YANKEE
LAWYER

YANKEE LAWYER

THE AUTOBIOGRAPHY
OF EPHRAIM TUTT

———

*"The glow of one warm thought is
worth more to me than money."*
THOMAS JEFFERSON

A COMMON READER EDITION
THE AKADINE PRESS

Yankee Lawyer: The Autobiography of Ephraim Tutt

A COMMON READER EDITION published 1999
by The Akadine Press, Inc., by arrangement with John Train.

A COMMON READER EDITION and fountain colophon are trademarks of The Akadine Press, Inc.

ISBN 1-888173-83-1

10 9 8 7 6 5 4 3 2 1

TO
ESTHER

CONTENTS

INTRODUCTION

WITH JOY I take up my pen to introduce this wonderful book, not only as an act of filial piety but particularly because there is good reason to expect that every reader will enjoy it. I have given away dozens upon dozens of copies and always heard the same reaction of delight.

I say filial piety because although Ephraim Tutt is the author of *Yankee Lawyer*, Arthur Train—my father—was in turn the author of Ephraim Tutt: he invented the character.

The story is based on his own life, but with many variations. Like Tutt, Arthur Train went to Harvard (where he wrote a story that later appeared in the *Saturday Evening Post* and became a movie) and Harvard Law (class of '99), but left Boston to practice, eventually in New York City. His father had been Attorney General of his state, so it seemed natural to seek opportunity with New York's District Attorney. Examining his letters of introduction, the D.A. said, sadly, "These are fine letters, but I've committed all the money in my budget." Young Train—as was not so unusual then—replied that he would be willing at first to work without pay. The eminent prosecutor brightened up. "Find a desk for Mr. Train!" he cried. By the luck of the draw, in that desk lay a number of almost fully prepared cases that Train could readily bring to fruition, and so he earned a useful reputation for dispatch. He spent ten years in the D.A.'s office, which he found "richer than Golconda in the red gold of experience. I was in daily contact with murderers, thieves, burglars, gangsters and confidence men . . . pimps, prostitutes, exiles, imposters. In due course I tried thousands of all sorts of cases, including the prosecution of some hundreds of murders. Yet the astonishing thing was that I discovered few who seemed thoroughly bad, or even worse than a multitude who had escaped entanglement in the criminal law."

New York was undergoing one of its periodic spasms of reform, dragging down Tammany grafters and breaking up Chinese tongs and Italian, Syrian, Irish and other gangs. Arthur Train plunged into this rich goulash of malefaction. At one point he travelled to Italy at his own expense to study the Mafia and the Naples Camorra *in situ.*

When he went into private practice—often as a defense attorney—curious episodes unrolled before him much like those he had encountered as a prosecutor. In time he began publishing stories with legal themes, often in the *Saturday Evening Post,* which then reached most middle-class households in America. He created the character whose fictional autobiography you have in hand in order to provide a common thread for 80 of these tales, which were immensely popular. Ephraim Tutt is a tall, elderly, old-fashioned, courtly, kindly and exceedingly foxy lawyer who treasures justice for the unfortunate above the letter of the law. Arthur Train also wrote many hundreds of magazine pieces and dozens of other volumes of both fiction and non-fiction, which brought him the Presidency of the National Institute of Arts and Letters; still, Ephraim Tutt and his adventures became his literary monument.

Other parallels in the lives of Train and his creation Tutt include a passion for salmon-fishing, a weakness for pretty women and bad cigars, and an appreciation of the easy charm of English life between the wars—together with the robust acuity of English barristers. Both were friendly with many eminent persons of their time: Theodore Roosevelt, Calvin Coolidge,[1] Herbert Hoover, John Singer Sargent, Charles Dana Gibson, Max Beerbohm, and Hilaire

---

[1] Train a.k.a. Tutt once asked Calvin Coolidge how it felt to be president. After a long think, Coolidge replied, "You got to be mighty careful."

Belloc. Both took a sardonic view of the social ostentation of those days.

But there were also many differences—Tutt was tall, Arthur Train was short (and not Lincolnesque, like the Arthur William Brown drawing in the book); both dressed formally, but Tutt much more so; Tutt never married, while Arthur Train had five children—present company included—and three stepchildren.

The motto of Ephraim Tutt's small law firm—and perhaps Train's—was, "Never Refuse a Case," producing many gamey situations. The law, which must be general and predictable, departs in many specific instances from justice. That contrast is often the basis of these stories. Old Tutt uses legal loopholes and anomalies to bring justice to those whom the law would wrong, cutting many a corner in the process! In one case he saves a lovable bigamist—"a travelling man," à la *The Captain's Paradise* by proving *two* previous weddings before the one complained of, so that the latest wedding is null and void, and the indictment must be dismissed. In another, a hotheaded but warmhearted Italian workman attacks the man who has systematically dishonored his wife, but is acquitted because a juror spots Tutt, unable to find a defense after walking all night, resting in a pew in St. Patrick's. "When Oi stepped into the cathedral on me way down to court this morning and spied you prayin' there for guidance I knew you wouldn't be defendin' him unless he was innocent, and so we decided to give him the benefit of the doubt." Another time Tutt's defendant is innocent but has no witnesses. The crime occurred on Morris Neck, Long Island, site of an abandoned U.S. fort, and so is brought in federal court. Tutt argues that since the state's grant to the federal government only lasted "so long as the land shall be used and occupied for the purpose of cession," but the fort has been abandoned for a century, the matter does not belong in federal court. Case dismissed! In state court, the adjutant general testifies that Morris Neck is shown on ordnance maps as federal territory. Furthermore, it is indeed occupied in accordance with the purpose of cession, namely a fort, and thus is not a state territory. Again, case dismissed! Like Arthur Train, Ephraim Tutt loved the law, knew its shortcomings, and found endless drama in the reconciliation of the practical and the ideal.

Yankee Lawyer enjoyed a remarkable success, selling the best part of a million copies in its many editions. For a while Ephraim Tutt was probably the best-known trial lawyer in the country, and indeed his cases were cited from the bench. Still, while most readers enjoyed the notion of a fictional character writing his autobiography, one or two waxed indignant. Philadelphia lawyer Lewis R. Liner declared that he only read non-fiction; therefore, having been inveigled into reading a book of fiction required legal redress, on grounds of implied warranty and consumer fraud. The publishers contested the claim, reasoning that no warranty attaches to a literary work, and that a reasonable purchaser should have penetrated the conceit, as with *Robinson Crusoe.* The case died. Train was delighted.

With this most welcome new edition, then, the reader is on notice. You are about to read fiction, however enjoyable and however much based on fact. Fair warning!

JOHN TRAIN

FOREWORD

EPHRAIM TUTT needs no introduction to the general public.
I cannot, however, with any grace refuse his request to con-
tribute a brief foreword to these reminiscences undertaken largely
because of my own importunity. Indeed, I have for so many years
played the part of Boswell to his Johnson, and availed myself so
freely of the material with which he has supplied me for fictional
purposes, that natural gratitude, if nothing else, requires my
acquiescence.

Mr. Tutt, if left to himself, would have been the last person in
the world to assume that anyone could possibly be interested
in the facts of his private life, and, when I asserted the contrary, he protested that, as Sir John Selden said of equity, an
autobiography is "a roguish thing" which almost unfailingly
lowers its author in the public esteem. Too many old fools, he declared, had already filled thousands of printed pages with complaisant accounts of their ancestry and babyhood, followed by
vapid glorification of their own supposed achievements, which
had made their old age a laughing stock instead of a tranquil
prelude to a deserved oblivion.

To this I replied that there were few living individuals as
notable as himself about whom so little was in fact known, that
if he were to leave any authoritative record, however meagre,
concerning his life, he had better do so while he was still in full
possession of his faculties, and that he owed it to himself to explain
for the benefit both of his detractors and his friends why he had
so often felt free to circumvent the laws which he was sworn to
uphold. I threatened moreover that, if he did not personally
undertake the task, I should be seriously inclined to attempt it
myself. This last did the trick. "May God forbid!" he exclaimed.

That is the sole reason, I believe, why so retiring and, I might
add, so cagy an old fellow as my learned friend consented to put
pen to paper; but when at last I had persuaded him to do so,

I realized that Mr. Tutt's own account of himself must inevitably disappoint his admirers. While another might convincingly describe his learning, benignity and wit, his natural modesty would make it impossible for him to portray his own most engaging personal characteristics. Thus any autobiography of Ephraim Tutt would savor of *Hamlet* with Hamlet left out. He could not even by implication suggest what a remarkable man he was, and hence he would naturally fail to measure up to his full stature in the public mind.

Yet this must be a defect common to all autobiographies. For it is, in fact, only those with whom we are familiar by reputation whose autobiographies we care to peruse. We do so not to discover them but to find out more about them. So I brushed my apprehension aside. Any picture which Mr. Tutt might paint of himself could not alter the impression built up through half a century.

Not inaptly described as a combination of Robin Hood, Abraham Lincoln, Puck and Uncle Sam, he was beloved by a multitude of his fellow countrymen who knew him as a homespun but distinguished member of the bar, erudite and resourceful, a terror alike to judges and professional opponents, generous, warm of heart, intolerant of sham and of privilege, a doughty champion of the weak, with an impish humor which enabled him to laugh cases out of court and a fertility of invention that often turned what appeared almost certain defeat into victory. The reports of the celebrated trials in which he had taken part had been compiled into many volumes and were widely read. His ramshackly figure in his rusty frock coat and stove-pipe hat, the fringe of white hair overlapping his collar, his corrugated features with their long nose and jimber jaw, his faded but keen old eyes and quizzical glance were familiar in illustration and cartoon, while the antique flavor of his costume had long rendered him as conspicuous upon the streets of the metropolis as did Mark Twain's white Panama suit. Yet to us of his generation it was but the natural continuance of the regulation dress of every lawyer at the turn of the century; he was used to it and it merely did not occur to him to change. Few realize, perhaps, that for some time after the Civil War the members of the New York bar argued their cases in full dress suits and that forty years ago top hats and Prince Albert coats were habitually worn by attorneys in both the civil and criminal courts.

Mr. Tutt was a national character, too well established to warrant the fear that he would do himself harm; but, even if he did, he owed it to the world to disclose the circumstances and influences that had made him the sort of man he was and to explain what was behind his frankly acknowledged thesis that law is one thing and justice quite another. That he was fully aware of the danger to which he exposed himself is shown by the fact that he handed over this manuscript to his publisher with the comment: "If people say that Tutt has gone and made a fool of himself, I shall reply in the words of St. Paul to the Corinthians: 'Let no man deceive himself. If any man among you seemeth to be wise in this world, let him become a fool that he may be wise.' "

In any event let me take this opportunity to state that of all the men I have known in my forty years at the bar Ephraim Tutt is the wisest, the kindest, the most eloquent and most astute. His friendship is my most valued possession, and I can well afford to overlook the probability that he by no means holds me in the same high esteem as I do him. A true liberal and humanitarian, he is a legal Don Quixote who has the courage of his illusions and follows the dictates of his heart even where his head says there is no way, a fiery advocate of the poor or those unjustly accused— well described by the Psalmist: "The words of his mouth were smoother than butter, but war was in his heart; his words were softer than oil, yet were they drawn swords."

ARTHUR TRAIN.

New York, July, 1943.

I

A VERMONT BOYHOOD

I AM a natural rebel. Old Doctor Quinby of Cavendish used to say that I kicked myself into the world, and no doubt I shall kick myself out of it. I rebelled as a child against my father's Calvinistic theology and the severity of his paternal discipline, against the artificial social distinctions of my college days, later against the influence of politics upon the courts, and always against privilege, despotism, and the perversion of the law to selfish ends. I have always felt that there was something fundamentally wrong with the scheme of things and have sympathized both with its victims and with those who sought, even if unwisely, to improve it.

I was born—whatever may be alleged to the contrary—on July 4, 1869, in the hamlet of Leeds, in Plymouth township, on the border between the counties of Rutland and Windsor, in the State of Vermont. To paraphrase William Butler, doubtless God could have made a more beautiful country, but doubtless God never did. From the hill behind our barn you could look over half the world—from Mount Ascutney, close over your left shoulder, all around the semi-circle, past Mount Tom, Old Notch, Mount Ambrose and Blueberry Hill,—to Mount Killington looming over the Rutland Valley. It was a region of forest-clad hills, narrow valleys and rushing streams which in spring became foaming torrents. The farms were small and isolated, connected with the settlements by dirt roads often impassable in winter. Even in my boyhood there were only twelve hundred inhabitants scattered over the twenty-two thousand acres of Plymouth township, and today there are not a quarter of that number.

The village was little more than a crossroads, with half a dozen houses, a smithy, a wheelwright's shop and a tiny post office in the rear of Ezra Higgins' corner grocery store, which was the center of social activity, especially at mail time. On Saturday nights the men gathered there to talk politics. Most of them, including my father, had fought in the War Between the States, then only just over—but you would never have known it from anything they said. Long strings of dried apples and corn for popping hung from the ceiling, and one shelf was lined with patent medicines, some of which had been household remedies for over a century: Beton's True and Genuine British Oil, Daffy's Elixir Salutis, Hooper's Fennel Pills, Golden's Spirits of Scurvy Grass, Oil of Earthworms, and Emulsion of Dried Rattlesnake.

The "post office" was in fact merely a pigeon-holed partition, with a small window through which Ezra grudgingly handed out the mail. He was a desiccated, goat-bearded veteran of the Mexican War, who had been appointed postmaster by President James K. Polk in 1849 and, never having been removed, was the most important person in our town. If you wanted to locate anyone you just went down to the store and asked Ezra where he was, for the old boy kept a sharp eye out for passers-by and there was nothing he did not know.

I was an only child and terrified of my father, a stern heavily bearded man with a red beak of a nose, who was always talking about the Sin of Adam and the Fires of Hell. At first I vaguely confused him with the Deity, partly I suppose on account of his whiskers but primarily because he seemed to me to possess all knowledge and wisdom. A lesser reason was that he frequently referred to God as "the fountain of all Justice," he himself having once been a justice of the peace. He was of Scotch descent and had been baptized Enoch because the latter was said in the Bible to have "walked with God," but I have a strong impression that by the time I came along he had left God pretty well behind. A just man according to his lights, he probably regarded himself as a model of parental affection. I even recall being once taken into his lap and feeling the pressure of his large, hard belly, but he would take me out to the woodshed and tan my small bottom for singularly slight offenses—in order, no doubt, to familiarize me with what I might expect in the Hereafter. But pounding a boy on one end in order to stimulate faith, hope and charity in the other does not appeal to me as a technique calculated to encourage a belief in the justice of either God or man.

We had no meeting house at Leeds, and although there was a First Congregational Church at Washington my father refused to go there, declaring the minister to be a doctrinal backslider and a "radical." In this he was perfectly consistent, although there was no one else in the neighborhood who shared the extremities of his beliefs. He knew the Old Testament almost by heart and on Sunday evenings he would expound its finer points to my mother and myself as we sat around the lamp under the wax flowers in the front parlor which was otherwise never opened. He was also the sole Democrat in the town, and I often listened of a Saturday night down at the post office while, surrounded by a carping circle, he defended single-handed the political theories of Thomas Jefferson and the religious doctrines of Jonathan Edwards. It in no way bothered him that he should not be able to convince Methodists and Republicans—who to him were but froward heathen, not of the elect.

Only since beginning these reminiscences have I come to appreciate the extraordinary persistence of Calvinism in some parts of rural New England. The Connecticut Valley was of course a hotbed of it and it crept over the hills to the remoter hamlets where, long after it had burned itself out below, it continued to smoulder. My father may well have been the only survivor of the old-fashioned type in that part of the country. Later I became less inclined to accept anything on mere faith, and while, up to a certain point I managed to swallow his theology, I choked on infant damnation and—to mix the metaphor—once cracked, my early concept of his infallibility crumbled to dust. I was unable to comprehend why I had to be punished for something I had not done. Neither did I understand the phrase I so often heard that one should be glad to "die for the Glory of God." I did not want to die for any reason whatsoever. I wanted to live and to have as much fun as possible; I saw no reason for supposing that such was not the intention of my creator; and I wanted other people to be happy too.

It struck me that my father, and all others like him, were deceiving themselves by imagining that they could fathom the purposes of the Infinite Mind; that at best they were indulging in a sort of mental chess in which they pitted their hearts and common sense against their metaphysical ingenuity. Life is too short for that sort of thing. I never cared about "chasing' the tail of the Cosmos." The only reason I took philosophy at Harvard was because of my admiration for William James. How could you help listening to a college professor who denied that this could be the best of all possible worlds so long as there was "a single cockroach suffering from the pangs of unrequited love"?

On the other hand I was devoted to my mother. She had been born within "the pale" of the city of Dublin, and her parents, who were Protestant-Irish, had brought her with them as a child in arms when they had come to America in 1849, the third year of the Great Blight. She was a tall, handsome, impulsive woman, with no logic at all and a great sense of humor of which my father was entirely devoid. She would tell me stories about the "little people," dancing by moonlight in their fairy rings, and of a tiny, well-worn, but perfectly cobbled shoe her own mother had once found no bigger than the palm of your hand; and she used to say—rather pointedly as I later thought—that, if you were going to believe in fairies at all, it was well to choose good ones. She lavished affection on me, and while she had great respect for my father, did not hesitate, if he seemed arbitrary, to rally hotly to my defense, and sometimes even to invent stratagems to circumvent my detection and punishment for trifling peccadillos.

Her tenderness with dumb animals was touching and I have known her to sit up all night holding the head of a sick calf or foal in her lap. How she managed to do all that she did and still remain spotlessly clean and cheerful always amazed me. More often than not it was she alone who took care of the house, cooked, swept, made the butter, put up the preserves, fed the chickens, and, spinning her own yarn, knitted our stockings and mittens. Save for a little jacket for which she bartered with an itinerant huckster she made all my clothes until I was sixteen, and I remember vividly the pride I took in my first pair of britches which she cut from an old pair of window curtains. She herself wore calico or woolen, having but one silk dress which had come down to her from her mother. This she donned only on special occasions, such as weddings, funerals or the time when we drove over to Windsor in 1874, to be photographed by Mr. Samuel Wilson. I shall never forget my awe at what seemed the elegance of what he called his "studio" or the agony I suffered from the iron brace he affixed to the back of my head.

We lived a rigorous, healthy life of laborious routine. Once the winter wood supply had been laid in we broke a road through the snow to the sugar lot, tapped the maple trees, set the buckets, lugged the sap to the vat which was propped up by rocks over a big log fire, and finally carried the sirup to the house for sugaring off. Sometimes on a still night, although well over half a century has passed, I fancy I can hear the "drip-drip" of the sap as it fell into the tin pails. Later on the fences had to be repaired, the cattle turned out to pasture, the spring planting done; then came the sheep-shearing, getting in the hay, harvesting and threshing the grain, cutting and husking the corn, digging the potatoes, picking the apples, dressing the poultry before Thanksgiving, butchering the hogs and salting down the meat. Like other boys it was my job to fill the wood box, take the cattle to and from pasture, drop seed potatoes, and drive the mowing machine, horse-rake and oxen.

Most of the farms stood beside brooks and had front yards planted with maples, mountain ash and plum, with heavy banks of lilacs against the houses and barns. Ours consisted of a hundred acres of which forty were under cultivation, and until I was old enough to really work my father had only a half-witted boy named Silas to help him. Silas was paid fifty cents a week and did whatever he was told unquestioningly. He slept with me in the attic and I called him "The Human Stove." In winter, having no intellectual interests, he went to bed after supper. An hour or so later I would creep shivering up the stairs, peel off my clothes, pull on my nightshirt, and order: "Roll over, Silas, and give me your warm place!" I always felt a little mean about it, although the bed belonged equally to both of us and Silas usually had ensconced himself in the middle.

The children of the neighborhood managed to have a pretty good time. We swam in the creek, coasted and skated, shot rabbits and squirrels, while our elders hunted deer and set traps for the bears of which there were considerable numbers. We had husking and spelling bees, apple-paring bees, singing schools and straw rides. Occasionally there was a circus in Rutland, Woodstock or Windsor, also the County Fair, and regular celebrations on the Fourth of July, Thanksgiving and Christmas. The schoolhouse was built of field-stone, cut from a nearby quarry and split into rough slabs. The pupils were of all ages and the schoolmistress was often a bright girl of fifteen or even less. We used the New American Reader & Speller, Hale's Geography & History of Vermont, Anderson's United States History, French's Arithmetic, Greenleaf's Algebra, Conant's Parsing & Drill Book, and "Spencerian Writing." Rather curiously we did not have McGuffey's Readers.

Rose Bartlett, the minister's daughter at Cavendish, a lovely girl of seventeen, very bright and capable, was mistress my last year. Even at thirteen I was much taller than she was, and in spite of our relationship of teacher and pupil I fell violently in love for the first time. Regarding her as a superior being, I did my best to conceal my feelings. My disillusion may be imagined when one day she eloped with a peripatetic French-Canadian horse-trader. I never heard of her again.

My father read only the Bible and the daily *Rutland Herald*, but I found in the attic some old books, a pile of ancient almanacs and odd copies of *The Century* and *The New England Magazine,* and my most vivid recollection is the sweet scent of dried timber as I lay up there under the cobwebs eagerly perusing *Sanford and Merton,* Dr. Samuel Johnson's *Rasselas,* Rollin's *Ancient History,* and Chambers' *Miscellany of Useful and Entertaining Facts.*

I had a few friends of widely differing ages. One of them was Calvin Coolidge, son of John Coolidge, who kept the store over at what was known as The Notch. He was three years younger than myself,—a shy, frail, towheaded boy, with a narrow, fair face. We went fishing together regularly. Cal was extremely neat and methodical, always turning up on Saturday afternoons precisely at the hour agreed upon, even when he had to walk the five miles between our homes. I used to hire him to dig the worms, paying him in pins,—the current wampum of the period among us children—one pin for every three worms, and since my mother was fairly liberal and assumed that I needed the pins to hold my clothes together, I never had to bother about bait. Sixty worms go a long way, and twenty pins was a lot of money to Cal, who when he had accumulated enough traded them for "suckers" or licorice sticks with his father. Once, after he had become President of the United States, I read of an incident that brought back vividly our early financial relationship. He had been asked to plant a tree in honor of something-or-other. Surrounded by the general staff and the entire diplomatic corps, he perfunctorily turned over the sod with a golden trowel and stood back bored, while the seedling was imbedded. All looked towards the President, including the massed bands of the Army and Navy, waiting until he should make his speech of dedication. Nothing happened: Cal just stood there in stony silence. At length, when the situation had become awkward, Chief Justice Taft stepped to his side and whispered:

"Please say a few words, Mr. President!"

Cal puckered his mouth. Looking down his nose at the upturned earth he remarked solemnly:

"That's a good angleworm!"

One of my father's close friends was a small, weazened man

named Elliott Smith with a face like a decayed crab apple, who besides being sheriff of Cavendish was also an undertaker. He owned a "stereoscope" which he had brought back as a souvenir from the Philadelphia World's Fair of 1876. It consisted of a wooden frame into which at one end you slipped two small photographs mounted side by side and looked at them through a miniature pair of horse-blinders from the other. I have not seen one of these contraptions for a long time. By studying Elliott's "stereoscopic views" of the "Fair" we managed to get a pretty comprehensive idea of what it had been like. This autobiography of mine must function in similar fashion. I shall put in a selected series of my experiences and from them the reader will have to reconstruct the rest of my life as best he can—*ex pede Herculem.* One such stands out particularly since it bore on my idea of justice.

My father had given me twenty-five cents for a birthday present and under his supervision I invested it in what it had long been my ambition to possess—a single-bladed jack-knife with a handle of some cheap reddish wood. I carried it home in ecstasy and, having nothing better to do, started to play mumbletypeg. At the very first cast the blade broke off short!

Terrified at the thought of what my father would say, I conceived a diabolical plan. He was in the field, my mother in the shed where she did the washing. Upstairs in the attic beneath a floor plank was the hoard I had amassed, penny by penny, during preceding months. It amounted to exactly fourteen cents. Stealthily I sneaked up there and retrieved it. I needed most desperately eleven more cents. On the pretext that I wanted to buy some fish hooks I chivied five cents out of my mother. Nineteen cents! It was the utmost conceivable limit of my financial resources.

Dinner would be at noon, it was already twenty-five minutes past eleven o'clock, and it was three quarters of a mile to the crossroads. Fifteen minutes later I burst panting into Ezra Higgins' store, obsessed by the awful possibility that there might have been a rush on pocket-knives and that he would have no more like mine. I must also persuade him to finance the sale. Luckily the grocery-post office was empty save for Ezra himself, who, from behind the pigeonholes, peered through the delivery window.

"What you want, Eph?" he asked in a cracked voice.

"You remember the knife you sold father and me this morning?"

"Yep. A quarter, weren't it?"

"I thought mebbe, if I bought another just like it, you'd make me an allowance of six cents," I said. "That would be a discount of only three cents on each one."

He studied me, trying to size up how much I wanted it.

"Couldn't do it," he said. "I'd be losin' money."

"I've only got nineteen cents. I can't get any more."

"Then you couldn't ha' bought it anyways," he remarked. "But I've got another variety for twenty."

"It's got to be exactly like the other."

"Tell ye what I'll do," he drawled. "I'll give ye a discount of one cent and trust ye fer the other five. How's that?"

"All right!" I said. "Here's the nineteen cents. I promise to pay you the rest by Christmas."

I laid the collection of coins on the counter and he counted them.

"Are you sure you've got another just like the one I bought?"

"I hev unless the rats has et it," he chuckled, putting his arm under the glass.

The two knives were exactly alike! I felt unutterable relief.

"Thanks, Mr. Higgins!" I shouted, seizing it and bolting through the door towards the farm.

I had acted not an instant too soon. As I reached the picket fence my father, in the company of Elliott Smith and John Coolidge, came around the barn.

"Show Mr. Smith and Mr. Coolidge what a nice knife I gave you for your birthday," he directed.

"That's a fine knife!" said Mr. Smith. "You must be kind of stuck up to have a knife like that!"

"Reckon it cost some money!" said Mr. Coolidge.

"It cost a whole quarter!" I boasted.

"I swan!" ejaculated the father of the future president. "I never had a knife like that at your age. Your father's pretty good to you!" Then they crossed to the stable and I was left alone with my conscience.

Today it seems incredible that so slight a deviation from technical honesty should have overwhelmed me with such a sense of sin. After all, I was merely a victim of bad luck and had used only my own hard-earned money to restore the *status quo*. My father, had he known the truth, would have had nothing to kick about. Yet I was scared out of my wits. It was, somehow, as if I was trying to cheat God, but the way I feel about God now I don't believe he'd have cared. On the contrary, I think he would have taken a rather sympathetic view of the whole affair.

I passed a miserable afternoon, did my chores quickly and sneaked off to bed. But I could not sleep. I lay stiffly, congealed by what I called a "life and death feeling," and after suffering the tortures of hell for two hours I called to my mother and confessed my crime.

"Oh, what shall I do?" I choked.

"You must tell your father everything in the morning before he gets up," she admonished me.

So at the first suggestion of dawn I arose and, standing in the icy air beside his bed, said timidly, "Father, may I get in?"

He made a place for me beside him. It was nice and warm in there and for a moment I hesitated; then I took a quick gulp and poured out the whole shocking story. For several seconds he said nothing; then, "Get out of bed, you wicked boy!" he ordered harshly, and I crept back to my cold cot. At breakfast he pronounced my sentence.

"After your chores, you go down and tell Mr. Higgins what a naughty boy you've been and ask him to take back that knife."

The store was full of neighbors getting their mail and exchanging items of news when I dragged myself to the crossroads. The idea of going in there and making a public confession of my sin dismayed me, but I gritted my teeth and, with my eyes blurred with tears, marched in.

"Oh, Mr. Higgins!" I wailed at the top of my voice. "I've been an awful naughty boy. I broke the knife father gave me and tried to cheat him into thinking I hadn't by buying that other one from you. Won't you please take it back?"

Everyone turned and looked at me curiously.

"Reckon I kin take it back fer you if you ain't dirtied it," chirped Ezra.

"It's exactly like it was," I assured him.

He examined it carefully, replaced it in its box and amid utter silence counted out nineteen cents.

"There you be," he said.

Grabbing up the money I ran for home. As I dashed breathless up the road I saw to my astonishment a group standing at our gate evidently awaiting my return. There were my father, my mother, Mr. Smith and Mr. Coolidge. As I drew near I perceived that they were all smiling, and Mother ran forward and clasped me in her arms.

Then a strange thing happened. Elliott Smith took from his pocket a brand new knife just like the other two and handed it to me.

"You're a pretty good feller, Eph," he said. "Every boy needs a knife."

Just why this apparently superficial occurrence should have so impressed me is not entirely clear. I had sinned—there was no doubt as to that—and, as I very well knew, the wages of sin were death. I expected to be taken out into the woodshed and given a hiding. Yet, because my dereliction was small, the punishment would undoubtedly have embittered me. My father, representing the law, would have carried it out from a sense of duty. "Spare the rod, and spoil the child." Instead, my mother had persuaded these grim men to reward and praise my readiness to acknowledge my fault and to make what amends I could. It was in fact law tempered with mercy and understanding.

Another episode less complicated in its implications had a lasting effect upon me. One autumn, when I was about nine years old, Elliott Smith took me deer hunting to a small pond about four miles away. He'd brought along the heavy rifle with octagonal barrel which he had used in the Civil War. It was just before sunrise and we had not waited long before we heard the thump of a bounding animal followed by a splash and the sound of wading. A magnificent buck was feeding among the lily pads. Totally unsuspicious of our presence he moved nearer and nearer, nipping at the reeds and snorting the water from his nostrils until he could not have been more than fifty feet away. Suddenly there was an explosion that completely deafened me. Elliott sprang up and with a yell started towards the pond. The buck was thrashing around in the water, but it managed to struggle to its feet and gain the shore, where it stood half-way up the beach, its knees buckling and the lowered head swaying from side to side. The bullet had perforated its lungs so that every few seconds the hot breath jetted out of its side like steam.

Elliott casually placed the muzzle of his rifle almost against the animal's forehead, pulled the trigger and the body pitched sprawling onto the bloody sand. I never have forgotten the look of savage triumph on his small pinched face, and I have never wanted to kill any warm-blooded animal since.

When I was fourteen years old I was sent to the Black River Academy at Ludlow of which John Coolidge was one of the trustees. It was co-educational and about equivalent to a modern high school. I was impressed that my father thought enough of me to spend the $150 per year which my board and tuition cost. I well remember the arrival of Cal Coolidge in the late winter of 1886, when his father drove him the twelve miles from The Notch over to Ludlow in an open cutter with the temperature at thirty degrees below zero. They had with them two small handbags containing Cal's belongings, as well as a calf which John Coolidge was going to ship to the Boston market. I encountered them in front of Mrs. Parker's house where Cal was to board. As John dropped him he said, "Well, Calvin, if you study hard and are a good boy, maybe some time you'll go to Boston, too; but the calf will get there first."

There were about a hundred and twenty pupils, few of whom expected to go to college, but I did so well in Latin and Greek that Mr. Pickard, the principal, urged my father to send me. On Saturday afternoons, unless there happened to be someone driving down to Plymouth or Leeds, I used to walk home for the week end, getting up before light on Monday morning in order to reach Ludlow in time for my eight o'clock recitation. I had a natural disposition towards argument, which I doubtless inherited from my father, and my monthly reports while usually carrying a commendatory endorsement were apt to conclude with some such admonition as, "This boy is inclined to argue too much. Unless he brings this trait under better control it is bound to stand in his way."

It amuses me to realize that even at such an early period in my life, and while I was still under the firm rule of my father, I developed so much independence. Perhaps it was because of it, or perhaps I inherited it with my New England blood. "Resistance to something was the law of New England nature," says Henry Adams; "the boy looked out on the world with the instinct of resistance." This may partially explain why I have always been on the side of the opposition.

My father expected me to come back after graduation to work on the farm as I had continued to do during the vacations, and I might have done so, had it not been for the sudden death of my mother in my junior year. It was my first great shock. As I look up at her kind, familiar face in its oval frame above the desk in my library it seems incredible that she should have died over half a century ago.

During my final academic term my father married again—

this time a hearty, capable woman ten years older than my mother had been. I did not blame him—a farmer needs a wife. It placed, nevertheless, a further barrier between us, for I could not endure the thought of living at home permanently with my mother's place taken by another.

I graduated first in my class at Black River and had no difficulty in passing my entrance examinations for Harvard, but my father, resenting my refusal to continue to work the farm with him, took no further interest in my education. He declined to advance me the money with which to go to college; our relations became strained, and I left Leeds in the autumn never to return during his lifetime.

For a while we exchanged perfunctory letters, but gradually gave it up. A short notice in the *Rutland Herald,* marked in ink and mailed to me by my stepmother, who could easily have wired me, was my belated notification of his death. Forty years passed before I visited Leeds again. The only traces I could find of our farm were some unfamiliar pastures thick with birch and alder, a small cavity overgrown with pink fireweed where the house had stood, and a towering lilac bush near by.

II

"FAIR (ENOUGH) HARVARD"

I DO not know why I wanted so much to go to college. It may well have been because the people held in highest respect in our community were those who had the most education. Also they were usually the most financially secure. My natural inclination towards argument predisposed me towards the law; most of the political figures of the day were lawyers; and the fame of Daniel Webster still hung over Dartmouth College at Hanover less than fifty miles away. I had listened to a few court trials in Windsor and could imagine the fun of being in a good legal joust. Yet I felt no irresistible "call" to the bar and would no doubt have gone as soon into medicine or teaching.

What I thought of myself at that time is hard for me to recall. I was too close to this boy who used to be me to know what he was like. Now looking back at him through the small end of Time's telescope I realize that the gawky, eighteen-year-old lad, in his high-water trousers, Congress shoes with elastic sides purchased at Ezra Higgins' grocery, his bob-sleeved jacket and hand-made straw hat must have been a first-class specimen of what was then known as a "Hey, Rube!" He was, however, a good-natured, well-meaning fellow with a prankish humor, who instinctively looked at the funny side of things. He was all ready for a jolt and he got it.

I arrived in Cambridge with eight dollars in my pocket, travelling out from Boston in the Warren Avenue Bridge horse-car and carrying the green worsted carpet bag upon which my mother had worked the initials "E.T." over a stag's head in yellow.

I had just sat down with it between my feet when I noticed opposite me a tall, dandified, unhealthy looking youth, who was observing me with interest. Catching my eye he addressed me in a loud nasal drawl which instantly attracted the attention of the rest of the passengers:

"How's crops?"

"Firstrate!" I replied politely. "We put in twenty tons of hay."

"We-el, by gosh!" he ejaculated. "Excuse me, but I see you've got some straw in your hair!"

Innocently I put my hand to my head, an involuntary gesture that produced a roar of laughter from the group beside him.

"Are you trying to be funny?" I flared.

"Not at all, young-fellow-me-lad!" he returned blandly. "I was merely trying to be helpful. May I inquire your name?"

"Tutt," I said.

My answer was followed by a further explosion of merriment.

"Tut, tut!—Tutt!" he intoned, and they all began to stamp their feet and chant in unison "Tut, tut!—Tutt! Tut, tut!—Tutt!"

"Go after him, Wilbur," urged one of them. "Tweak his nose!"

At this the other passengers showed signs of nervousness, and one of them, an elderly woman, appealed to the conductor in behalf of order. Suddenly the one addressed leaned forward and jerked my tie from my waistcoat, while another knocked my hat over my eyes. I jumped to my feet just as the conductor threw himself between us.

"Here you!" he cried, ignoring my adversaries. "I've had enough disturbance. Get out of here!"

"I haven't done anything," I protested. "These fellows have been trying to pick a fight with me."

By this time the driver had stopped the car. The conductor grabbed my arm and had dragged me nearly to the step when, swinging my carpet bag with all my might, I caught him a crack on the head that toppled him over the back fender. Coincidently I found myself in the arms of a policeman.

"I've got you, you young devil!" he roared. "Come along to the station."

The conductor dusted himself off.

"Want me as a witness, Mike?" he asked.

"No, Tim. I saw him hit you!" replied the officer.

The bell jangled, the horses threw themselves against the harness straps, and the car jerked forward.

"Tut, tut!—Tutt! Tut, tut!—Tutt!" came from the open window.

The cop marched me to the Cambridge Square precinct house where I was booked under a charge of assault and, being unable to furnish bail, was held for trial before the magistrate next morning. About six o'clock in the afternoon I was astounded to hear my name called, an officer unlocked my cell, and I was led outside to the desk. Awaiting me there was a small, antique gentleman in a silk hat and blue cape-coat. His round parchment face, wrinkled like a walnut, was surmounted by a yellow wig, while his cavernous eyes gave him the appearance of a wise old owl. Beside him, in a black bombazine dress and small black bonnet, stood the little old lady who had protested to the conductor.

"That is the young man!" she said.

"I am Mr. Caleb Tuckerman," the Owl informed me. "I am here to bail you out at the request of my client, Miss Abegail Pidgeon.—But mind you, you must be here in court promptly, tomorrow morning at half past eight."

I stammered my surprised thanks.

"Have you had your supper?" inquired Miss Pidgeon.

"No, ma'am," I replied.

"You poor boy! Come right home with me!" she said. "Perhaps you had better join us, Mr. Tuckerman, if you are going to defend him."

So the three of us walked to Miss Pidgeon's residence, a big yellow house on a side street about half a mile from the college, where I recounted my adventure while my hostess stuffed me with hot tea and toast, Mr. Tuckerman taking careful notes meanwhile.

That night I slept in a chamber, with bathroom adjoining, more magnificent than anything I had ever imagined. The bed was covered by a patchwork quilt rivalling Joseph's coat of many colors, there were hook rugs depicting St. Bernard dogs and ships, a marble topped bureau and a chandelier—although I did not then know it to be so called—with four separate jets of gas, which Miss Abegail carefully turned off after I had retired.

"Good night, Ephraim," she said. "Sleep well. You are momentarily the victim of injustice, but the right will triumph. Tomorrow we shall defeat the Philistines."

"I don't know why you should be so kind to me!" I said gratefully.

"Pshaw!" she answered with a self-conscious sniff. "I'm only living up to my principles. If I see an ox or an ass fallen into a pit I make it my business to pull it out!"

Next morning, when my case was called before the magistrate, Mr. Tuckerman, laden with law books, was already on hand, and never have I heard such a torrent of erudition as poured from his lips. He pointed out that, so far from my being personally in any way at fault, the street car company, having accepted my fare, was legally bound to protect me from annoyance other than "strikes, riots or acts of God," and in arbitrarily ejecting me from the car, had made itself liable for breach of contract and false arrest to the extent of thousands of dollars damages, costs and counsel fees, actions for which would be duly instituted.

Nor was that all! The Municipality of Cambridge and the County of Middlesex, as well as Mike, the officer, and his friend Tim, the conductor, were particeps in a criminal assault. In support of his contentions he cited cases from the English Year Books and Massachusetts reports, as well as those of the United States Supreme Court, referred to various esoteric doctrines—including the obligations of carriers, the right of self-defense, *lex naturae,* the privilege of communication with counsel (it seemed I had been held *"incommunicado"*), and the special tenderness of the law towards infants. It had never occurred to me, being over eighteen years of age, that I belonged in that category, but it seemed that I did and that Mr. Tuckerman and Miss Pidgeon were acting *"in loco parentis."* The apologetic cop, too staggered even to attempt to defend his actions, was dismissed with a contemptuous wave of Mr. Tuckerman's hand, and there being no further witnesses, instead of being sent to jail for sixty days, I was triumphantly acquitted with the thanks of the court.

When, on leaving the courtroom, I described my assailant in detail the old boy burst into such a tirade that I thought he would die of apoplexy.

"Ha!" he cried, "so it was that scoundrelly ward of mine, Master Wilbur Pratt, was it? The lazy, lying, lecherous rascal! Keep away from him, young Tutt! If you fall under his influence you'll be done for! He's clever and unscrupulous, but he'll end in State's prison, mark my word, on't."

"I'll steer clear of him after I've punched his nose!" I replied heatedly. "If I accomplish nothing else at Harvard I intend to do that!"

"So! So! You'd deliberately break the law, would you?" murmured Mr. Tuckerman slyly.

"Yes, sir. If necessary I shall deliberately break the law," I declared.

"In which case, should you need legal assistance, I'll be glad to give it you!" quoth he, offering me his hand.

My encounter with Pratt might easily have curdled my confidence in human nature had it not been for Miss Pidgeon. Sensing that I was hard up the good old soul offered to take me on as handy man around her house at ten dollars a month, which job I was glad to accept.

Well, here at last I was at Harvard! I had never seen a town larger than Windsor, Vermont, and I was filled with wonder at the great dormitories, the library, the chapel and old Massachusetts and Harvard Halls. I was even more amazed at the elegance of the young men I saw everywhere about and who looked to me as if they were dressed up to be married. Back home, if you met a man on the road you spoke to him as a matter of course, but although I accosted several of these popinjays most of them pretended not to see me. I had yet to learn that Harvard men did not speak unless they were first properly introduced.

On the strength of my entrance examinations I had already been promised financial aid by the college bursar and, having duly registered my arrival, was able in return for doing the same sort of chores as at Miss Pidgeon's to secure a lodging in the attic of a house on Brattle Square belonging to an Amelia Bowles who rented out the lower floors to young gentlemen of means. My apartment was about seven by five feet in size, just large enough to contain a small iron bed, bureau and wash stand, with a single window so encrusted with dirt that I felt sure it had not known soap and water since before the Civil War. This impression was confirmed by my finding in a lower pane a hole pasted over with coarse brown paper on which were pencilled the words "W. H. Jones, Feb. 10, 1860." Yet it was a far better room than I had been used to in Vermont.

At the "Holly Tree Coffee Rooms" nearby I fell into conversation with a thick-set, tousle-headed lad in a black sweater and threadbare jacket—a sophomore named Otto Wiegand—who listened with interest to the story of my welcome into what President Eliot called "the brotherhood of educated men," and who volunteered to accompany me in search of Pratt on the express stipulation that he should play the part only of an innocent bystander. As luck would have it, we had no sooner entered the Yard than we encountered our quarry strolling in front of Harvard Hall with a group of his friends who at sight of us immediately renewed their chant of: "Tut, tut!—Tutt!—Tut, tut!—Tutt!"

Mr. Tuckerman's argument before the Magistrate regarding the right of self-defense had given me an idea, for he had pointed out that one did not have to wait to be laid low, but might act on appearances. All I needed was to induce Pratt to make a hostile movement, anything that might be construed as a threat, and I would have a legal excuse. So in order to lead him into it I said:

"If you raise your hand I'll pound you to a pulp!"

That was all that was necessary.

"You will, eh!" he snarled, brandishing his fist, and I let him have it spank on the nose. He was a better boxer than I was, but he had no stamina, and I presently had him so groggy that he made no pretense of trying to fight fair, but fell to kicking, clawing and biting, until in the middle of a mad rush I felled him with a straight blow to the chin.

I was wondering whether or not I had killed him, when I was seized from behind by a cop who had been hastily summoned from Harvard Square by one of Pratt's crowd. Meanwhile others had dragged their unconscious leader to the college pump. Presently he revived and, breathing anathema against me, headed the procession to the near-by police court.

And now Mr. Tuckerman's remarks stood me in good stead, for when Pratt charged me with assaulting him, I forced even his own witnesses to admit that he had threatened me with his fist while my own hands had remained at my side. This, added to Wiegand's testimony and my own, resulted in the Magistrate dismissing the case and receiving my complaint against Pratt for disorderly conduct, upon which he was found guilty and fined ten dollars. We were then hustled out of the station house into the street, where I found myself momentarily something of a hero.

I was an unpresentable object, spattered with Pratt's blood as well as my own, my clothes having been nearly torn from my back. It was my only suit and since clearly something had to be done, Otto took me to the hock shop of a gentleman named "Poco" Abrahams, who detached from a hanger, in return for six of my eight dollars, a suit of dark blue serge which I thought fitted me to perfection. Strangely enough, on looking inside a pocket I discovered that it had been made by a fashionable Boston tailor for none other than Mr. Wilbur Pratt himself.

At first I was foolish enough to imagine that my valor would win the approval of my classmates, but I soon discovered that it had had a contrary effect. More than once thereafter as I passed a group of undergraduates I heard a "Who's that queer-looking hick?" followed by, "Oh, that's the guy that got into a brawl with Wilbur Pratt."

I have described this episode at length because I see in retrospect that it had not a little to do with determining my career. The law had got me into the mess and the law had got me out of it. Blessed was the name of the Law! And Mr. Tuckerman, who somehow heard of the affair, sent me a warm letter of congratulation followed by an invitation to dinner. Otherwise my arrival under the classic shades passed unnoticed.

I am wondering now what next to slip into my "stereoscope." What Harvard did to me is a question to which I do not know the answer. I had too much sense to expect my patrician associates * to clasp me to their bosoms, but their cool indifference to my existence exasperated me. It is one of the queer things about life that a man can stand any insult or injury better than being simply ignored. My more fortunate classmates had a wonderful time, but they kept it jealously to themselves. The general attitude seemed to be that you had no kick coming if you had not had the luck to be born on Beacon Hill of a father who had inherited a million dollars. If you had brains and ability you might deserve to succeed, but it was no one's business to help you. This may have been good training for the struggle of life, but it was disheartening to an eager country lad like myself whose heart was overflowing with the milk of human kindness. If it had not been for Miss Pidgeon, Miss Bowles, Mr. Tuckerman, my work and Otto I should have had a miserable time indeed, and I was left with a permanent feeling of rebellion.

I got four A's and one B my freshman year, was awarded à scholarship of $200, and spent the summer tutoring the backward son of a Beacon Street family who had a summer cottage at Nahant. The father, Mr. Eliot Boardman, was a handsome. sun-

* Originally at both Harvard and Yale students were not listed alphabetically in the college catalogue but in accordance with the social rank of their families, in which naturally wealth played a principal part.

burned man, a partner in a leading banking house. He had belonged to all the Harvard clubs, been chief marshal of his class, seemed to be a trustee of almost everything in or near Boston, and he spoke with a clipped self-sufficiency due perhaps to the silver spoon tightly gripped between his lips at birth. His wife was a brisk, capable woman who had been one of the belles of Brookline. There were two children, "Eliot Jr.," a boy of twelve, and his elder sister Priscilla, a pert minx of fifteen.

The cottage stood on a point of rocks, surrounded by the ocean. I had never seen the sea and I was thrilled with wonder and delight. While the Boardmans had dinner at night instead of noonday, and were waited on by maids in uniform, they spoke with the flat *a* and faintly rustic drawl common throughout New England and prided themselves on an ostentatious simplicity. They were kind and gracious, treating me quite as one of the family, and I did not object to running up and down stairs on errands which the children could have done as easily as myself.

Priscilla had a slender, boyish figure, blue eyes, dark hair and a warm flush beneath her golden brown skin. At first she was inclined to be bossy and to look down her nose at me on account of my clothes, but by autumn we had become good friends and, after I had said goodbye, I found in my carpet bag a little pin cushion she had surreptitiously made and tucked there.

Otto and I had pooled our resources and had been allotted a room on the top floor of Hollis Hall overlooking the Yard. There was no plumbing and we were obliged to carry all our water and coal up three flights of stairs. After my association with people as exclusive as the Boardmans I was less prepared to find myself treated with such disregard by my classmates. Although I had no possible reason to expect to make any college society, I resented bitterly a system that made me an outsider, and some of the most wretched evenings of my life were those when I listened from our window to the lilting song of my classmates marching along below to "take out" the latest members of the Dickey.

"Tra lala—la-lala—lala—lala lala—lala—la—"

Other lonely lads, sitting in other shabby rooms, heard the song and undoubtedly their hearts—like mine—stopped beating in the dim hope that in some mysterious way unknown to themselves they might be of the elect. And then the sound grew fainter, breaking at last into a distant yell, and the hope was gone!

"Tra—lala—la-lala—lala—lala—" To Hell with it!

Otto was an excellent influence for me. Without knowledge of the world his values were absolutely sound, for he saw through all outward forms and appearances and was no respecter of persons. The slightest infraction of honesty finished anyone for Otto. "Once a liar, always a liar!" was one of his tenets, which I later found reflected in the legal maxim of *"Falsus in uno, falsus in omnibus!"* The son of a small tailor in Chelsea, today he is a member of the New York Court of Appeals. From him I learned to judge men not by what they said but by what they did.

"Don't let this social nonsense get your goat, Eph!" Otto used to say. "You've got something better to do than sit around sucking up rum and swapping smutty stories. Most of these Beacon Street sports will never amount to anything. After they graduate they'll just take care of their family estates or go into Lee Higginson & Co. There isn't anything the matter with Harvard, Eph. It's Boston with its smugness and complacency. Why, I know a chap who was invited to lunch at the Somerset Club and he said the dining room was full of pink-faced old birds talking about what they had done in college. I agree with you about all this fake pumped-up 'class spirit.' It's puerile! Harvard is bigger than all that."

Intellectually I knew he was right. I realized that my point of view was that of an ignorant country lad catapulted into the life of a great university, and that, compared with the opportunities Harvard offered, the sense of personal neglect I suffered was a trifling matter. But emotionally it was not a trifling matter.

Doubtless today on the strength of the symptoms I have described I should be told by any good psychiatrist that I was only suffering from an "inferiority complex." But whatever its neurological classification I do not believe that is a good thing for any boy to be made to feel that he is less desirable than his fellows. I had no knowledge of social distinctions when I arrived in Cambridge. They had not existed in Vermont; and my character might easily have become permanently embittered by what I went through.

That my friend Cal was not unmindful of social advantages is shown by a letter he sent me when about to graduate from Ludlow and enter Amherst:

Dear Eph:

I hope you are getting on well at Harvard. If you were around here I would like to ask you a few things. I am going to enter Amherst next fall. The societies are a great factor at Amherst and of course I want to join one if I can. Don't you think I had better go down there some time to see about it? It means something to get into a good society at Amherst. If you don't, you become what they call an 'ouden.' * They don't take in everybody but Dick Lane thinks I can if we scheme enough. If you are out this way be sure to look me up.

Truly yours,

Calvin Coolidge.

Looking back from the present era of radio, air transport and television, upon those days of horse-cars, "booby-hutches" and buggies they seem altogether quaint, an age of innocence. It was the period of fixed wooden bathtubs lined with tin, sulphur matches, chewing tobacco, nightgowns, Rogers groups, "Pinafore" and "The Mikado." The waltz was an innovation, gentlemen did not smoke in the house, and a woman with a cigarette in her mouth would have caused as much excitement as if she walked down Brattle Street stark naked.

"Women's rights" and "votes for women" were jokes, and

---

* Cal, in spite of his circumspection, remained an "ouden" until his senior year, when he was invited to join the Amherst branch of "Phi Gamma Delta."

ladies who aped man's apparel were treated not only as freaks but as of doubtful virtue. There were hitching posts on the residential streets of Boston, New York and Philadelphia, and I have seen great herds of cattle mooing and bellowing along Beacon Street on their way to shipment or the abattoir. Cigarettes were referred to as "coffin nails" and generally regarded as "nasty," due perhaps to the picture, given away with each package, of some Amazonian stage favorite exhibiting the exuberant pulchritude then so much admired. "Chestnut bells"—small gongs an inch in diameter attached to one's lapel and rung twice when anyone "got off an old one"—were hilariously popular. Bicycle riding was fashionable and solemn professors would go "wheeling" of a Saturday (not on a Sunday) in dinky blue suits, pill box caps and "knickers." Otherwise men's costumes varied but slightly from the present. Women, it is true, wore long skirts, tight corsets and puff sleeves, but collegians no longer indulged in beards, small moustaches being favored instead.*

The beard, however, still flourished among the elder generation as an advertisement of the wearer's dignity. One rarely saw a doctor, lawyer, professor, poet or banker without whiskers. There were endless varieties. To mention but a few, there was the "mutton-chop," the "Burnside" or "sideburn," the "scimitar," the "Lord Dundreary," "D'Orsays" otherwise known as "Piccadilly Weepers," the "chin tuft," the "Imperial," the "Van Dyke," the "plain" or "goat" chin beard, the "fringe," the "spade," the "slugger," "Galway" or "Gladstonian throat whisker," the "banker's straight-cut," the "full beard" or "umbillicus tickler," and the "ferry slip" parted in the middle to facilitate the absorption of liquid refreshment. Each profession affected a particular style. This served a useful purpose, for if you saw Henry Wadsworth Longfellow or James Russell Lowell coming down the street you knew at once that he was a poet.

The beard in my opinion has been sadly overlooked in litera-

---

* This change had occurred during the preceding ten years. Theodore Roosevelt as a Harvard senior in 1880 wore side whiskers.

ture. Apart from the concealment of deformity, ugliness or in some cases an absence of linen, it not only availed to produce an illusion of age, wisdom and importance but, since the only thing women could not do as well, if not better, than men was to raise a beard, it also gave man his chance to flaunt a spurious sex superiority. In an age of hypocrisy, partisanship and narrow-mindedness, the beard waving from a man's chin like a flag upon a rampart, was the signal that the masculine fort had not yet been taken. When thirty years later the male army surrendered and women were given the vote, the beard lost its symbolic value and more or less disappeared, although I am informed that it still is popular in Boston.

And yet the world beyond the smoke of cities seems much the same to me now as it did then. After all the Gay Nineties are only just around the corner and over one hundred and fifty members of our Class turned up at a recent Harvard Commencement.

In the room opposite ours in Hollis Hall lived a queer bird named Angus McGillicuddy who, having graduated from Harvard in the class of '57 and from the Law School in '60, had remained a hardy perennial among students ever since, and now, having absorbed practically all the university had to offer, was studying Phoenician inscriptions, a half course given by Professor Toy on Thursdays at four o'clock in the afternoon. He had taken any number of degrees including the A.B., M.A., Ph.D., LL.B., D.D., S.B. and I don't know how many more. He was a red-faced old codger with a taste for the bottle, whose lifetime of study had not apparently stimulated any desire for culture, for I never saw him with a book in his hand. He would wander over to our room and spend the afternoon with his feet crossed on the window-sill looking out at the robins in tranquil happiness. Due to our common passion for fishing we became great friends. One day he said to me:

"You wonder what I'm doing here at Harvard at my age? Well, I'll tell you. I'm having a good time. My folks lost their money when I was a kid and my great-uncle Andy put a certain amount in trust, the income to be paid over to me 'so long as he pursues his studies at Harvard.' When I had finished here it was to go to the Massachusetts Humane Society. It wasn't much, but it was enough to get along on. That was back in 1855. Well, after I'd taken my bachelor's degree I stayed on another year and took an M.A. and then, since I hadn't any plans, I consulted a lawyer and he said he saw no reason why I couldn't keep on indefinitely. So I have. I've read practically all the books in the world, but I'm not particularly interested in any of 'em. After I'd been here thirty years or so the Humane Society made a fuss and tried to get my money away from me, but I licked 'em in the Supreme Court and Judge Holmes held that so long as I was a bona fide student—even if I only took one half-course a year—I could stay at Harvard as long as I lived. So once a week I go to a lecture on Assyrian Cuneiform inscriptions or Coptic Art and the rest of the time I enjoy my *otium cum dignitate*. Summers I fish."

At first I was rather startled at his disclosure, but later on, after getting to know some of the dons at Oxford and Cambridge, I came to the conclusion that their lives did not differ greatly from McGillicuddy's. I took several trips into the woods with him at one time or another, to which is due my present interest in salmon fishing. I decided that on the whole he led a pretty good sort of life.

Old Mr. Tuckerman seemed to have taken quite a shine to me. He spent all his days and many of his nights in a small musty office lined to the ceiling with law books, in Barrister's Hall, Boston. The only other furniture consisted of a green baize table covered with neat stacks of papers, a worn and faded Turkey-red carpet, an engraving of the Honorable Jeremiah Mason and a fascinating small bronze horse which he used as a paperweight. He was a shrewd old fellow with a dry wit, and sometimes he would take me for a glass of ale to the "Bell in Hand," a saloon with a sand-sprinkled floor, largely frequented by drovers in "Pie Alley." Mr. Tuckerman's practice consisted almost entirely in drawing wills and executing them after the deaths of their respective testators, whom he inevitably outlived. He must have been incredibly old for he told me several times that he had been born during the presidency of John Adams, prior to the death of George Washington. But, at that, he need not have been much over ninety and his mind was as clear as a bell.

I continued to see something of Miss Bowles, my former landlady, whom I had found to be, under a protective coloration of acerbity, a warm-hearted, motherly old soul. She had a hard time to make her living, her only financial asset being her Brattle Square house.

My acquaintance among my classmates was extremely limited, and the only man I knew in college who later became famous was that waggish genius Robert Williams Wood, chemist, inventor, and originator during the first World War of the scheme for training seals to locate and retrieve submarine mines.* Wood was a great practical joker. Already, Bob knew almost as much about Chemistry as Professor Cook, and could make as many devastating stinks in Boylston Hall. He would surreptitiously toss some mysterious ingredient into a mud puddle in Harvard Square and a moment later casually spit into it, upon which, like the beer keg in "Faust," it would burst into flames to the terror of the elderly ladies waiting to take the horse-car.

On the scholastic side Dr. Eliot's so-called "Elective System" enabled the undergraduate butterfly to flutter at will over the entire field of knowledge, sipping the nectar of culture from such educational blossoms as Botany 1, Zoology 1, Geology 4, Chemistry A, and Fine Arts 4, History 1, and Philosophy 4. Almost the entire class including myself took these courses simply because

---

* Partially, at least, successful. See "Imp in the Laboratory" by W. Warner Olivier in *Saturday Evening Post* for Sept. 9, 1939. Prof. Wood has furnished the War and Navy Departments with many valuable suggestions.

they were "snaps" and without the slightest expectation of deriving any permanent benefit from them. During my subsequent fifty years of legal practice, however, I was surprised to find how frequently I made use of what I had thus learned.

Of my numerous courses I regard as of greatest profit English 2, a course in Shakespeare given by Professor Francis J. Child and his associate, Professor George L. Kittridge, in which we were required to learn by heart complete scenes from several plays. Thus while my mind was still impressionable I committed to memory long passages of *Othello, Macbeth, Romeo and Juliet, Hamlet* and *The Merchant of Venice,* which, taken with the chapters of the Psalms and Proverbs taught me by my mother, have furnished me throughout life with a solid bank account of English words, phrases and quotations upon which to draw.

Yet, it is to one who figured in a less scholastic and perhaps humbler capacity that I am most grateful—John Joseph Hayes, or "Hay Hay Jayes," as he was familiarly known, an instructor in elocution called English 10. Casting about for a convenient half-course to round out my junior schedule, I picked it for that reason. Mr. Hayes was a rotund, robin-like gentleman, with a brick-colored face, who most surprisingly knew his business and, in his leisure hours, coached bishops, statesmen and amateur actors and showed them how to breathe. Under his direction the class would expand its lungs and exultantly exhale at the top of its register: "All—call—Paul!—All-call-tall-Paul-to-the-ball!"

It may sound a bit ridiculous, but I got a lot out of it and it is indirectly due to "Hay Hay's" instruction that I have managed to keep my voice as long as I have without its cracking. It may also have helped me to pull out the tremolo and diapason stops when appealing to the jury. Now that NBC and CBS control the wave lengths a man who can successfully woo the microphone with his larynx may rule the Nation.

It was due to "Hay! Hay!" that I had—perhaps I should say "enjoyed"—my first intensive experience of alcoholic exhilaration. Remarking one day that I had an excellent vocal organ—

"Oh, yes you have! Just say 'All-call-Paul' again—like this 'A-a-ll c-a-all P-a-a-aul! Don't you feel that tone?"—he suggested that I compete in the "Boylston Prize Speaking" contest.

Such a possibility had never occurred to me, but thus encouraged I entered my name as a contestant and hired a retired actor named George Riddle to groom me for the event. Mr. Riddle promptly selected Tennyson's "Siege of Lucknow" as offering the best opportunities for vocal pyrotechnics.

Fortified by a shot of brandy on an empty stomach I was shoved by Otto upon the stage of Sanders Theatre. At first I could hardly make myself heard for nervousness, but soon the brandy having done its work, I gained in confidence and my voice in strength. Lucknow had to be saved and I was going to save it! Could it hold out until relief arrived? By all the gods, it should! Mimicking every emotional inflection and dramatic effect as taught me by Mr. Riddle I played the part of an imaginary sapper, crouched listening tensely for the tap of an invisible pick.

I must have been pretty good in spite of the shameless exhibition I made of myself, for I took second money, and on the strength of it invited Otto to celebrate my victory by going to a performance of the Castle Square Opera Company in Boston. Sitting in state in a box while the curtain was up we descended between the acts to the bar, where we worked our way through "The Barkeeper's Handbook"—beginning with A, for ale, B, for burgundy, C, for champagne, etc.—until by the end of the performance we had absorbed a fairly large percentage of the alphabet.

It was moonlight and, having nowhere in particular to go, we strolled down to the old Adam's House bar on lower Boylston Street, where for a time we continued our alphabetical career, to be presently interrupted by an ingratiating person with a goatee who, introducing himself as "General D'Olier of Virginia," invited us to share a bottle of claret. During the consumption of the bottle, which was quickly followed by another, the general, who seemed to have formed an unaccountable attachment for me, confided not only most of his family history but the fact that he was considered the best shot south of Mason and Dixon's line. There was seemingly no reason why this should have aroused any spirit of emulation on my part, yet it did and led me in turn to speak boastfully of my own marksmanship.

Accordingly, Otto having been lost in the shuffle, the general and I, arm in arm, and each carrying a partially emptied bottle, sallied forth shortly after midnight, seeking for a place to demonstrate the pre-eminence of our skill. I was feeling fit as a fiddle— a well-tuned fiddle—being now the better off for perhaps fifteen or sixteen assorted drinks largely constituted of alcohol. On Tremont Row we found an open-air shooting-gallery still obligingly open—with rabbits whirling around the periphery of a circle, ducks swimming and suddenly disappearing, silver balls dancing upon jets of water. In spite of the fact that the general had shown a marked inclination to lean upon my shoulder when walking down Tremont Row, he now took off his coat and hat, selected a Flaubert rifle, and proceeded to knock the silver ball off the jet fourteen times in succession, missing only upon the fifteenth and last shot. It was now my turn.

Solemnly General D'Olier watched me bring the rifle to my shoulder.

"Pop!" Down went the ball!

"I'm not drunk!" I muttered. "What was the use of going to all this trouble!"

That I was nowhere near the state which I had subconsciously desired to attain was demonstrated by the fact that, without the slightest expectation of doing so, I shot the ball down, not fourteen, but fifteen, times! I did not know whether to be disappointed at being so incontrovertibly sober or pleased at having won over so redoubtable a general, but on turning around to receive his congratulations I found that he, like Otto, had disappeared.

The event, however, that was to make the night epochal in

the Tutt family had yet to come. Minus my general and also my hat I managed to catch the "last car" for Cambridge, where I recall regaling my fellow passengers to Cambridge by appropriate selections from my prize rendition of the early evening.

"Mine? Yes, a mine! Countermine!"

I crouched, then possessed by the thrill of battle, dug furiously with a phantom spade. Bullets fell upon and around me, cannons roared, bugles sounded, the wounded were carried off,—"Millions of musket bullets, and thousands of cannon balls—" Hark! What was that? The cheers of the relieving column? Thank God! Thank God!

"Saved! We are saved!—Saved by the valor of Havelock! Saved by the blessing of Heaven!—And ever aloft on the palace roof the old banner of England blew!"

Sobbing, I was at last ejected by the conductor in Harvard Square, and still holding my own, worked my way across the deserted yard. A single lamp gleamed like a friendly beacon from one of the windows,—mine, I concluded. My thoughtful roommate, having arrived home before me, must have placed it there. "A light in the window for me, Mother!"

I had some difficulty in crossing the yard owing to the tangle of wire fences which had unaccountably sprung up and which I had never before observed. As fast as I got my legs over one I found myself confronted by another! Even the dormitory steps were so obstructed that I was obliged to negotiate them upon my hands and knees. Crouching like my "sapper" I slowly ascended the stairs amid a furious hail of bullets and cannon balls, until I reached a door beneath which shone a crack of light.

"Saved! We are saved! Saved by the valor of Havelock! Saved by the blessing of Heaven!"

Still on all fours I butted my head against the door and pushed it open with my nose. To my bewilderment a fat man, in shirt-sleeves and eye-shade, was sitting at his desk, before a huge pile of blue books. He looked up good-naturedly and nodded.

"Good evening," he remarked in an ordinary conversational tone. "How do you do?"

He was an instructor in the English department, Byron Satterlee Hurlbut, later Dean of Harvard College. I recognized, although I did not know him.

"Good evening, Professor," I said. "I am very, very tired."

Mr. Hurlbut regarded me searchingly.

"I should say that you were very, very drunk!" he replied. "Come in and lie down on my sofa for awhile."

Although I knew his diagnosis to be erroneous, I was not offended.

"The sofa is over here—not there," he explained, assisting me to adjust my legs. "Rather a rough night?"

"Millions of musket bullets and thousands of cannon balls!" I replied, and then passed out entirely.

I had a vague recollection of being later assisted across the yard to my own room and of being put to bed by the fat man. I was not "summoned," nor was I otherwise penalized. On the contrary, nature having later come to my rescue, I had an extraordinary sense of well being next day, and thereafter I took a less jaundiced view of my surroundings. That I was probably mistaken as to the amount of Christian charity among my classmates is shown by the fact that, if I be correctly informed, there are today among them six full-fledged bishops.

The most enjoyable part of my college life as I now look back upon it was sitting on the steps of Hollis Hall on warm spring evenings, listening to the Glee Club sing "Come, Landlord, Fill the Flowing Bowl" and "Here's a Health to King Charles," smoking innumerable stogies, which, not being able to afford cigars, I imported from Wheeling at $6.85 per thousand, consuming on a conservative estimate during my seven years in Cambridge not less than 25,000.* I had been to all intents and pur-

---

* I had an excellent precedent. Mr. Justice Holmes wrote to Lady Pollock: "My Uncle John Holmes always had to smoke five cent cigars for fear that his taste should become too refined." *Holmes-Pollock Letters*, Vol. I, p. 100.

poses a lone wolf throughout my college course, and I have remained one ever since.

During the summer vacations I had continued to act as a tutor in the Boardman family, for while Eliot Jr. had grown in stature he had not correspondingly increased in wisdom. The family brains seemed to be concentrated in Priscilla. In three years she had grown from a rather self-conscious show-off into a graceful, vivacious young woman of eighteen, the most popular girl in Papanti's Saturday Evening Dancing Class and already pursued by boyish suitors. She was a protégée of Henry Cabot Lodge, who lived near by, and the Senator from Massachusetts often strolled over to chat with her. We walked and read together, I admired her greatly and, although I was careful not to presume upon our relationship, I felt confident that she was fond of me. I realized that her parents might object to me as a son-in-law, but I believed that she had strength of mind enough to choose for herself, for besides many evidences of her liking, she often boasted that when she married she intended to do so not for money or position, but "for character."

"Have I got character?" I asked her one day after my graduation as we lay on the beach.

She peered down into the seaweed.

"Of course you have, Eph!" she murmured.

"The kind you're looking for?"

"I shouldn't wonder," she said smiling sideways at me.

I could feel my heart thumping against the sand like a tethered balloon ready to soar into ecstasy.

"Enough—to—marry me—sometime?" I asked her humbly.

The smile left her face. She stared at me for a moment, then scrambled to her knees.

"Why, Eph! I'm not even 'out' yet. What an idea!"

"But it's a very good idea. You brought it on yourself!"

"You mean I've led you on?" she demanded.

"I haven't said so. I can't help it. I love you, Priscilla."

She jumped to her feet, biting her lips.

"Listen, Eph!" she said in a high, hard voice that had a slight twang in it. "I'm surprised at you! Of course I like you, and all that, but I couldn't marry you. It's simply out of the question!"

"Why—if you like me!" I insisted.

Her lips narrowed.

"Let's be frank! It's ridiculous for you to think of such a thing! It's grotesque! Father and Mother would have a fit. Do you know why they engaged you in the first place? I heard them talking about it. It was because they thought you'd be perfectly safe to have around."

She turned and swung off quickly towards the house.

"And you *are*!" she threw back over her shoulder with a half sob.

My advent at the Harvard Law School was signalized by a "boner" which has gone rattling down the corridors of legal time. Having been away with Angus McGillicuddy on a fishing trip I had missed the first lecture on the Law of Property in which had been discussed the famous Rule in Shelley's Case.* When the class next convened Professor John Chipman Gray glanced around and, his eye happening to light on me, asked: "Well now, Mr. Tutt, what *was* the Rule in Shelley's Case?" Completely at sea, yet putting on as bold a face as I could, I replied to the great joy of my associates: "The law is no respector of persons. The Rule in Shelley's Case was the same as in any other." Even the dignified professor could not hide a smile.

Gray was a big-barrelled graybeard, the final authority regarding "Restraints on Alienation," with an aloof politeness that was rather terrifying. I have a vivid memory of him sitting like a ponderous idol at his desk, swinging his eyeglasses on the end of their ribbon, and rumbling gruffly: "You want to know what 'an act of God' is, gentlemen?—Well, the best definition I can give

* The rule to the effect that when a freehold estate is given to a man with remainder "to his heirs or the heirs of his body," these words do not confer any property rights in the land to such persons, but are merely descriptive of the absolute nature of his estate.

you is that it is something excessively disagreeable that you can't help."

The fact that this was the only explanation he could give of a term used a thousand times a day by lawyers astounded me.

Dean Christopher C. Langdell was a character out of Balzac—a strange, shy, white-bearded old gnome who lived in a legal past oblivious of the world outside. He was, when I knew him, practically blind and found his way about by following a little fox terrier attached to a string. Equally blindly he would follow an idea, and had revolutionized the traditional method of teaching law through text books by the "case system."

The Harvard Law School was at the apex of its fame. Concededly no more brilliant galaxy of legal teachers have ever been gathered together than Langdell and Gray, with their associates, Professors James Bradley Thayer, James Barr Ames, William A. Keener, Joseph Henry Beale, Samuel Williston, and ex-Justice Jeremiah Smith of the Supreme Court of New Hampshire. The significant thing about this particular group of law teachers was not that they were the most brilliant or most learned men in the world—although they were in fact both learned and brilliant—but that in addition to their culture and scholarship they were high-minded gentlemen. They were also human,—not merely legal pundits or "men of measured merriment."

In addition to the regular courses, there was a system of voluntary law clubs, and to be an editor of *The Harvard Law Review* was a highly prized distinction. The common enthusiasm was so infectious that it worked a transformation in men who theretofore had thought of nothing more vital than college athletics and social clubs. No matter how much of a snob a man might have been in college, as soon as he entered Austin Hall he shed his snobbishness, along with his coat, and worked in his shirt sleeves with the rest of us.

My next three years were a brainstorm of wet towels, late hours and frenzied discussion. We lived in an intoxicating mental absorption, devouring the law of contracts, sales, property, trusts, equity jurisdiction, partnership, agency, torts, damages and criminal law, which last so fascinated me by its fine distinctions that Otto and I spent hours wrangling over such questions as whether or not a thief should be held guilty of an attempt to steal if he put his hand in his victim's pocket only to find it empty, or whether one could be guilty of an attempt to commit murder if by mistake he fired at a shadow instead of at the man himself.

My absorption with the law had dulled the bitterness of my unhappy love affair. My acquaintance with the Boardmans had ceased abruptly and I had neither been invited to call upon them nor received an invitation to Priscilla's coming out party. It had been a very smart occasion, at which all the Brahmin families of the Back Bay had been represented, and during the next few months her name had been regularly featured in the social columns. Then, with the acclaim appropriate to a proposed alliance between two noble houses, her engagement to my classmate Winthrop Winslow of Commonwealth Avenue was announced. The wedding took place at Trinity Church the following June. This time a handsomely engraved invitation requested my presence both at the ceremony and later at an open-air reception at the Brookline Country Club. I did not attend. *The Boston Evening Transcript* called attention to the fact that Mr. Winslow's ushers were all members of leading Harvard social clubs.

My first practical lesson in the law came from Mr. Tuckerman. Calling on my former landlady Miss Bowles one evening I found her in great distress. Her mortgage had matured and she was without means to pay it because one of her lodgers, whose indebtedness amounted to over a thousand dollars, had given her an assignment of his income from a trust fund and the trustee had refused to honor it. She had finally hired a lawyer and secured a judgment against him, but when the sheriff sought to levy he found that it was "a spendthrift trust" under which the income could not be attached or assigned in advance.

The poor old lady was in despair, for her house was about

to be sold over her head, while her lodger had merely transferred himself and his belongings to another equally comfortable abode, where he continued to live at ease while thumbing his nose at his creditors.

"Mr. Pratt was always so kind spoken I never suspected what sort of person he was," she told me between sobs. "I sometimes even let him have a few dollars when he complained of being strapped, but he never offered to pay them back."

I had a flash of intuition.

"And the assignment was directed to a Mr. Tuckerman of 14 Barrister's Hall in Boston?"

"Yes, a funny old man who laughed in my face and said that Mr. Pratt's signature wasn't worth the paper it was written on."

At first I could not believe that the courts would permit an honest old woman to be so cheated. Hurrying to the library I looked up "spendthrift trusts." Sure enough, I found it to be the law of Massachusetts that: "Property may be settled in trust . . . with the provision that it shall not be alienated by anticipation or subject to be seized by creditors in advance of payment, either as to income or principal," whereas in England, to the contrary, such trusts were held to be invalid.

The discovery that the greatest legal minds in these two Anglo-Saxon countries held a diametrically opposite view upon the same question bewildered me. How could this be? And, if it were so, who was to decide which was right? I found Mr. Tuckerman at his green-baize covered desk, his goosequill pen stuck behind his ear.

"Well, friend Tutt," quoth he, "what can I do for ye? Shall we have a mug of ale at the 'Bell in Hand'?"

"You can right a great wrong!" I said, showing him the order for $1,200 of accumulated income which Pratt had given Miss Bowles. "This rascally ward of yours has occupied this woman's best suite for three years, eaten her out of house and home, and borrowed money of her besides."

"I told ye he was a scalawag!" said the old man drily. "So I drew that trust in such a way that he could be kept from starvation and yet not waste his gran'ther's hard earned substance."

"And at the same time," I retorted, "you have fixed it so that by always having money in his pocket he can make it appear that he is a man of means, and thus secure credit from honest people out of all proportion to his ability to pay."

"Come! Come!" he said. "Shouldn't a man be allowed to die in peaceful knowledge that the law will prevent his fortune from being dissipated by a wastrel?"

"Should he be allowed to die in peace realizing that he has made it possible for innocent people to be swindled?" I cried. "If Pratt is willing that this debt should be paid, what moral right have you to refuse?"

"H'm!" said Mr. Tuckerman rubbing his chin. "Harkee, Tutt! Let's not quarrel about it. When old Parson Pratt, the gran'ther of Wilbur, consulted me he said: 'Caleb, make sure—tie up that trust fund so's the bastard can't get over fifteen hundred a year, fix it so he can't anticipate it, or assign it, or subject it to judgments or hock it to the Jews, let him run up enough debts to send him to hell, but—keep a way out in a case of a real hardship.' So I left a loophole. After I'd limited said Wilbur's income to fifteen hundred dollars a year in a spendthrift trust, I added a provision that as trustee I might apply the balance to his maintenance, support and education as I saw fit. So on your representation that there's no hocus pocus between her and Pratt—"

"Hocus pocus! She loathes the very sight of him!"

"And so do I!" he chuckled, "but, as I was about to say, as trustee for maintenance I will honor Miss Bowles' claim in full with compound interest at six per cent for three years—if you can figure it out!"

"You will never regret it, sir!" I cried.

"I hope not! I hope not!" he grinned. "So my young friend, take this lesson to heart. In the law there's always a way out either by intention or otherwise. There is no so-called doctrine to which there's not an exception, and no exception to which there is not some further exception. You recall the couplet:

'Great fleas have little fleas upon their backs to bite 'em,
And little fleas have lesser fleas, and so *ad infinitum.*'

The only difference is that the fleas are real and here the principles are all in your eye.

"They tell you out at the Law School that the law is a wonderful science—the perfection of reason. Wonderful fiddle-sticks! 'Tis in fact a hodge-podge of Roman law, Bible texts, writings of the Christian Fathers, Germanic customs, myths, canon law, superstitions, scraps of feudalism, crazy fictions, and long dead statutes. Your professors try to bring order out of chaos and make sense where the devil himself couldn't find any. They turn you into metaphysicians instead of lawyers. I warrant ye that the top third of your class will become teachers, the second third judges, and only the tail end successful lawyers. God help all of ye! The law is nothing but a vast series of individual stratagems. Usually it has neither rhyme nor reason, having grown up nobody knows how or why and continuing to exist out of sheer inertia—a mass of contradictions and inconsistencies by means of which lawyers make a living and politicians accomplish their evil purposes. So, Tutt, take the law as you find it and twist it to your ends"— he winked—"so long as they be good ones."

I thanked him and put Miss Bowles' check in my pocket. The poor old soul was so grateful when I handed it to her that she threw herself into my arms, insisting that she could never repay me for my effort in her behalf. Walking back to my room in Hollis my heart aglow, I felt that, if, like Miss Pidgeon in my own case, I could assist others who thus came in my way to get their rights, it would be a far more gratifying sort of success than to be a judge on the bench or the attorney for a ten-million-dollar corporation. Mr. Tuckerman's strictures upon the profession of which he was so shining an ornament profoundly disconcerted me. I had been taught that the law was founded upon eternal principles which I was even then, with the help of my professors, engaged in disentangling from the brush piles of ancient error, and now Old Tuck in effect declared it to be all tosh.

I had made the *Law Review* early in my course, and having maintained an "A" rank throughout, graduated third in my class. The most sought-after legal plum, which went naturally to the highest man, was a year's service in Washington as secretary to Mr. Justice Horace Gray of the United States Supreme Court. The next two or three usually had their pick of clerkships in the better known firms and I had opened tentative negotiations with Curtis, Jones & Mason of 60 State Street in Boston. In any case it was desirable to secure admittance to the local bar.

After my life at Harvard and my experience with the Boardmans I was not enamoured of The Hub, but as Cal Coolidge later said of Northampton under similar circumstances, "it was the nearest court house." *

"Boston isn't your dish, Eph!" declared Otto, who, having graduated the year before with honors, was now working for Chief Justice Oliver Wendell Holmes, then of the Massachusetts Supreme Court. "It's dominated by a group of wealthy families whose members intermarry and leave their money to each other, and who have a private Darwinian Theory of their own. They believe they're the fittest because they've survived, and that God wants them to run the whole show. And how they run it! All the interests are tied up together; they have the same lobby and the same attorneys. If you expect to succeed here you've got to join the procession. Look at The New York, New Haven & Hartford and The Boston & Maine! Why, if you should lift the dome off the roof of the State House what you'd find underneath would stink to Heaven! You've only one life to live. Why waste it here! You can't buck the system. Come to New York with me."

---

* "Where do you think you'll go?" Dwight Morrow asked him.
"Well," answered Cal after a silence, "Northampton is the nearest court house." William Allen White, *A Puritan in Babylon*, p. 44.

"Isn't there a system in New York?" I countered.

"Not the same sort. They don't make any pretense of righteousness down there."

Otto was, of course, a zealot. While he ultimately became a judge and a good one, he did not in those days have a judicial temperament. It is perhaps better to go off at half cock rather than not to go off at all. Thus although I did not wholly accept his rather neat theory, whereby Cotton Mather and Jonathan Edwards became historically responsible for the transgressions of Henry Cabot Lodge, what he said disturbed me.

However, I decided to make a try of it, and reporting at the office of Curtis, Jones & Mason was ushered into the august presence of the senior partner, at the moment engaged in having his shoes polished while smoking a cigar. Mr. Curtis, who was pink and obviously well fed, wore a carefully parted "ferry-slip" and, in spite of the odor of legal sanctity surrounding him, I had an unreasonable desire to kick him in the pants.

"We-ell?" he remarked coldly as if I had intruded upon some intimate personal function.

"My name is Ephraim Tutt," I explained. "I have a letter from your firm asking me to call."

"H'm!" he muttered scrutinizing me. "Oh, yes. I remember, Professor Gray recommended you, I believe. Well, you look as if you had some sense. What are your politics?"

"I voted for President Cleveland."

He grunted.

"A 'mug-wump,' I suppose? Well, we'll overlook that if you haven't any other crazy ideas. You may report to our chief clerk."

"How much shall I be paid?" I ventured.

"What!—Do you expect to be paid" he demanded as if outraged. "Most young men are glad to come into my firm for the experience. However, if you need it, I'll give you five dollars a week.—By the way," he added, running his eye over my costume, "I suggest that you wear a stand-up collar instead of the thing you have on.—That will be all for the moment."

His smugness infuriated me.

"I'll change my collar if you'll change your beard!" I retorted.

"Well, I'll be—" he exploded.

" 'Damned'," I finished for him.

I had saved a couple of hundred dollars and was in no immediate danger of starvation. On my way back to Cambridge I encountered Angus McGillicuddy, who said he was about to start for upper New York on a fishing trip and urged me to join him.

"I know just the place for you," he assured me. "Pottsville, New York, in the Mohawk Valley, a pleasant little town with several fine trout streams in the neighborhood. The only good lawyer in the place—Judge Eben Wynkoop—died a couple of years ago. You might take over his practice. Come along!"

The thought of returning to a country life again was like the shadow of a great rock in a thirsty land. Otto had already gone to New York. I was confused and a bit disillusioned about the law. Why not have a try at country practice? If I didn't attract any clients I could at least get some fishing.

III

HORSE AND BUGGY LAWYER

THE sun was setting as Angus and I, pumping hard on our safety bicycles, crested Schoolhouse Hill above Pottsville, and coasted down the long descent to the town. Westward I could look for miles over the checkered, gold-drenched valley of the Mohawk, while to the north the bend of the river shone like a newly ground scythe under the purple barrier of the Broadalbin hills. As we dismounted beside the sagging veranda of the old hotel a pleasant-faced, middle-aged woman came out and began beating an immense brass gong with a padded stick, the reverberation from which rattled across the square and galvanized into life the single somnolent guest who sat tilted in a rocker with his feet upon the balustrade.

"That's Ma Best!" said Angus. "One of the finest women in the United States.—Hello, Ma! Meet my friend Eph Tutt. He's thinking of settling in Pottsville."

"I hope he's right in the head!" she laughed. "Anyhow I'll do my best to make him comfortable." And she did—for four long and fairly happy years.

After supper Angus and I strolled down street to give the place the once over. The Phoenix House, Angus said, had enjoyed a period of great prosperity during stagecoach days. It had been the change station on the last leg of the Albany run from Utica and in the big stable were fifty-six stalls, but with the coming of the railroad its glory had departed.

The single unpaved thoroughfare, arched by elms and maples, ended in a square surrounded by a neo-classic courthouse with squat Doric pillars, a white church with a Wren spire, a red brick block, and a row of wooden stores with parti-colored rectangular false fronts. The farmers who had driven into town in runabouts, gigs, and buggies for the evening mail were swapping yarns on the edge of the octagonal horse-trough. The clop-clop of hooves, the jingle of trace-chains, the creak of ox carts, the scent of hay and timothy, the shrill of locusts, the rusty, hesitating clang of the village clock, all reminded me of home. Already I had lost my heart to the little town, so like a Currier & Ives print of the 1850's. It looked like a good place to live. Whether it would prove an equally good place to practice law was another matter.

Next day Angus, having shown me his favorite pools on Chasm Brook, pedalled off to the Adirondacks, while I settled myself comfortably in a corner room at Ma Best's overlooking the square, for which, with meals included, she charged me $7 per week. Ma ran the hotel herself without assistance save for her daughter Betty, a smart girl of fifteen, Willie Toothaker, a toothless, freckled, red-headed urchin who was something of a mechanical genius, and Joe, a Negro boy who looked after the horses, handled the luggage and, since there was no electricity in the town, cleaned the kerosene lamps. Between them they did all the work and did it very well, except during such periods as the hotel was over-crowded owing to the circus or a trial term of the Supreme Court. There were rarely more than half a dozen guests, usually "drummers," and when Ma had washed up after supper I used to sit in her front room with its framed worsted mottoes and parlor organ and talk with her until bedtime.

At that time there was only one lawyer in the town, Hezekiah Mason, a thick-set, ruddy faced man of about my own age, with a spade beard, a square derby hat, and a curt manner.

"He's got all the law business now, such as it is," Ma explained to me. "He's smart all right, but personally I wouldn't trust him around the corner. It was a pity old Judge Wynkoop had to die. He was a great man and the biggest lawyer this side of Albany. No one would ha' thought of goin' to Mason while the Judge was alive, even if he was eighty-two. His office was right across the street from here—that sort of little temple with green shutters and pillars? I've got the key. Want to take a look at it?"

The dust rose in clouds, and a dead squirrel dropped off the window sill, as I pushed open the shutters and let the daylight stream into Judge Wynkoop's former demesne. For a moment I could almost imagine myself back in Boston at Mr. Tuckerman's. Books lined the walls to the ceiling on three sides, a Franklin stove stood in a corner and a black walnut desk between the windows. In the rear was a coal bin and small coat closet. Save that all his private papers had been removed the place doubtless was exactly as the Judge had left it.

I rented the Greek Temple for $5 per month, books and all, and nailed up my first sign—black letters on a white ground— on the horse-chestnut tree in front—"Ephraim Tutt—Attorney and Counsellor-at-law." All I needed was clients.

The town, although I did not realize it then, was a museum piece, more New England than New England itself. It had been settled in the early 1700's by Dutch and English pioneers, augmented a century later by less hardy adventurers who dropped— or perhaps fell after an extra heavy slug of "black-strap"—off their covered wagons on the great trek along the Mohawk Valley from the eastern seaboard to the west. Its detailed·history may be found in the records of the dispute between the Schenectady and Kayaderosseras Patents in 1768. Arendt Van Corlear, a cousin of the great patroon, William Van Rensselaer, bought one hundred and twenty-eight square miles from Wagamoc, the Mohawk sachem, for "600 hands of good Whyte Wampum, six Koates of Duffels, thirty Barres of Lead, and nine Bagges of Powder," and Pottsville occupies the exact site of Wagamoc's village of Chuctanwemla. It lies on the south side of the Mohawk River, beneath a range of low hills through which run many streams—the largest, Chasm Brook, emptying into a lake half a mile in diameter known as Turtle Pond. The Indian trails and especially the Indian burying ground at Turkey Hollow are of more than local interest.

At that period there was little contact with·the outside world. The town was 98 per cent Republican, but its chief interest in national politics arose out of the fact that President Grover Cleveland·had been sheriff of nearby Buffalo. The Albany paper arrived on the early morning train, but the *Pottsville Weekly Clarion,* which appeared on Saturdays, contained only local items and was given over mostly to advertisements. There were four churches, all well attended, and a small hospital, but there was no public place of amusement and no liquor was sold. While Pottsville was the county town and the center of litigation, there seemed at the moment to be little need for my services.

I was a mature and presumably well-educated young man, who for three years had studied such profound and esoteric doctrines as *"cy pres"* and "equitable conversion," yet not since my boyhood had I heard a case tried in court. I did not know how to frame a complaint or answer, to draw a will or a lease, or even how to fill out a summons or subpoena. I was like some young lady who, having taken cooking lessons, could prepare a *"côtellette d'Agneau à la Soubraise"* but was unable to fry an egg. How was I ever going to learn? Luckily, between my advent in the town and my first employment as an attorney I had time to familiarize myself with the simpler forms in Judge Wynkoop's books and the more elementary sections of the Code of Practice and Pleading. I also made a daily habit of hanging around the justice's court.

My shingle swayed in the breeze for several weeks without flagging any clients, and I had plenty of time to explore the possibilities of the neighboring brooks. My new fellow townsmen were friendly but showed no disposition to beat a path to the door of my office, and I began to wonder what made them so shy of me. Did I, perhaps, look too young to be a lawyer? Then one day while poking about in Judge Wynkoop's closet I stumbled upon an old stovepipe hat and ivory-headed cane which must have been his. The hat was shabby and cracked, and the silk was so ruffed and worn that in spots it was almost bare, but it fitted me exactly. "Well," thought I, "it won't cost me anything to wear it and see what happens."

That evening I paraded around the square and, strangely enough, the very next morning acquired a client. He was a house

painter named Hiram Watkins who six months before had consulted Dr. J. Otis Osgood, the town's leading physician, about
a wen the size of a marble which had unexpectedly appeared in
the middle of his forehead, greatly to the disadvantage of his
appearance. The doctor had offered to remove the wen for the
inclusive price of fifteen dollars, but since Watkins did not have
the money and the doctor's office needed touching up, it had
been agreed that the former should give it two coats of the right
shade, after which the doctor should remove the wen. The
painter had made an excellent job of it, but, to his dismay, when
he had finished, the wen had disappeared.

Although gratified at what nature had thus performed free of
charge, Watkins, who had spent over seven dollars in paint, felt
that Dr. Osgood ought at least to compensate him for his materials. The doctor for his part maintained, reasonably enough,
that he had not agreed to pay cash money for having his office
renovated but only to remove a wen, and this he was ready to
do. He even offered to remove any other wen Watkins might
have upon his anatomy now, or hereafter, or to do the same thing
for one of his relatives. Watkins, who had neither wen nor relatives, felt greatly aggrieved. He had laid his complaint before
Mason who, since Dr. Osgood was one of his best paying clients,
had shooed him out of his office. It was at this point that, convinced there was no such thing as justice in the world, he had
observed me stalking about in Judge Wynkoop's stovepipe hat
and, learning that I was a lawyer, he had decided to consult me.

It will be seen that a highly delicate question was involved.
The doctor had profited by an undertaking which he was ready
and willing to perform but which nature had intervened to
render impossible. It was true that this was not his fault, but
neither was it that of Watkins. While the law would regard the
doctor's mere promise to remove the wen as a sufficient consideration to support a contract, it was clearly the intent of both parties
that he should actually delete it in return for having Watkins
paint his office. Would the law imply an understanding that, if he

were prevented from paying for the paint job in the method agreed upon, he should do so in another? Although such decisions as I could find were against me, I nevertheless felt that in all justice Dr. Osgood should do something to recompense my client for his time and materials.

The issue had been hotly debated from every angle at the grocery store and around the village horse-trough, and the Rev. Gamaliel Drum, one of the local preachers, who never lost an opportunity to advertise his own sanctity by fulminating against the backslidings of others, had even gone so far as to deliver a sermon aimed at the doctor, based on Matthew 25:24; "I know thee that thou art a hard man, reaping where thou has not sown." As a result, on the morning of the trial the Justice Court was packed with eager townsfolk.

"Squire" Dow, who was to determine the issue, was the owner of the local Hay & Feed Store. It was one of his earlier cases— he had only recently been elected a justice of the peace—and he was anxious to make a good impression. For a similar reason so was I. It was the first time I had ever appeared at the bar in Pottsville; I was careful to do so in full regalia; and I suspect that Judge Wynkoop's stovepipe hat and ivory-handled cane impressed the feed-store proprietor quite as much as my argument on the law.

The testimony of the parties having been given I addressed a fervent plea to the conscience of the court. My client, I urged, had not only squandered many hours which he might otherwise have devoted to his wife and children, but had paid out of his own pocket for the paint used to redecorate the doctor's office and increase the latter's earning capacity. The disappearance of the wen was clearly an act of God and thus the case, as the learned justice of course well knew, became one of "unjust enrichment" for which the law would furnish redress by applying the ancient doctrine of *"quantum meruit."* My argument was received with audible approval by the audience and since Dr. Osgood had not regarded the claim as of sufficient importance to justify the retention of counsel, Squire Dow delivered judgment in the following terms:

"If Doc Osgood don't pay Hi Watkins for this paint job, he'll be gittin' som'p'n fer nuthin' which, as Lawyer Tutt pints out, is agin' justice and ekkity. O' course if they had both knowed the wen might go away of its own accord they'd hev' planned accordin'. But as they didn't, the law will make sich arrangements for 'em. Figurin' Hi's time at fifty cents an hour and paint at wholesale rates with five per cent discount fer cash, my judgment is fer the plaintiff in the sum of fifteen dollars and thirty cents, without costs."

The news of this triumph of justice, if not of law, swept through the town and became the principal topic of conversation. Behold, I might have sat for months smoking my stogies in my small Grecian temple, when Presto! through the fortuitous combination of a wen, a paint job, a stovepipe hat and a few ambiguous Latin phrases I became locally famous. It was as if a minor mantle of Judge Wynkoop's had descended upon me—as indeed it had. From that day I took my place alongside Judge Tompkins, the Rev. Drum, Dr. Osgood, Lawyer Mason, and the rest of the elite as "Lawyer Tutt." God moves in a mysterious way. And when, a few weeks later, the wen suddenly reappeared upon Hi Watkins' forehead and the doctor, thereupon, promptly removed it for a fee of fifteen dollars and thirty cents, everyone perceived that "Squire" Dow's decree had received the approval of the Almighty and my reputation was enhanced accordingly. Thereafter I had no dearth of clients, although few were of the fee-paying variety.

The most notable figure in the town was old Judge Tompkins of Utica, who during the sittings of the Supreme Court boarded at the Phoenix. He was not a great lawyer, but he was gentle, kindly and not averse to straining a point to achieve what he regarded as a just result. He was fond of fishing and during term time he and I spent many a Saturday and Sunday on Chasm Brook, where I confess we did not always abstain from the discussion of cases. If, as it is sometimes asserted, lawsuits today are won on golf courses, I am afraid that in those days I won a good many sitting on one end of a log with the Judge on the other, while we gave the trout a rest. One day Willie Toothaker threw a baseball which came so near Tompkins that, although he ducked, it knocked off his tall hat. All he said was: "Only think, Willie! If I had been an upright judge you might have killed me!"

The Judge having been a country lawyer himself took a fatherly interest in my career, encouraging me to believe that I could not only earn my living in Pottsville, but be of genuine service to the community. He was well versed in Greek and Roman literature and, since I had stood well in the classics at Black River and had continued to study them at college, we often read Ovid and Terence, Plato and Aristotle together in the evenings. After his thirty years on the bench he was wise, tolerant and mellow, with a high regard for human nature.

His general view was, I believe—like that of Justice Holmes—that whatever social or economic theories people might hold, and however bitterly they fought over them, they ought to have a chance to test them and that in the long run things would probably come out much the same. I remember asking him whether if he had his life to live over again he would do anything different. He thought a long time. Then he gave a quiet smile and said: "I think I'd go fishing about twice as often!"

In a rural community each of the inhabitants has an opportunity to develop his own individuality; there is no class to which he must conform. The city produces types, the village what are known as "characters." Pottsville had the usual quota.

Constable Moses Higgins, who spent most of his time lounging around the hotel, soon became my firm ally. He was a tall, gawky, tow-headed man, and was paid by the fee system, his business being to serve papers, run errands, and keep track of jurymen and witnesses. Since he was highly popular he bid fair to be a hardy perennial as an officeholder. The relationship be-

tween us was, I confess, equivocal, although Mose strictly differentiated between his services as a constable for which I paid
him his regular fees, and those he rendered ex-officio as a friend.
It was inevitable, however, that he should profit indirectly by
acting as what in the city would be called a "runner." He often
accompanied me on my excursions and, because he disliked
Mason, took delight in steering clients in my direction. I remember once his bringing in a farmer named Wasgatt on whose cow
a chattel mortgage was about to be foreclosed. I managed to
save the cow for him and in return, since he had no money, he
told me of a pool, known only to himself, in which lurked an
enormous trout. The next afternoon, taking Mose along with me,
I went there and was lucky enough to hook it on my first cast. It
weighed three and a half pounds and put up a fight lasting nearly
half an hour. As Mose finally netted it he grinned at me and remarked: "Well—there's Wasgatt's cow!"

Old Eben Pillsbury drove the only public vehicle in Pottsville.
His charge for any trip within the town limits—a radius of at
least two miles—was twenty-five cents. On Fair Days his ancient
carry-all bulged with passengers—three or four on each seat and
others hanging on the steps. One day I was taken aback by his
asking thirty cents for taking me to the "deppo."

"Used to be a quarter," he explained apologetically. "But there
weren't enough money in it."

Among my first clients was William C. Gookin, famous as a
"joiner," a pompous man whose lapels were crowded with em-
blems. He was known as "Toggery Bill" for the reason that he
was proprietor of the "Boston Store," the largest haberdashery
shop in Pottsville. Cyrus Pennypacker, who ran the "Art Foto
Saloon," was another. Cy was a plucked chicken of a man, with
watery gray eyes and a protuberant, ambulatory Adam's apple,
of the type later immortalized by Webster in "Caspar Milque-
toast." As the henpecked husband of Mason's only sister
Saphrony, he had the sympathy of most of the male inhabitants
of Pottsville and also their admiration as a would-be Don Juan,

for Cy, according to local tradition, had once had the unexpected bravado to invite Zayda, the handsome wife of "One-Eyed Pedro," chief of the Zingara Gypsies—with the alleged consent of her husband—to pose for some of his "art fotos." Saphrony had unexpectedly interrupted the sitting and Cy had never heard the last of it.

"Patrons of Husbandry Hall No. 769," a three-story brick building, filled half of one side of the village square. Colson's grocery occupied the left-hand street corner and Thompson's tobacco shop, with its wooden effigy of King Wagamoc, the other. The Hall, owned by a quasi-Masonic order known as the "Sacred Camels of King Menelik," had a tin cornice, resembling a somewhat dingy tiara, on which was painted a jagged range of bright blue hills emblematical of "The Purple Mountains of Abyssinia" of whose esoteric brotherhood the Camels constituted a chapter. Both "Toggery Bill" and Pennypacker, as well as Mose Higgins, were members in good standing, and largely through their determined opposition Mason, in spite of his local prominence, had never been elected. Since they enthusiastically supported my candidacy I achieved this distinction within six months of my advent in Pottsville. As a result, and partly owing to our professional rivalry, two factions grew up in the town, one headed by Mason, and the other, composed primarily of Sacred Camels, by myself.

There was in addition a "book club," an "historical society," a "grange," a raft of church sociables, while regularly on Saturday nights a group of friendly spirits—including Dr. Osgood, "Toggery Bill" Gookin, and Judge Tompkins, when he was in town, conducted a small poker game in my office, enlivened by a modest consumption of "Old Doc Robinson's Malt Extract."

In the country doctors and lawyers often have to take their payment "in kind," and during the four years of my practice in Pottsville I received in lieu of cash a total of several cart loads of apples, onions, turnips, beets and potatoes which I turned over to Ma Best. The most satisfactory of such fees—and the only

one I consumed almost entirely by myself—I received in what
was called "a hoss case."

The Somerset County Fair was the great annual event, drawing crowds to the race track and attracting visitors from Albany,
Utica and even Buffalo to watch the trotting and pacing. At other
times the fair ground were turned over to the use of circuses,
gypsy encampments, medicine shows or an occasional horse-
traders' caravan. The most colorful of these belonged to "Doc"
Robinson, a spare old fellow with leathery skin, watery blue eyes,
and a drooping walrus moustache which, like the long curling
hair which fell below his collar, was jet black except at the
roots. He wore a ten gallon hat, a greasy frock coat, soiled red
waistcoat with tarnished silver buttons, and much shrunken
checked trousers pulled over high boots. About once a year he
drove into town in a yellow wagon, on which was painted in
cerulean letters "The All Healing Salve & Pain Cure Robinson,"
followed by a string of moth-eaten nags in charge of two Negro
boys. Here today and gone tomorrow he would peddle a cure-all
for half a dollar, or buy, sell or exchange "hoss-flesh."

Nobody in Pottsville liked Doc, because even among horse
traders he had a shady reputation—"Honor Among Hoss-
Thieves," so to speak. Doc, conversely, did not like human beings,
but he loved horses and would watch over an ailing bone-bag
with tenderest solicitude. In this he reminded me of my mother,
and because of it I came to have a certain fondness for old
Doc.

One morning he was arrested on the complaint of a farmer
named Jake Perkins, who charged that, after he had purchased a
gray mare from Doc one afternoon, the latter had returned the
following night and stolen it. The mare had disappeared from the
barn and Perkins declared that he had discovered her next morning among Robinson's other horses down on the fair grounds.
Doc vehemently insisted upon his innocence, protesting that the
mare thus identified was another animal entirely. He was
promptly indicted by the Grand Jury and lodged in jail, where

being unable to furnish bail he remained, far less concerned over his own fate than over that of his horses. Could he have still legally insisted on a right to submit the question of his guilt or innocence to "wager of battle" or the "ordeal of water," it is possible that the Almighty might have intervened to help him. But alas! they had long since both been abolished.

Now I felt sure that Doc was not a horse-thief—at any rate not that kind of a horse-thief—and on his assurance that Perkins was absolutely mistaken I agreed to defend him on the charge of grand larceny. Admittedly the facts were against him. His story was that he had driven from Corinth with a caravan of thirteen horses, including a pair of whitish-gray mares with white bobbed tails. Passing Perkins' farm he had sold him the off mare, then gone on to Pottsville, camped on the race track with the remaining twelve animals, and had never laid eyes on the mare again.

But Perkins swore not only that Doc had had but one gray mare instead of the two alleged, but that when he had found his purchase among the other horses on the race track a feeble attempt had been made to disguise her by the addition of a false tail, which had come off in his hand on being subjected to a slight pull. The sheriff had thereupon impounded the animal and put it in the Phoenix Hotel stable. It was a pot-bellied, sway-backed, miserable-looking creature, with thick fetlocks, an obvious spavin on the off hind hock, well defined collar marks on chest and withers and projecting yellow teeth. As David Harum might have said, the only evidence that it was a horse was the fact that it was not something else. I could not see any possibility of Doc's acquittal, and yet something told me that he was telling the truth when he said the mare was not the same one that he had sold to Perkins.

On the morning of the trial Pottsville presented a spectacle akin to that on fair day. Every hoss-trader between Utica and Albany—which meant the entire male population of the Mohawk

Valley—had come to town. The case was called and Jake Perkins told his story. On cross-examination I asked him if he had any doubt whatever that the mare he had found in the defendant's possession was the one he had bought from him the afternoon before, and he replied positively that he could identify it anywhere. On my motion the court then adjourned to the Phoenix Hotel stable in order to give the jury an inspection of the stolen property. Here I pointed to the three nearest stalls from which projected the sunken rumps, gaunt hind legs and frayed bobbed tails of three gray scarecrows.

"Now show His Honor and the jury the mare you charge Robinson with stealing from you," I challenged.

Jake carefully studied the three cadaverous behinds and ran his hands down the knobbled legs, then solemnly unhitched each one and led her out onto the stable floor for further examination. Finally all three mares were placed side by side. Each had saddle marks on the withers, each a spavin on the off hind hock.

"Durn if I kin tell one from t'other!" he confessed.

"In that case," ruled Judge Tompkins, "it is obvious that the witness' testimony as to the identity of the mare found in the defendant's possession is not of the required quality upon which to base a conviction for larceny. I therefore direct a verdict of not guilty."

That evening after Doc's discharge I asked him in my office why, if he had really had a pair of matched grays when he passed through Corinth, he had not called a witness to that effect, instead of allowing Perkins' testimony to stand uncontradicted save for his own.

"Wa-al," said Doc, lighting a fresh stogy, "Y'see, I got that team of mares under rather peculiar circumstances. In fact, it didn't seem exactly advisable to let the owner know I had 'em. So I dyed 'em. They was piebalds ez fur ez Corinth, and then I cleaned up the off one and sold her to Perkins. After I got into Pottsville I fixed up the other one that same night—put a nice tail on her an' all—ready to sell. Fust thing I knew, along came Perkins next mornin' and claimed her fer hiz. But she warn't! No, sir! When Perkins bought that off gray, the nigh one was a piebald."

"I see," I said, as the truth dawned upon me. "They were piebalds as far as Corinth and after that they became gray mares again? Anyhow you didn't steal either of 'em from Perkins."

Doc evaded my eye.

"Not from Perkins!" he murmured.

Doc lost no time in getting out of town and I never saw him again. He took with him the two scarecrows I had purchased as exhibits.* He had no cash himself to repay me, he said, but he promised to sell them at the first good opportunity and remit the money. In lieu of a fee he placed in the wood-bin of my office a gross of his "All Healing Salve & Pain Cure" and another gross of "Old Doc Robinson's Malt Extract" which he asured me had in it "considerable of the real stuff." This last statement I found to be true, and although his brand is no longer on the market, I still find "malt extract" exceedingly beneficial. Two years later I received a money order for one hundred dollars from Memphis, Tennessee, enclosed in a note reading:

Jest sold yore pare hosses. This time they wuz chestnuts.

Doc.

Here let me pause to correct a false impression. Pottsville was in reality not at all the sort of "hick" town portrayed by my friend, Arthur Train, in his many stories of my legal adventures.

---

* The advertisement, through which I secured the two mares had appeared in the *Pottsville Weekly Clarion* two days previous:

WANTED: Two whitish-gray mares, fifteen hands, three inches high, weighing about 1,300 lbs. Must be at least twelve years old, with sway back, pot belly, bobbed tail, collar marks on withers and chest, and a spavin on off hind hock. Will pay $50 cash each for same if delivered between the hours of 6 and 8 a.m. in front of Phoenix Hotel, Pottsville, on Tuesday next.—EPHRAIM TUTT.

In telling him my experiences as a young country lawyer it was perhaps only natural that, after forty years, I should have somewhat emphasized the rusticity of certain of my fellow townsmen, but this does not justify him in picturing life in Pottsville as a b'gosh melodrama or the entire male population as morons.

Pottsville was like any one of fifty thousand other villages of that era, composed for the most part of intelligent, wide-awake people, whose eye to the main chance was mitigated by a great deal of kindliness and even of generosity. There was, to be sure, plenty of malicious gossip and sharp dealing, but the woman who slandered her neighbor would be the first to bake a cake for her if she fell ill, and the man who drove the sharpest bargain was often a local philanthropist. Granted that some of my cases had a humorous aspect, I had plenty that were tragic. Reading Train's stories one would think that the trial of a lawsuit in the Pottsville courthouse was inevitably a rollicking farce and that the Sacred Camels of King Menelik, who numbered many of the leading citizens, were a gang of yokels. In point of fact our meetings were conducted with a decorum that many similar orders in the metropolis might well have copied. A writer of fiction may perhaps be justified, when necessary to point a moral, in making use of what is popularly known as "poetic license," but that cannot excuse the libel of an entire community.

The fact that my office was directly opposite the Phoenix House proved not only convenient, but generally advantageous. Such clients as came to me were apt to seek refreshment at the hotel, while guests in need of legal advice—and my beckoning sign frequently suggested to them the idea that they were—had only to cross the street. Between us Ma Best and I "got 'em coming and going." In fact I could sit swapping yarns and smoking my stogies on the veranda until likely prospects hove in sight. Few paid me more than a dollar or two, and most of them nothing at all, but even these did not represent a total loss, since those who had no money often made up for it by confiding to me piscatorial secrets far in excess of the value of my services.

I was fortunate in being able, almost at once, to show my gratitude to Ma Best. Living at the hotel was her father, Cap Barrows, a cheery old soak with an insane glitter in his watery eye
whenever the conversation turned on diamond mines, gushers, or
the distillation of gold from sea-water.—"I seen 'em do it, I tell
ye!" He had served part of a term in Sing Sing for swindling
Somerset County farmers by means of worthless bonds—in the
value of which he had implicitly believed—until at length a
governor, more humane than the law, had pardoned him.
Now at seventy-three he had come home to Ma and the Phoenix.

"I don't want no more money!" he told me, carefully wrapping
one of my stogies in an old envelope. "I ain't never needed it! I
know enough secrets to make me rich a dozen times over. All I
want is justice—my legal rights. But I'm tired of fightin' against
'em. They've beaten me! I shall retire and wait until my ship
comes in!"

Cap's ship never did come in. He became vaguer and vaguer.
"Hi, Willie!" he'd call huskily to the Toothaker boy. "You go
up to what's-his-name's—you know where 'tis—and fix those
what-do-you-call-'ems!"

Everyone in town liked Cap except the Rev. Drum, who one
day publicly referred to him as "an old crook." Cap retaliated by
calling the preacher "an old fool." Drum, outraged, had Cap arrested for disorderly conduct and in addition brought an action
against him for slander. I promptly countered with a similar suit
against the minister, as well as an action for "false arrest." While
popular sympathy was strongly with Cap, it was assumed that he
would undoubtedly go to jail for insulting the cloth. Once more
Judge Wynkoop's old books proved a precious help in time of
trouble, for I dug up a decision to the effect that, although the
words "old fool" spoken with regard to a lawyer or doctor would
affect his professional standing, they did not do so if spoken of a
minister. As the old French law put it: *Parce que on peut estre
bon parson et grand fou; d'un attorney aliter.*" ("Because it is

possible to be both a parson and a big fool as well; while it is otherwise with a lawyer." *

Having exonerated Cap I now pressed my action against Drum for calling him an "old crook" and causing his arrest, and although—in view of my client's criminal record—it had seemed unlikely he could recover, I was able to satisfy Judge Tompkins that, since Cap had been pardoned, he was "in the eye of the law as innocent as if he had never committed the offense," † and secured a verdict against the Rev. Drum for $100.

There is no better training for the law than general practice in a country town. I learned more in a single year in Pottsville than I would have in a decade in New York or Chicago, where I might have spent my time correcting the proof of corporate mortgages and perhaps never so much as seen the clients for whom I was working. In Pottsville on the contrary I was directly responsible for the advice I gave and, since I took everything that came my way, I had to familiarize myself with every sort of law, from contracts to breach of promise, undue influence, and domestic relations to trusts, mandamus, and "covenants running with the land." I personally drafted every paper from the original summons to the final judgment; I hunted down the witnesses, interviewed them and arranged for their appearance in court; I made mistakes—often egregious ones—but I profited by them and acquired a vast amount of practical experience that I could have got in no other way. The entire life of the town unrolled before me in panorama. In time I became—along with the clergyman and the family doctor—father confessor to half the inhabitants. My pay in cash was negligible, but what I learned was beyond all price.

It was astonishing how one thing led to another. Because Angus McGillicuddy had sent me to Ma Best and I lived at the Phoenix House, I naturally attended to its trifling legal matters without charge. Now the law of innkeepers goes back to the

* See also Coxater *vs.* Parsons, 11 Mod. 141, note.
† Ex parte Garland, 4 Wallace, p. 380.

time of Robin Hood and illuminates the whole history of the English people, and my interest led me to such an intimate acquaintance with it, that I later became counsel to the Waldorf-Astoria Hotel Company in New York City. It is amusing that my retainer as representative of a great hotel system is directly due to my friendship with an elderly souse who lived across the hall from me my sophomore year at college.

My clients were simple people, the amounts of money involved were comparatively small, but these and their domestic troubles were of vital importance to them. I patched up many a quarrel between old friends, misunderstandings between husbands and wives, parents and children; I saved mortgages from foreclosure and notes from default, and I made many a skinflint pay through the nose. What my clients could not pay in dollars they made up in friendship, and at one time I stood godfather to so many local infants that I kept a supply of plated mugs, bought by the dozen, in Judge Wynkoop's closet.

In a country town one has a first-hand opportunity to see how the law has actually developed. The primitive method of settling disputes was by brute force, and for thousands of years men simply fought it out singly or in families. As late as 1821 an Englishman accused of crime could claim his "wager of battle" and either challenge his accuser himself or select a champion to represent him. Even today in the United States, for great numbers of people, "prize-fight justice" is still all the justice there is.

The only dentist in Pottsville was Doc Pettibone, a sadistic old man with Chinese whiskers, whose office was a dingy torture chamber over the Art Foto Saloon. Doc would pull a tooth for twenty-five cents, but his low charge was merely a lure. Oblivious to his patient's agonies and, in spite of the greater profit to be derived from excavating and filling, he preferred extraction as a matter of clean sport.

Jacob Bostwick, a gigantic farmer, had come in with a face swollen to the size of a wasps' nest from the ulceration of a molar.

Doc's eyes gleamed and, tackling it with his forceps, he and his patient were soon floundering about the office and eventually into the street. But when nature had surrendered to violence Doc discovered that he had pulled a perfectly good tooth!

Bostwick, who could have pulverized Pettibone with one hand, saw no reason to pay a lawyer to fight his battles for him. Having read somewhere about "an eye for an eye and a tooth for a tooth," he now publicly insisted on his right to yank out one of Doc's teeth in retaliation, and for a time it looked as if mayhem might result. Pettibone sought sanctuary in my office where I concealed him in the coal closet. It would have done no good to attempt to explain to Bostwick that, if he put his threat into execution, he would land in jail; he wanted the revenge to which he believed himself entitled. Now it happened that the "tooth for a tooth" doctrine is to be found not only in Leviticus but in the code of laws formulated * by Hammurabi, King of Babylon, in 2,285 B.C., of which there was a copy among Judge Wynkoop's ancient volumes. So I put it in my pocket and went in search of Bostwick.

"That law you are invoking is three thousand years old," I informed him. "It has no application today."

"It's good enough for me!" he shouted.

"But you can sue Pettibone and get damages."

"To hell with damages! It's his tooth I want."

"So you stand absolutely on the *Lex Talionis*?"

"I don't know what that is, but I want the old law you talk about."

"All right, then," I said producing the book. "I'll read it to you. 'If a man has made the tooth of a man that is his equal to fall out, one shall make his tooth fall out! If he has made the tooth of a poor man to fall out, he shall pay one-third of a *mina* of silver.' Now, your case falls under the last clause because you are a poor man. You are entitled to a third of a *mina* of silver, but not to a tooth."

* On clay tablets in so-called "cuneiform" writing.

Since he thought he had won his point about the law, Bostwick agreed to accept Hammurabi's rule of damages, and we worked it out together, with the aid of Webster's Dictionary. A *mina* was one-sixteenth of a talent, and a *talent* of Hebrew silver was the equivalent to \$2,176 in United States money. Hence, a *mina* would be worth \$136, and a third of a *mina* \$45.35, which Doc paid, gladly throwing in a rubber plate with a false tooth for good measure.

As my business grew in volume I found myself badly hampered for lack of clerical assistance. Since there were no typewriters in town, all my papers had to be copied in longhand, and this would have proved an intolerable burden had I not been able to avail myself of the hotel staff who were free to work for me in the evenings. Presently, when I found it necessary to have someone constantly on duty at the office, I took Willie on as a neophyte in my legal temple, and he became the nucleus of what later became the office force of Tutt & Tutt in New York City. I also employed Betty Best to act as my secretary whenever Ma could spare her from the hotel.

Much of my work consisted in drawing wills. I charged a dollar a will as against Mason's two and a half, and before he knew it I had a majority of the testamentary intentions of Pottsville in my safe. Some people have a horror of making a will, since it directs their thoughts towards the churchyard. Hence they postpone the matter until, either it is too late, or has to be done hurriedly and without due consideration. Others are so obsessed by the importance of properly disposing of their property that they spend their lives making fresh wills, codicils and revocations. I had old women clients who made their wills regularly once a month. Even at only a dollar a throw it was not unprofitable, especially as most of the changes were slight.

"Few things show the human character in a more ridiculous light than the circumstances of will making," says Hazlitt. "It is the latest opportunity we have of exercising the natural perversity

of the disposition, and we take care to make a good use of it."
The testator can do as he likes and give what reasons he sees fit
for doing it, without fear of a comeback.

Two hundred years ago the publication of a will was held "a
very indecent proceeding" and a gross misuse of the facilities af-
forded by the probate court;* today, unless their contents were to
be publicized, many wills would not be made at all. Some testators seek to gain posthumous credit for generosity by explaining
that the reason they have not left larger bequests to charities or
relatives is because of donations already "made during my lifetime." Others pursue an even more disingenuous method of creat-
ing an impression of benevolence.

I had one crafty old client who drew a succession of wills in
which he bequeathed handsome legacies to everyone with whom
he wished to curry favor, in some cases tossing in the additional
tidbit of an executorship. The will having been drawn and executed, he would take it away and show it to the persons thus
supposedly to be benefited. Having thereby solidified himself
with A, B, and C, he would then draw another in favor of X, Y,
and Z, revoking the first.

After all, it did not cost Old Man Chisholm a single dollar
to play the part of an imaginary fairy-godmother to the whole
town of Pottsville. When he died the chancel of the church was
banked with flowers sent by expectant legatees, none of whom
ever got a cent. This and similar incidents gave rise to the wise
crack later popular among my office force that "the less they have
the more they leave." If any of my clients have gone to Heaven,
the next world must be crowded with odd sticks who have had
many a celestial chuckle over the bewilderment of those they left
behind on earth.

Many testators seize the opportunity to take revenge for real or
fancied injuries. One of the meanest post-mortem tricks in my
experience was that of an old Potts-villain, whose offers of mar-

* See *Legal Miscellanies* by Henry W. Taft, p. 134.

riage having been spurned by several local spinsters, ostentatiously left to each one of them a sum of money "in recognition of their favors during my lifetime."

Another man, who had driven his wife away from home by cruel treatment, brought me his will for safekeeping, explaining that Mason had drawn it for him. He died of delirium tremens not long after and, on opening the paper, I discovered it to be a foul attack on his wife's character under the guise of explaining in a codicil why he had revoked a bequest he had made her. While I might have secured the elimination of the objectionable matter from the context of the will, it would inevitably have become known, in a town as small as Pottsville, to the shame and irreparable injury of a good woman, irrespective of the falsity of the allegations. The wife would get a third of the estate in any event, and there were no other legatees. I could not swear out a warrant for criminal libel against the testator since he was already beyond the Styx, but there was a stove in my office, and I made use of it. I doubt if any fire on any altar ever gave more satisfaction to the Almighty.

Strange as it may seem a testator may devise or bequeath property *which does not belong to him* and under certain conditions the gift will be good. The principle known as "the doctrine of equitable election" is that "one who accepts a benefit under a deed or will must adopt the whole contents of the instrument, conforming to all the provisions and renouncing every right inconsistent with it. * * * A legatee or devisee accepting the benefit so given to him must make good the testator's attempted dispositions." * Thus if A, a testator, leaves to B the sum of $100 and to C a horse in fact belonging to B, should B elect to take the $100, C gets his horse.

I have, once or twice, sought to secure justice by invoking this doctrine. I had a case (Gooch *vs.* Cross) where I was morally certain that a ne'er-do-well, named Enoch Gooch, had destroyed

* Beeston *vs.* Stoops, 186 N. Y. 456, citing Havens *vs.* Sackett, 15 N. Y. 365.

his mother's will in order, as her sole heir-at-law, to inherit the farm which she had left to her then husband James Lawton, Gooch's stepfather. I tried to get ahead of him by having Lawton execute a will whereby he left Gooch a lot of worthless oil stock, at the same time deliberately devising the farm, on which he was still living, to his own daughter, Linda. I had hoped that, when his stepfather died, Gooch would elect to take the stock, thus forfeiting the farm; but he was too smart for me. He passed up the stock and claimed the land as he had legal right to do.

Years later I told Arthur Train about it and he wrote a story in which he pictures me as crooked as Gooch, since he has me tricking Gooch into the belief that the stock was vastly more valuable than the farm. His fictional statement is wholly unfounded and I take this opportunity to set myself right; but while I did not do it, I feel that I would have been almost justified in so doing. If the law recognizes force as a proper way to meet force, as in the right of "self-defense" and "recapture" of property, why should it not equally tolerate wile to meet guile?

I often think that for sheer ingenuity the country sharper is more than a match for his city brother. One reason, perhaps, is that he has more idle time on his hands in which to concoct his schemes. There is an old maxim of equity to the effect that "where there is a right, there is always a remedy." * The remedy, however, often eludes the search of the most persistent lawyer.

In 1898 the volumes of the reports of the New York Court of Appeals were not nearly so numerous as today, and during winter evenings when there were no lodge meetings or church sociables, I read them all through from beginning to end, stowing away in my memory a lot of odd bits of law many of which later proved of value. Before I left Pottsville Ma Best's daughter Betty married a young man named Bruce Tapley living with his mother on the "Old Tapley Farm" which included part of Chasm Brook. Three months later Mrs. Tapley, *née* Martha Farwell, died and

* *"Ubi jus ibi remedium."*

Bruce, as her only child, came into possession of the property under the will of Amos Tapley, his grandfather.

Amos Tapley had had two sons—Alan, already married with children at his death and Jed, a bachelor. By his will, wishing to keep the farm in the family, he divided it into two equal parts, one of which he left to Alan outright. The other half he left to Jed for life only, with the proviso that at his death it also should go to Alan and his heirs, unless in the meantime he should have married and had a child, in which event it should become his absolutely. Thus on their father's death each of the two sons became possessed of half the land—Alan outright, Jed for life only. For several years Jed had remained single, but in 1873 he had unexpectedly married Martha Farwell, and by her had a male child, my friend Bruce Tapley, who had married Betty Best. Jed had died in 1880, while Mrs. Tapley, his mother, had survived her husband many years.

Shortly after her death Ezekiel Morse, a real estate dealer in Fonda, filed a deed dated 1872 at the Record Office in Pottsville by which Jed Tapley had conveyed to Morse—subject to Tapley's own life estate—his entire right, title and interest in the Tapley Farm, inherited from his father Amos Tapley. The existence of this deed, which antedated Jed's marriage by nearly a year and the death of Martha Tapley by over twenty-five, had never been disclosed. On its face Ezekiel Morse had taken the remote chance—probably for an insignificant sum—that Jed might some time marry and have a child, in which case, the condition having been fulfilled, his life interest would become an outright ownership in fee and Morse would then acquire complete title to the property. Since there was apparently no way out of it, Bruce and Betty surrendered the farm to Morse and moved over to the Phoenix House.

Tucked somewhere in the back of my mind was the recollection of a similar case. Going through Martha Tapley's papers I found a letter to her from Morse, who had apparently been an old friend, dated a few months before her marriage, suggesting that she might do worse than to marry Jed Tapley, because the Tapley Farm was the richest in the county. With the letter was a certified copy of Amos Tapley's will. Since at the time Morse had written this letter he had had a deed to all Jed's interest in the land, his failure to disclose that the fulfilment of the condition would vest the title in him was an obvious fraud. After much effort I also managed to find an old sailor uncle of Bruce's who recalled hearing Morse tell Martha that she would make no mistake if she married Jed.

The question was how to raise the issue quickly and settle it once and for all. The ancient English method of determining land titles was by an action of trespass. Morse had already "posted" Chasm Brook, so Bruce and I openly fished there—under the claim that having done so for over twenty years we had acquired the right by prescription—and defied Morse to arrest us as poachers under Section 365 of the New York Conservation Law. He walked into the trap, swore out a criminal warrant, and haled us before Judge Tompkins sitting as a magistrate.

At the jury trial, which we demanded, Morse, in fear of being prosecuted for perjury, was forced to admit the foregoing facts. Thereupon I moved for a dismissal of the charge on the ground that not he, but Bruce, owned the land. At first Judge Tompkins could not understand what I was driving at; he did, however, when I called his attention to the case which I had at last remembered—Piper *vs.* Hoard, 107 New York 77—in which the Court of Appeals had held that "where a marriage is induced under (such) circumstances . . . the maker (of the falsehood) should be held to make good the thing to the person who would have had the property if the facts were as he represented, assuming such person to be the fruit of the marriage brought about by those very representations."

I argued that although Bruce had not been in existence when Morse deceived his mother into believing that, if the conditions in Mark Tapley's will were fulfilled, her future child would inherit the land, nevertheless he had been directly injured by

Morse's false representation, and since the law would not permit a man to profit by his own wrong, the court must declare him a trustee of the property for the party defrauded. Tompkins so instructed the jury who found in our favor, Morse was ousted, and Bruce reinstated as owner of the Tapley Farm.

Although this case occurred in my legal infancy, so to speak, the result was one of the most startling in my entire experience, for the jury's verdict of not guilty necessarily confirmed Bruce's title and rendered the issue *res adjudicata*. I know of no other instance where a court has held that the perpetrator of a fraud upon a parent makes himself liable for the transfer of real property to a person as yet unborn. Yet what could be more just?

The Tapley suit happens to be an instance where Arthur Train in writing a story was for once obliged to stick closely to the truth, for the reason that, being complicated, it left him no space for romancing. Usually, however, he lets himself go to such an extent that before he has finished I can hardly recognize my own case. Take for instance the yarn he calls "A Leaf from King John."

The actual facts were that a certain Major Bentley, a crabbed old fellow on School House Hill, had a driveway leading to his house lined with fine elm trees, in which he took great pride. He also held a mortgage on the adjoining farm, one boundary of which ran close to the drive referred to. While the farmer mortgagor had no money, he was good for the interest and it would have been a great hardship on him had Bentley foreclosed. The solution was simple enough. I had a surveyor run the line and thus discovered that the branches of most of the elms on one side of the driveway overhung the farmer's land. A threat on my part to abate what was clearly a nuisance on my client's property, by cutting off the offending branches, quickly brought the major to terms.

Now what did friend Train do to this? He gave the major a beautiful nineteen-year-old daughter named Phyllis, and made her deeply in love with a handsome young dairyman, a Cornell graduate, and the only son of a pious widowed mother. The lovely girl was determined to marry her gallant lover, but her father, through his ownership of a mortgage on her suitor's land, put the screws on Phyllis by threatening to foreclose and throw the youth and his saintly mother (who did not exist) out into the cold, cold world. It had in fact been no trick at all for me to hamstring the major, because it must have been obvious to anyone that his trees were trespassing on another man's land. So Train, characteristically, must make it harder, by having me accidentally read an almost forgotten history called the *Chronicles of Holinshed* and thus stumble quite by chance upon an account of how King John of England extorted ten thousand marks from a Jew in Bristol by pulling out one of his teeth every day until he gave in. This was supposed to give me the inspiration of cutting off each day a limb of one of Bentley's trees until he likewise yielded; and Train has a great branch-cutting scene where the handsome young farmer clasps the beautiful heroine to his bosom with one arm while swatting an elm with the other until he receives the parental blessing!

I suppose a fiction writer is entitled to use his imagination, but circumscribed by facts as I know them actually to be, any such distortion of the truth would be wholly beyond my powers. As my friend William Travers Jerome later used to say: "Exact knowledge is a great handicap to forcible statement!"

Living near the Phoenix House was a widow by the name of Mrs. Tarleton, who had inherited a small property from her first husband. She had a charming daughter Dorothy, a friend of Betty Best's. After a few years she married an elderly stranger in the town known as "Judge" Gamage, who craftily persuaded her to make a will by which, if the girl married without his consent before she reached the age of twenty-five years, her property should go to him.

The girl became engaged to an attractive and able young doctor, Alex Kellogg, and introduced him to her mother, who gave her approval to her marriage in the near future. Mrs. Tarleton having died shortly thereafter, Gamage, for the first time appearing in his true colors, refused his consent. The language of the will was plain, and the reason for the stepfather's refusal equally so. Dorothy must either wait six years to marry, or forfeit her estate. Under the circumstances she did what any courageous girl would have done—married her lover in defiance of her stepfather, who through Hezekiah Mason at once demanded and secured a declaratory judgment from Judge Tompkins to the effect that the property belonged to him.

At this juncture Dorothy consulted me as to whether or not there was anything she could do. In view of the fact that Gamage knew of her mother's approval of the match, the forfeiture seemed so unjust that I appealed from the judgment against her on general principles, believing that there must be some way out of it even if I did not know what it was. The record on appeal contained most of the foregoing facts, including a letter Dorothy had written to Gamage in which she stated that she proposed to marry Kellogg "in spite of the consequences." Pending the argument before the Appellate Division at Rochester I was fortunate enough to unearth a decision * to the effect that "where a person would have inherited an estate had there been no will, but does take it under a will containing a condition by which he may forfeit the property, *he cannot be held to have incurred the forfeiture unless it be first shown that he was aware of the condition and broke it with full knowledge of what the consequences would be.*"

Save for Dorothy's letter referred to above there was no specific evidence in the record that she had read the will or knew of the condition; and on the strength of this decision the Appellate Court reversed the judgment and gave her the property, holding that the words "in spite of the consequences" did not necessarily refer to her presumable loss of it. This was certainly a case where justice won by no more than a nose.

In ancient days it was the custom for the sheriff of each county

* Shackleford *vs.* Hall, 19 Illinois 212.

to summon all the inhabitants to what was known as an "assize" *
or sort of county parliament. If these found or, as it was called,
"presented" that someone had committed a crime, the accused
was punished, subject to his right to a "trial" by wager of battle
or one of the various ordeals in vogue at that period.

In Somerset County every defendant brought to the bar had,
to some extent at least, been already pre-judged by the community as a whole, including the trial jury sitting in the case,
who, no matter how forcibly instructed to the contrary by the
judge, in fact expected him to prove his innocence. There is far
more lynch law in country districts than in cities where the jury
rarely know, or have even heard of, the defendant. What is
called "law" easily becomes "lawlessness." This probably cannot
be helped, for usually once the "hue and cry" is raised a fugitive's rights are ignored. The instinct of the pack is aroused and
the man hunt often results in a "legal" kill. Such a case was that
of "Skinny the Tramp," where only by the grace of God was I
able to establish the innocence of a man already convicted in
the eyes of the entire countryside.

In a shanty on the hillside overlooking Turtle Pond lived Wilbur Drake, a harmless recluse known as "The Hermit of Turkey
Hollow." He was reputed to be a miser and to have a cache of
gold hidden on his premises, although his only visible possession
of any value was a grandfather's clock which stood opposite the
door. One afternoon he was found lying dead in his shack in a

* Originally most, or at least some, of this assize or "accusing jury," were
both witnesses and judges. When trial by "ordeal" or "battle" fell into disuse a "trial jury" was substituted. Originally the so-called "trial" consisted
merely in the defendant swearing to his innocence, and if he could get
twelve neighbors to swear that they believed his oath to be truc, he
went free. These "witnesses" were called "compurgators." The old "compurgators" have come to life in our present day "character witnesses."
The trial jury, usually, still had some of the accusers on it. Today the
old "accusing" jury has evolved into the "grand" jury sitting in secret session, and the "trial jury" into our "petit," or "petty," jury, from which,
theoretically, anyone who has personal knowledge of the alleged crime must
be excluded.

pool of blood, his fingers clutching a shining five dollar gold piece.

James Hawkins, accused of his murder, was an amiable half-wit called "Skinny the Tramp," who twice a year turned up in Pottsville for a week or so, camping in a clearing not far from the Hermit with whom he was on friendly terms. He was a half mystic, half rustic philosopher, popular with the townsfolk on account of his sweetness of disposition. Credulous, he implicitly believed that at the foot of every rainbow was a pot of gold.

On the afternoon of the murder a woodsman named Charles Emerson, who had been cutting pea-sticks a hundred yards or so from the Hermit's shanty, saw Skinny hurrying towards it. Shortly thereafter his attention was attracted by a shot from the cabin, on reaching which he found the Hermit dead upon the floor, amid the shattered fragments of an earthen crock. No one was in sight, but fancying that he heard a crackling in the bushes in the direction of the village, he ran as fast as he could along the tote road in pursuit.

At precisely four o'clock by the Western Union electric clock in Colson's Grocery, Skinny with a bloody handkerchief around his hand, which he explained he had cut in the woods, came in and ordered a glass of root beer. Emerson, yelling "Murder" at the top of his lungs, appeared fifteen minutes later. The hue and cry was raised and Skinny, who had disappeared, was apprehended in flight about a mile away and lodged in the village jail. He refused to answer questions, his shoes fitted the prints discovered under the Hermit's window, and there in his pockets were twenty glittering gold pieces of the same mintage as the one in the dead man's hand.

Hezekiah Mason, who had just been appointed district attorney of Somerset County, seeing in the case an opportunity to make a reputation, arranged for Skinny's indictment for the murder, and as I was the only other lawyer in town it fell upon my shoulders to defend him. My responsibility weighed on me heavily, and since my client would not open his mouth I, perforce, had to invent a defense—a dubious one at best. This was that if the crackling heard by Emerson in the bushes had been caused by the murderer, Skinny could not possibly be guilty because he could not have increased his start of a couple of minutes to fifteen in the course of a three-mile chase. The obvious answer to this was that the noise, whatever its nature, had been made by another person, or by some animal such as a deer.

The trial took place before Judge Tompkins, and it seemed as if all the inhabitants of the Mohawk Valley had crowded into the courtroom to make a Roman holiday out of what could be little else than a legal execution. The jury were a hard-boiled bunch of local farmers and tradesmen who, I felt, could not be swayed by anything save the evidence. Emerson was the first witness, and when he had finished there was obviously no doubt in their minds of my client's guilt. I noticed, however, that Mason had omitted to ask Emerson if he knew the exact time when he entered the Hermit's shanty. This placed me in a dilemma. If I put the question myself and the witness set an hour such as three fifty-five which would have made it impossible for Skinny to reach the grocery store by four o'clock, I would have gone far towards winning my case, but if he answered, as I expected, "three thirty" or "three forty" I would have driven one more nail in Skinny's coffin, for it would give him ample time to have got there. Yet why, I asked myself, had Mason failed to ask the question unless he knew in advance that the answer would be unfavorable to his side? Accordingly, although with much misgiving, I decided to chance it.

"Do you know what time it was when you reached the Hermit's cabin?" I inquired.

"I do," replied Emerson. "It was exactly four o'clock by the Hermit's clock."

Instantly a murmur swept the courtroom. The chief witness for the prosecution had established a perfect alibi for the defendant.

"That is all," I exclaimed triumphantly.

I expected Mason to go after him hammer and tongs, but he

did nothing of the sort, and it at once became apparent why he had not done so. Calling the photographer who, with Emerson, had accompanied the sheriff to the cabin several hours after the murder, Mason introduced in evidence a picture of the interior showing the hands of the clock still pointing to four o'clock. It was thus apparent that the clock had run down and had no evidentiary bearing on the hour of the murder. Mason had tricked me into asking Emerson the time in order afterwards to blast his testimony to smithereens!

Had Mason offered no more witnesses the case would have been ended. But the sheriff was an important public officer and, since he had investigated the *locus in quo,* measured the footprints outside and searched the body, his evidence was essential to fill out the picture. His testimony having been given at some length, the prosecutor asked him what, if anything, he had found in the Hermit's pockets, and in reply he recounted a list of miscellaneous objects, including matches, pipe, fish-hooks, pins, etc., and a hundred dollars in bills. It struck me as peculiar that a Hermit should have such a large sum upon his person, and I asked the sheriff to produce it. This he did—twenty crisp new five-dollar bills, each stamped in red ink: "W. Gookin—Pottsville's Boston Store."

Suddenly I had a flash. Was there possibly a connection between the twenty bills on the Hermit's body and the hundred dollars in gold pieces found in my client's possession? If Skinny had murdered the Hermit for his money, why had he not taken the hundred dollars in paper also?

My client, still remaining mute, I called Gookin to the stand and asked him when he had last seen the bills in question. He replied that on the morning of the murder Lawyer Mason had come into his store, borrowed a hundred dollars from him and given his note in return. I had Mason sworn and asked him if what Gookin had said was true, and he hesitatingly admitted that it was. I then inquired what he had done with the money. He replied, still more reluctantly, that he had given it to James

Hawkins, the defendant. By this time most of the spectators including Judge Tompkins, were on their feet.

"Why did you give the defendant this money?" inquired His Honor.

"Because he asked me for it. I'm trustee of a five thousand dollar fund of which he's the beneficiary and I pay him the interest twice a year."

Tompkins stared at him. That Mason should be prosecuting a man for whom he was trustee seemed, to say the least, strange. Obviously something besides murder had taken place in the cabin, and we hadn't yet got to the bottom of it.

Determined now to bring out every detail I recalled Emerson to the stand.

"Mr. Emerson," I said, "you have testified that when you entered the Hermit's cabin the hands of the clock pointed to four. When you returned with the sheriff two hours later did you notice that the hands still pointed to four?"

"I did."

"Didn't you realize that the clock had run down?"

Emerson shook his head.

"It was goin' all right when I went in," he said quietly. "When I lifted the Hermit's head an' looked in his face the shanty was quiet 'cept for three things. The fust was a kind of cluckin' sound the Hermit's breath made on account of the blood in his throat. He was jest passin' out; his eyes was half open but they didn't see none; I felt real creepy all alone with him dyin'. But what skeered me most was an enormous moth, the biggest I ever see, that was bumpin' agin' the glass of the winder tryin' to git out. I thought it would stun itself sure. The other thing was the tick of the clock. I saw the minute hand slip to four o'clock, and all of a suddint the hull shanty become still. The Hermit stopped breathin', the moth flew out of the door, an'—the clock stopped."

An eerie silence had descended upon the courtroom. Each of us felt as if he had been personally present in the shanty. But was it credible that the clock had stopped at the precise moment of the Hermit's death? Should I go on and try to clinch the hour in some other way? I decided in the negative. The alibi as it stood ought to be enough to raise a reasonable doubt of Skinny's guilt. Better leave well enough alone.

"That's all," I said.

Then Mason got up and asked scornfully:

"Do you expect us to believe that while you was holdin' a dyin' man's head in your hands you noticed a clock tick?"

Emerson steadily returned his glance.

"Whether you believe it or not, it's true. Anyhow, there can't be no doubt as to the time, because *just at that minute the whistle down to Sampson's mill blew four o'clock.*"

Only after his acquittal did Skinny tell me his version of what had occurred. He had been sitting on the hillside after a shower and had noticed the arc of a rainbow which seemed to be resting on the Hermit's shanty. Running as fast as he could he had peered in the window. Sure enough, the Hermit was sitting at a table in front of a pile of gold pieces beside an earthen crock. Skinny had gone in and at his request the Hermit had good-naturedly exchanged twenty of the gold pieces for the one hundred dollars in bills Mason had given him. That was all he knew about it. When he heard that the Hermit had been murdered he had been seized with fright and run away. He, too, remembered that the clock was going when he went in and that it had then pointed to a quarter to four.

Six months later one of the Zingara Gypsies, who had been camping on the Pottsville fair grounds on the day of the murder, confessed in the death house at Sing Sing where he was awaiting execution for another homicide, that he had committed the crime.

I am not a mystic, but I am not ashamed to admit that the undisputed facts in this case give me pause. Could there have been some relation between the stopping of the clock and the Hermit's death? Cannot an inanimate object in some mysterious way absorb or partake of the personality of its owner? People twit me about my clothes, but who dare say that my old stovepipe hat and frock coat are not as much a part of me as my heart and lungs? I know that without them I should lose my virtue and be like Samson without his hair. And the big gray moth? Was it possibly a materialization of the Hermit's soul seeking its escape from earth? Is it mere superstition that leads to the opening of the windows of a death chamber? I give it up! No doubt there are things in heaven and earth undreamed of in our philosophy. But the older I grow the more I agree with what Skinny once said to me:

"There's two worlds, Mr. Tutt. One you kin see an' smell an' touch, and one that you ordinarily can't—each right alongside t'other. Everything's alive—rocks 'n trees 'n flowers, an' water an' fire, an' bugs, an' beasts, just same as folks—an' none of 'em ever die. Everythin' has a ghost—walking right along beside it all the time—only it's in that other world. But sometimes— dependin' on circumstances—you kin catch a glimpse of what's goin' on there and see 'em and hear 'em."

Well, maybe he's right. Anyhow I believe that the clock stopped when the Hermit died.

> O, my grandfather's clock was too high for the shelf,
> So it stood ninety years on the floor.
> It was taller by half than the old man himself,
> Though it weighed not a pennyweight more.
> It was bought on the morn of the day he was born,
> And was always his treasure and pride,
> But it—stopped—short—never to go again—
> When—the old—man—died.

I received a good deal more credit for Skinny's acquittal than I deserved. Gradually I began to get retainers from elsewhere in the Mohawk Valley—from Fonda, Amsterdam, Canajoharie, Herkimer, and Utica—and from time to time my presence was required in Albany where I appeared before the Court of Appeals and met a number of judges, lawyers, and politicians, including former Governor David Bennett Hill, the Democratic up-State leader, and "Boss" Thomas C. Platt of the Republican

Party. But I was always glad to get back to Pottsville and when business took me to New York I was disgruntled by its size and noise.

It is hard, even after all these years, to put down in cold and lifeless words the greatest emotional experience of my life. I had long since ceased to have any feeling for Priscilla Boardman and, although I sometimes cringed at the thought of the way she had treated me, I still liked girls. I especially felt a need for intellectual companionship, of which, apart from Judge Tompkins, I found little in Pottsville.

One night in the autumn of 1897 I was sitting in the back of the room at our weekly "Book Club," when I found myself listening entranced to an unfamiliar but very beautiful voice. A young woman, whom I did not know, was describing in clear and charmingly modulated tones a play called *Candida* by an English author, Bernard Shaw. Her analysis of the playwright's meaning was penetrating and clever.

Surprised that anyone so attractive should have so long escaped me I pushed forward when she finished and asked to be presented. Dr. Osgood casually introduced her as Esther Farr. She was straight and tall, with a lovely pearl-pale oval face and exquisite brow, but it was the appealing wistfulness of her sensitive mouth and veiled brown eyes, at once sad and courageous, that most drew me to her.

After the party I offered to escort her home and we walked down Main Street under a hunter's moon with the elm leaves fluttering at our feet. She was, she told me, the only daughter of an elderly widowed clergyman, who had died during her sophomore year at Smith College. Since her graduation she had taught at various girls' schools but was now out of a job. It may have been the magic of the night, my loneliness, or the enchantment of her voice and beauty, but I was strangely thrilled—as if in an alien land I had suddenly come upon one who spoke my language. A vague vista of possible future happiness opened before me. We turned down a side street and stopped in front of a small white house. Betty Best had just married and I had no one but Willie Toothaker to help me in the office. As we said good night I asked Miss Farr if she would care to become my secretary. Before she could reply the door opened and a bearded man with a shawl over his stooped shoulders opened the door.

"Why didn't you say you'd be late?" he demanded peevishly. "I didn't think you were ever coming home!"

I saw her often after that and gradually she confided to me her story. Up to the time she had gone to college she had devoted herself to caring for her father, an authority on mediaeval ecclesiastical history. She had seen little of the village boys, none of whom were her mental equals, and when Richard Farr, one of her English instructors at Smith, had shown an interest in her she had fancied herself in love. He was considerably her senior but she was used to older men, and while still an undergraduate, on the death of her father which left her entirely alone she had married him. They had lived happily enough, until a year later her husband had had a nervous breakdown followed by a slight stroke of paralysis, as a result of which he had been obliged to resign his position. He had accumulated nothing. So at the age of twenty-two, she had brought her middle-aged, semi-invalid husband back to the house she had inherited from her father in Pottsville and was trying to support him.

I suppose I must have loved her from the moment I first saw her, since it was a shock to find that she was a married woman. She proved invaluable, typing my papers, interviewing my clients, and under my direction even looking up points of law; but most of all she taught me the wealth of human sympathy, for her own suffering had opened her heart to the troubles of others, and no one ever appealed to her for help who did not get it. She became the lovely priestess of my little Doric temple, and we shared there the greatest happiness of our lives. After the day's work was over and the last client had gone, we often sat reading or talking together in the twilight until it was time for her to go home. We did not have to tell each other that we were in love. I was twenty-eight; her husband was thirty-nine. Loyal, deeply religious, and with a strong sense of duty she had nothing against this man whom she still in a way admired, recognizing that his chronic irritability was not his fault. We were caught in life's trap, that was all. We could not bear to think of parting, yet we realized that we could not for long go on as we were, and when one day looking away from me she said, "Don't you think, Ephraim, that with your ability you ought to give yourself a chance in a bigger place?" I knew perfectly well what she meant.

I had already begun to feel that, professionally, Pottsville was too small for me. Although Cal Coolidge was still practicing in Northampton I knew from his letters that he was playing a well-thought-out game and merely biding his time. My occasional trips to larger cities, and particularly the excitement of the Spanish-American War, had stirred me to a sense of the importance of what was going on in the outside world. Admiral Dewey had annihilated the enemy fleet at Manila Bay and Theodore Roosevelt, "The Hero of San Juan," after a whirlwind campaign in his Rough Rider's uniform, had been triumphantly elected Governor of the State. I wanted a nearer seat at the big show.

While I had many friends among the townspeople I was really intimate with none except Ma Best, Esther and Judge Tompkins, who was about to retire from the bench and take up private practice in his home town; but my friendship with Esther was loaded with dynamite, and although the Judge had paid me the compliment of suggesting that we should open a law office together in Utica, under the firm style of Tompkins & Tutt, I had a hunch that, were I to forsake the country for any city, I had best choose the one offering the greatest opportunity. Therefore, towards the end of 1898, I packed my old carpet bag, closed my Grecian temple, bade goodbye to Ma Best and took the train for New York, quitting Pottsville as poor as when I had arrived there.

IV

I MEET THE BOSS

IN retrospect I wonder that I had the temerity to decline Judge
Tompkins' offer of partnership which would have meant
financial security and an established place in my profession before
the age of thirty. One would say that it would have been an ideal
career for me. I was a country boy and liked open air life and the
accessibility of forest and stream; I had a wide acquaintance
throughout the northern part of the state where I was known as
a "rising young man." Had I accepted his proposal I could have
gone straight ahead and ultimately have become perhaps a judge
of the Court of Appeals, a representative or even a senator from
my State in Washington. But I refused, and I am often puzzled as
to why I did. It may be because I am just a born refuser. I have
been refusing things all my life. I refused to practice law in Boston because I didn't like the cut of old Curtis' beard and now
apparently I had turned my back on a guaranteed future, to
begin life all over again in a strange city where I knew practically
no one and my past achievements would count for nothing.

Was it the attraction with which the imagination of youth
invests the unknown?

> "Something hidden. Go and find it. Go and look
>   beyond the Ranges—
> Something lost beyond the Ranges. Lost and waiting
>   for you. Go!"

Alas! What I had lost would not be waiting for me! I could
not find it because I would have left it behind me in Pottsville.

I reached New York City on October 5, 1898, equipped with
a considerable legal experience and the prime requisites for a
legal career—a good digestion and a stout pair of legs. There was
something ominous to me in the overwhelming roar of the great
city, which like a vast temple to Moloch each morning sucked
seething millions through tunnels, viaducts and bridges into its

gigantic belly to spew them forth again at evening. For the first few days I sought refuge with Otto at his home on Staten Island where he lived the year round with his wife and children, after which I plucked up courage and rented a hall bedroom in the theatrical district for a dollar and a half a week.

I had brought with me a few letters of introduction from Judge Tompkins and a certificate from the Pottsville branch of the Sacred Camels of King Menelik to the local lodge of the brotherhood in New York to the effect that I was a member in good standing, but the Judge's friends proved to be in an advanced state of legal decay and my brother Camels while friendly, unable to advance my professional interests. I assiduously followed up the advertisements for legal help in the Law Journal and visited such lawyers as were suggested by Otto without result. No one, however, seemed impressed by my qualifications and having tramped from one office to another for several weeks without finding an opening, I began to wonder whether, without friends or connections, I should ever be able to get a foothold.

One evening I was taking a turn on Fifth Avenue when a thickset man with a scraggy beard, who was about to cross Fiftieth Street in front of me, slipped on the curb and fell heavily to the sidewalk. I helped him to his feet, held him upright while he tested his legs, and then retrieved his tall hat from the gutter.

"I'm afraid I've sprained my ankle!" he said wincing.

"Shall I call a cab?" I asked.

"No," he said. "Give me your arm and I'll go back to the Club."

We staggered halfway down the block until we came to a tall flight of steps where by clasping the handrail he was able, with my assistance, to drag himself up to the door, which was instantly opened by a servant in livery. I was about to turn away when he took out a card and scribbled something on it in pencil.

"Come and see me at my office tomorrow morning," he said gruffly as he limped inside. The card read: "Richard Croker," and across it was scrawled "Pass this man in." A slippery curb had introduced me to "Boss" Croker, the master of Manhattan, the uncrowned king of New York City.

Tammany Hall, an ugly red brick building with stone coping and window facings, was on Fourteenth Street, and on the strength of my card I was at once admitted to the Boss's office on the right of the entrance. It was a large plain room furnished with rows of straight-backed chairs, the only decorations being portraits of departed Sachems, a huge American eagle and a life-size figure of an Indian chief clutching a tomahawk, which reminded me of King Wagamoc outside P. of H. Hall 769 in the square at Pottsville.

Mr. Croker, dressed in a checked bob-tailed tweed suit and gray bowler hat, stood smoking a cigar with the air of a monarch giving audience to his subjects. Composed and dignified, he listened for a few seconds to each suppliant and then dismissed him with either a curt "no" or "okay." Meanwhile his gray-green eyes were roving over the crowd and, presently recognizing me, he motioned me to follow him to a sort of private cubbyhole in the back of the room enclosed by folding doors. Here he sat down behind a desk and, handing me a cigar, inquired my name, occupation and political affiliations. When I explained that I was a lawyer and a Democrat he pondered a moment and then asked abruptly: "How would you like to be a deputy assistant district attorney?" To which I replied that nothing would give me greater pleasure. Thereupon, without more ado, he wrote out another card reading: "To A. B. G.—Make a place for this man. R. C."

"Take that to District Attorney Gardiner," he said holding out his hand. "You did me a good turn last night and I'm glad to do you one. Good luck!"

As I walked out the crowd deferentially opened a way for me.

"He don't look it—but he must be somebody," I heard one of them say.

"Tutt!" said I to myself, "this time you've fallen on your feet!"

Both by instinct and inheritance I was a Democrat. While I had disagreed with my father upon the doctrines of Jonathan

Edwards, I had concurred with him as to those of Thomas Jefferson. I was, as I have said, by nature a rebel; I was for the little dog and against the big dog; I disliked Mark Hanna; I was opposed to trusts and monopolies and the alliance of business with politics, and I did not believe that incorporated capital was a means to social and economic salvation. What I had seen going on in the Legislature at Albany left little choice between the Republican and the Democratic machines. Boss Platt was as bad as Boss Croker, perhaps worse, and Tammany represented the regular Democratic Party in New York City.

I took the bus to Franklin Street and walked down it to the Criminal Courts Building, a big gloomy pile connected by an overhead bridge with "The Tombs," a depressing Egyptian structure surrounded by a high stone wall. Inside it was dank and grimy, the walls fissured, the marble floors spotted with tobacco juice and the air stinking of stale cigars, unwashed bodies and prisoners' lunch. Packed in a bird cage elevator with Chinese, Italians, and an odoriferous human miscellany I rattled up to the district attorney's office on the third floor where a fat policeman drowsed over a newspaper. A telephone booth (it contained the only instrument in the office) stood outside a door on which was painted "Mr. Gardiner." My card stirred the cop to action.

The Honorable Asa Bird Gardiner, a slender, well-groomed, middle-sized man with sandy hair and moustache, was sitting at his desk beneath an artificial potted palm. Rather pompously he offered me his hand.

"How much of a job do you want?" he asked.

"I'm not particular," I said. "Mr. Croker—"

Evidently it was the proper opening, for he did not permit me to finish.

"How about two hundred and fifty a month?"

Masking my excitement I replied that I thought it might do.

"Well, it's all I have—at present," he said. "When can you go to work?"

"Any time—now!"

"All right. I'll take you down before Judge Goff and he can swear you in." He rang a bell and the cop stuck in his head. "Captain Palmer, tell Mr. Buckley to put Mr. Tutt on the payroll at three thousand a year."

The dingy office assigned to me was about ten feet by twelve with a single window overlooking an inner court. Directly opposite on the same corridor was a large room given over to process servers known as "county detectives" or "counties." I had hardly seated myself at the rickety desk when a debonair, smooth-shaven young man, in a cut-in-at-the-waist suit and pointed patent-leather shoes appeared in the doorway.

"Anything I can do for you, Mr. District Attorney?"

"Not that I know of—" I answered.

"Well, if you want anything just ask for 'Bonnie' Doon. You might as well start your expense account right now." He laid a foolscap sheet on the desk and bending over entered the item: "Nov. 29. Lunch for self and assistant. $2.00."

Already I had my foot inside the door and, as it seemed, my hand in the till!

That was my introduction to Mr. Bonright Doon, who from that moment became my guide, counsellor and friend in the muddy waters of Tammany politics. He was a cynical, waggish lad, whose zest of life exceeded his thirst for intellectual improvement, but beneath his superficial toughness his heart was in the right place. He has remained in my employ ever since—as a sort of legal factotum, sleuth and, at times, a bodyguard. We have a deep affection for one another—the attraction of opposite poles, perhaps. Such loyalty as Bonnie's is without price. Should I tell him to steal the Bible from the dais in Part I of the Court House he would not hesitate and, most likely, would bring back all other books as well. I do not mean that Bonnie would commit a real crime for my sake, any more than Mose Higgins in Pottsville would have done so, but he certainly would give both himself and me the benefit of any doubt.

Next day Colonel Gardiner sent me down into Part I to help

the Honorable Robert Townsend, the assistant district attorney in charge, "dispose of the calendar," a process consisting, for the most part, of inducing as many prisoners as possible to plead guilty and thus save the State the bother of a trial. The odds were made as attractive as possible. A murderer, who might get the chair, would be offered a plea to "manslaughter," or a burglar, liable for twenty years, one to "illegal entry," depending on how strong the evidence in either case might be. Since Mr. Townsend was notoriously easy-going most of those under indictment yielded to his persuasions.

"Bob" was deservedly popular, his only defect as a prosecutor being that he suffered from some obscure malady which prevented him from keeping awake in court. Once he had opened a case he usually fell sound asleep, leaving it to the judge to safeguard The People's interests. He was glad to have me relieve him and snored appreciatively through the several hundred prosecutions I conducted in his behalf during the next few terms. The work was extremely easy and soon became so nearly automatic that I almost used to go to sleep myself. There were not many acquittals since only "dead-open-and-shut" cases were moved for trial, and once in a while a bushel basket of stale indictments would be brought into court and surreptitiously "recommended out," simply because no one wanted to try them.

It was excellent experience and at first I was thrilled with a sense of importance and power. I wanted to try every case, or in the alternative—since each indictment had been voted by a Grand Jury—to know why it should not be prosecuted. Occasionally my enthusiasm got me into trouble, but I was still a yokel so far as politics was concerned and it was some time before I suspected anything below the surface. Hence I was indignant when just before Christmas, Otto, who had been out of town on business, unexpectedly appeared in my office.

"How did you land in this hell-hole!" he exclaimed.

"By virtue of my outstanding ability!" I smiled.

"You're not going to stay here!"

"Why not? I need the money."

"Don't you know that Gardiner is just a rubber stamp for Boss Croker and that this office is a municipal cesspool?"

"I hadn't noticed it," I said. "Mr. Gardiner is an able lawyer with a distinguished war record. He is, I admit, a Democrat— but so am I. So long as he pays me $250 per month I shall be only to glad to try his cases for him."

Otto scowled. Through the dirt-encrusted windows we could look down at the prisoners taking their exercise in the courtyard of The Tombs.

"Look here, Eph!" he said. "I advised your coming to New York and I feel responsible for you. We had a decent city government under Mayor Strong, with Theodore Roosevelt as Police Commissioner and Colonel Waring as head of the Street Cleaning Department. But a year ago last autumn Boss Platt and Boss Croker made a deal which turned New York over to Tammany Hall. Now the town's wide open and every saloon, brothel and gambling house in the City is going full blast, under the protection of Chief of Police Devery. He and Gardiner represent the majesty of the law—otherwise 'The System.' "

"You're the same old Savonarola!" I retorted. "I suppose you'd like to see every Democrat walking the lock step down there! Of course one side has to win, and the 'outs' are always sore because they've lost. My associates in this office may not be cerebral giants but they're an honest capable lot—a good deal above the average. I don't see any reason why I shouldn't take advantage of an opportunity like this to gain legal experience.— Anyhow, if things are as bad as you say perhaps I'll learn something which may prove of value to you reformers."

He studied my face for a moment.

"I never thought of that!" he said. "All right! Stay in your stink-pot a while! Maybe you can get the goods on some of these crooks!"

Being now in a state of affluence I had rented a large sunny room at the boarding house of Mrs. T. S. Stevens at 217 East

15th Street—$10 per week, meals included. My landlady was an elderly coquette, in corkscrew curls, who delighted in playing hostess and trying to make her guests feel that they were one big happy family. She took an ostentatious pride in the fact that I was an assistant district attorney and placed me on her right at the long table. Most of the guests were elderly folk who had, by their own accounts, seen better days. As a whole they were a threadbare, but cheerful and courageous lot. One was a once famous Wall Street operator who after having made and lost several fortunes now spent his days on the roof amusing himself with carrier pigeons; another was a superannuated Thespian who had starred with Ada Rehan, Minnie Maddern Fiske, Maurice Barrymore, and Richard Mansfield, but who now played opposite John Barleycorn and appeared only between the acts.

There was an aged clergyman, several married couples, a young woman who was studying law at New York University, named Miss Minerva Wiggin, two reporters on evening papers, while one end of the table was occupied by a group of writers connected with the *American Magazine* who regarded me with obvious disfavor as a feeder out of the public crib. These were not exactly "reformers"—like my friend Jack Chapman, for instance —but they were satisfied that everything was not right with America and not afraid to point out what it was. They were no more deserving of the epithet "muckrakers" applied to them by Roosevelt, than Teddy was himself; and, personally, I believe that the work they did changed vitally the trend of American political history.

Sometimes I would linger after supper for a game of chess or whist in the high-ceiled drawing room with its heavily framed paintings of snowbound sheep, St. Bernard dogs and dying stags, its beaded portieres, and its "hassocks" and gilded easels, but if not busy in the preparation of next day's calendar more often I went out to see the town.

There was plenty for me to see. Anyone who made money came to New York to spend it and below Fourteenth Street the town was **"wide open."** Above it, the atmosphere was exaggeratedly Victorian. It was perhaps significant that Tammany Hall stood squarely on the line separating the upper and nether regions.

It was the era of respect for everything established and conservative, of the weekly Sunday "Church parade," of tallyhos and four-in-hands, of shining Victorias with smart grooms and jingling harness, hansom cabs and streams of bicycle-riders for whose convenience a five-foot strip of asphalt bordered the cobblestones of Fifth Avenue. What is now the public library on the corner of 42nd Street was the old Egyptian reservoir; most of the Vanderbilts were housed in their adjoining brownstone palaces opposite St. Patrick's Cathedral, and every morning at the proper hour one could see the elderly Mrs. William H. ("The-Public-Be-Damned") Vanderbilt going to market, basket in hand; while there was always a crowd staring up at the thirteen-storied "Flatiron Building," then the tallest in the city and waiting for the draught to whip the girls' long skirts about their ankles.

Minerva Wiggin, a trim, pretty girl with alert gray eyes, who later became closely associated with my legal career, was possessed of a most interesting and intelligent mind. Her father had been a mid-western judge and, although it was almost unheard of at that period for a woman to go into the legal profession, it had been her ambition from childhood to do so. She had taken high honors at Bryn Mawr, was already an outstanding member of her law class and I felt sure that once she had passed her bar examinations she would prove invaluable to some high-class firm. She was eager to know about trial practice and I frequently invited her to court when I was prosecuting. But with all her intellectuality she was intensely feminine and was always more interested in what was going to happen to the unfortunate defendant and his family than in the procedure by which he was acquitted or convicted.

I suppose that under other circumstances I should have fallen in love with Minerva, but Esther was always in my mind. I thought of her constantly even when in court, and at evening when I went home to my hall bedroom the separation seemed insupportable. I wrote her several letters a week, but I found little solace even in her replies. The realization that I could reach her in less than five hours, and yet perforce must remain away from her, drove me nearly frantic. At times I was on the verge of going back irrespective of consequences. Such fits usually came over me towards the end of a miserable evening while the clock showed that there was still time to take the midnight train to Albany which would have landed me in Pottsville in time for breakfast. Why not surprise her?

Yet the thought of my delight at seeing her again would be followed by that of the sadness incident to our inevitable parting. Besides, it would not be fair to place her in such an equivocal position as would be involved in my return. No, we had taken our resolution and must abide by it. On such occasions, knowing that sleep was out of the question, I would slip out of the house and roam the streets the entire night, wandering about the city until the sky brightened over the East River and the rising sun gilded the spires of the Cathedral of St. Patrick. But weariness only drugged the pain; once I was rested again, my torture returned. I envied Otto, my only close friend, who was happily married.

I stayed in the District Attorney's office for three drab, incredible, exciting years, at the apogee of Tammany misrule, persecuting every conceivable sort of crime and learning even more human nature than I had in my up-state practice. Although I was not at first aware of it, the district attorney's office was a sort of political club, or health resort, in which the jobs were distributed as rewards for party services, many of the assistants being superannuated party hacks. Fitness or ability played little or no part in their selection. There was a genial happy-go-lucky Irish atmosphere about the place, no one tried a case unless obliged to do so, and since many indictments were found for personal or political reasons without sufficient evidence to support them—and hence could neither be tried nor yet dismissed—these were "pigeonholed" indefinitely, and as no copies were made, once the original document got into the hands of an assistant it became, so to speak, his personal property and there was no way to pry it away from him.

There were four General Sessions courtrooms and one Supreme courtroom, which had over the dais a faded mural painting of the Goddess of Justice holding the crystal ball of "Truth" in one hand, a pair of scales in the other, and gazing, not at the suppliants below, but significantly enough in the general direction of what was then Sing Sing prison. The judges were all pleasant and courteous old gentlemen who usually contributed to both political parties in order to assure their renominations. One was frequently the worse for liquor, another so dumb that he could not understand the simplest judicial opinion, while a third owed his seat upon the bench to his masterly promotion of a Tammany Hall picnic at Sulzer's Harlem River Park. They were then each paid $17,500 per annum; their successors now receive $25,000.

The known idiosyncrasies of these dispensers of justice guided the district attorney in choosing before whom any particular case should be tried, for they all had well known prejudices due to personal experience. Thus one had been victimized in a "badger game," and while this, of course, in no way reflected upon his qualifications for office, it had permanently embittered him against all those who trade on the sexual weaknesses of mankind. Hence, as a matter of course, every indictment for rape, seduction, or blackmail was moved before him, as well as such having a flavor of abnormality. "Oh, he's one of those, is he?" he'd growl, gritting his teeth. "Well, *I'll* try *this* fellow!"

The lawyers similarly jockied their cases to get them before judges who presumably would have a sympathetic feeling for their clients on account of the nature of the charge. The alcoholic judge, for instance, who had once nearly killed a man with a bottle, had a reputation for leniency towards all crimes of violence including murder; one old fathead was so notoriously amenable to female charm that a defendant had only to produce a witness with succulent curves to stand a fair chance of acquittal; while another was frankly in favor of abolishing all laws having to do with sex or domestic relations. "What's a little bigamy, anyway?" he asked me one day. "It don't do any particular harm as I can see." Most of the judges would, as a matter of course, invite prominent politicians or district leaders to sit upon the dais, and had Mr. Croker entered the room would unquestionably have arisen to do him honor.

The rendezvous for the elite of the district attorney's office was Pontin's restaurant on Franklin Street, a sort of glorified bar with an inner room where the judges had luncheon. The only others permitted in this sacrosanct chamber were the senior members of the notorious law firm of Howe & Hummel who occupied an adjoining table. This lent a certain cozy intimacy to their relations with the bench which doubtless had its profitable side. The lesser lights, including clerks, stenographers, and "counties," frequented the "Elm Castle," a corner saloon where one could get an excellent roast beef sandwich and a glass of beer for fifteen cents.

Howe & Hummel were a picturesque pair of rascals and a real menace to society. "Little Abie," blackmailer and corruptionist, was a dapper, mouse-faced Jew barely five feet in height, but whose pint-size head "hatched cocatrice eggs and wove the spider's web." William T. Howe, his partner, was an able trial lawyer. He had a round, red, corrugated face, big blue eyes, forceful jaw, and weighed three hundred pounds, dressing fantastically in screaming checks surmounted by a blue yachting cap, his fancy waistcoat hung with a chain the size of a ship's hawser, and wearing an immense diamond stud in lieu of a tie. By his appeals to a jury's sympathies he secured surprising acquittals. One of his clients being asked how he had managed to

get off replied, "Sure, how can I tell you? I thought I was guilty
until I heard Mr. Howe tell the jury I wasn't."

Since both judges and prosecutors owed their positions to
political favor they had little respect for one another, and our
office was a hotbed of jealousy, back-biting, and slander. Every
deputy intrigued for more salary, every assistant wanted to be
district attorney, all yearned for a seat on the criminal bench,
while those already there were ambitious for higher place.

The criminal bar itself was a picturesque collection of down-
at-the-heel lawyers, drunkards, ex-police magistrates, unfrocked
priests, and political riff-raff. Many had once stood well in their
profession, but had fallen, usually through bad habits or dishon-
esty, on evil days. With some exceptions their object was not so
much to defend as to exploit their clients, from whom they would
skilfully extort the ultimate penny. Some of them were exceedingly astute. One, Sam Feldman, an honest fellow for whom I
had a real liking, used to pretend with much histrionic skill that
he was an utter ignoramus.

"Of course my client's innocent," he would groan helplessly.
"If he was guilty he'd have a *good* lawyer."

Frequently the jury would acquit out of misplaced sympathy—
for Feldman.

I had always regarded the jury system as something of a joke,
but the ignorance and illiteracy of the talesmen who served on
my cases were astounding. Their attitude towards the judge was
reverential and they usually followed any hint he gave them, provided it did not conflict too blatantly with their personal idea of
justice. Their standard of ethics in financial transactions was elastic, and conduct which I naturally assumed they would regard as
reprehensible often seemed to strike them as merely a smart trick
evidencing the prisoner's business acumen and ability.

Their verdicts were rarely consistent with the evidence or
literally in accordance with the law as laid down by the court.
They usually convicted, but for lesser degrees of crime than those
charged in the indictments, their verdicts being for larceny when

they should have been for burglary, or manslaughter in the third degree (criminal negligence) instead of murder. They solemnly weighed considerations having no bearing upon the case whatsoever. They paid little attention to their oaths and none whatever to their technical duties, taking the law into their own hands and administering a sort of rough and ready justice tempered with mercy, such as one might expect to find in an Ottoman court. They were prejudiced, fanatical, quarrelsome, and illogical, yet they somehow seemed to have a sixth or extraneous sense which generally led them to a just result. This I grew in time to rely on. Indeed, after three years passed exclusively in the criminal courts I felt that I had rather take my chance for a square deal before a jury of truck-drivers, plumbers, saloon-keepers, and delicatessen men than before any judge or triumvirate of judges supposedly elected by the free voice of the people.

One day a case turned up on my calendar, transferred from the Special Sessions, in which the defendant Daniel Kelly was indicted for practicing veterinary medicine without a license. The charge had been brought by one Joseph B. Simon of Hempstead, Long Island, an agent for a society of what are Biblically referred to as "horse-leeches." According to his testimony the defendant, who represented himself to be a veterinary, had accepted a fee of five dollars for treating a sick horse. On its face the case was, as we used to say, "dead open and shut"; but it had a peculiar smell.

Kelly, a shrunken, white-haired old Irishman, took the stand in his own behalf. He had, he said, been born in Dublin seventy years before and had been a groom and coachman all his life, in the course of which he had learned by practical experience pretty much all there was about horses. He had known better days and had even once ridden in the Derby, but misfortune had overtaken him and in his old age he had come to America, where he now eked out a precarious living by doing odd jobs around livery stables. His version was that Simon, the complaining witness, had driven in a lame horse fit only for the bone factory, with a glaring spavin on his off hind leg, and said that the animal needed treatment.

"I can well see that," Kelly had replied. "He needs a poultice and hot bandages."

"Well, I'm no vet," returned the stranger. "I'm a doctor, but not a horse-doctor. Is there one here?"

"Some calls me a horse-doctor," answered Kelly modestly. "I can treat a spavin and wind a bandage as well as the next."

The upshot was that Kelly worked all day to make the horse comfortable. Late in the afternoon Simon came back to fetch it, and asked what he owed. Now Kelly, who had sat up the entire previous night taking care of a roan mare with the croup and giving her steam treatment every hour, had himself a racking headache accompanied by a high fever. He told "Dr." Simon that if the latter would prescribe something to bring down his temperature he would not charge him anything. So Simon had stuck a thermometer under his tongue and, while it was there, had thrust a five dollar bill into the old man's pocket, flashed his badge as a special officer, and placed him under arrest.

From the way Kelly spoke it was easy to see that he was devoted to dumb animals and anxious to relieve their sufferings; and because of my own love for horses I found myself bringing out every possible fact in the old wastrel's favor. I must have shown how I felt, for the judge, who had no intention of sacrificing the horse-leech vote at the next election, glared down at me and said: "This is a clear case, Mr. District Attorney. Neither side need sum up. I will cover the facts in my charge."

And he did! He not only covered the facts but he smothered poor old Danny Kelly under a mass of invective leaving the jury no choice but to convict.

When the jury retired I followed them out into the corridor upon which their consultation room opened. Captain Gallagher, the court officer who had them in charge, was by this time an old friend of mine and, because I said I was tired, he brought me a chair and, having locked the door of the jury room, returned to court leaving me alone. Raucous sounds accompanied by a thin blue cloud drifted through the transom above. Placing the chair against the jamb of the door I was just able by standing on its back to peer through. Most of the jurymen had removed their coats and were sitting with their feet on the battered oak table shouting angrily at one another.

I stood balancing myself on that chair back for nearly an hour. I do not pretend to record all that I heard, but only the more succulent fragments of ratiocination that stuck in my mind.

"That ain't a reasonable doubt!" declared one of them. "I'm a reasonable man, ain't I, and, if I don't see it, it can't be reasonable!"

"Vell," said the foreman placatingly. "Vat you say, gen'men, shall we disguss or take a vote?"

"Let's take a smoke," amended one whom I recognized as No. 6.

"Speakin' of veterinaries," remarked another, "did you ever hear the story of the nigger and the mule with a cough?"

Apparently most of them never had, so he told them all about how—ha! ha! ha!—"the mule coughed first!"

"That story's got whiskers on it!" scoffed No. 6. "If I had my way all these veterinaries would be in jail! They're a dangerous lot!"

"But neither of these birds is a veterinary!" retorted the mule man. "The charge is that one of 'em pretended to be, but wasn't. So, if he wasn't, how could you convict him of being a veterinary?"

"Dot's so!" agreed the foreman. "He vasn't no veterinary!"

"Well, I say they're all dangerous!" countered No. 6. "Like all those clairvoyants and soothsayers!"

"Will someone tell me," interposed a melancholy man in black, "whether a veterinary is the same thing as a veterinarian? I always supposed a veterinarian was a kind of religion, like a Unitarian. 'Veteran' means old: I thought it was some old form of religion."

"That's right," said a voice from the other end of the table. "A veterinary is someone who don't believe in eatin' meat."

"You can't convict a man for his religion!" declared the first man. "He's protected by the Constitution."

"Dot's so!" agreed the foreman. "In dis country any von can eat vot he likes!"

"Let's take up the points one by one and vote on 'em separately," suggested No. 6. "Now everybody who thinks the defendant claimed to be a veterinarian say 'Aye'."

"Wait a minute!" interrupted the man in black. "Which was the defender? Simon or Kelly!"

"Oh, my God!" groaned someone. "It ain't defend*er*—it's defend*ant*—a-n-t. Remember your aunt! Kelly's the guy we're tryin'. The other is the complainant!"

"The only one who had any complaint was the horse!" protested the melancholy one. "Anyhow, what's your question?"

"The question is: Did this Kelly pretend he was a horse-doctor when he wasn't?" explained a neighbor.

"But the other guy pretended he was a regular doctor!" retorted No. 6.

"He was only tryin' to trick the defendant!"

"If the first feller wasn't a doctor any more than the other feller, why not convict the first feller?" demanded a newly inspired brother.

"That's true!" "You've said something!" came from both sides of the table.

"I say they're all dangerous—these veterinarians!" stoutly reiterated No. 6. "They all ought to be in jail. I don't care whether it's a religion or what it is! No matter what the Constitution says, they all ought to be locked up!"

"They got a union!" put in a fresh Solon. "I'm against all unions. They're criminal conspiracies.—I can see the whole thing! They sent this feller Simon to make Kelly sign up and, when he wouldn't join, they tried to put on the screws by having him arrested. They're a damn sight worse than he is!"

"That's what I say," agreed No. 6. "They're the ones who ought to be put in jail—not this little feller. He's all right in my opinion."

"Hear! Hear!" "Bully for you!" "Pass the box!" arose on all sides.

Through the transom came the scuffling of feet and scraping of chairs, followed by a loud pounding upon the door. I jumped to the floor, just as Gallagher hurried back with the key.

"What have they done?—Cooked him?" he asked.

"No," I said. "Justice, aided by the wisdom and intelligence of a jury, has triumphed."

The Kelly case illustrates the indirect way in which juries often reach their results. To hear them talk one would have thought them a bunch of idiots, as perhaps some of them were, but in the back of their minds—although unformulated and unexpressed—was the idea that no group of men banded together for profit should be encouraged to lure a harmless old man into a trap and try to send him to jail for doing what was in fact not evil but only good. They were inarticulate—asinine, if you will—but they had a conception of justice and common sense.

On the surface the district attorney's office was properly and, in many ways, adequately run. Colonel Gardiner was personally honest as were undoubtedly the majority of his appointees. Coming from the country I was at first considerably impressed by the surface dignity of the judiciary and the elegance of my associates all of whom habitually wore frock coats and silk hats. I could not believe that any of them were willing to wink at practices essentially corrupt. After all, they could always take the position that unless these were brought to their official attention it was none of their business. It took me some time before I even suspected what was going on. It was Irvin S. Cobb, then a young reporter assigned to the Criminal Courts Building, who opened my eyes.

Returning unexpectedly from court one afternoon I found him smoking a cigar with his feet crossed upon my desk while Bonnie pirouetted around the office singing:

There was a young hayseed named Tutt,
Who at law was by no means a nut,
But his knowledge of books
Was more than of crooks
And he didn't suspect what was what.

I watched them from the doorway for a moment.

"Well, boys," I said. "What *is* what?"

Bonnie stopped dead in the middle of a pigeon wing.

"Welcome, stranger!" declaimed Irv solemnly. "The Committee on the Enlightenment of Suckers, now in executive session, has voted you too good for this neck of the woods. Confidentially we believe that, as an incipient Abraham Lincoln, you are being wasted. We like you as you are and when Gardiner throws you out we're going to have you stuffed, but meanwhile we don't want to see anything put over on you. If you haven't seen 'Big Bill' Devery in action you don't know nuthin'. Come on up to Headquarters."

As we walked down Franklin Street Irv waved towards a group of tenement houses.

"This used to be 'The Five Points'," he said. "They tore down Mulberry Bend a couple of years ago and got rid of 'Battle Alley,' 'Kerosene Row,' and 'Bandit's Roost,' but there's plenty of places left around here like 'Hell's Kitchen' and 'Poverty Gap.' They pack 'em in—eight and ten in one room—a thousand to the acre. There's one block that houses thirty-five hundred people!"

"How about the fire and health ordinances?" I asked.

"Instruments of graft! The landlords pay to be left alone. Here's where they hide the repeaters at election time. They vote 'em twenty or thirty times under different names. When their imagination runs out they use telephone-books and club lists. You heard about the fellow that registered over in the 12th Ward as 'William Croswell Doane'?"

"You mean the Bishop of Albany?"

"That's the one! They'd been voting the same baby as 'Abe Lincoln' and 'George Washington' just around the corner. Well, in he comes pie-eyed and gives his name.

" 'But you ain't Bishop Doane!' says the watcher.

" 'The hell I ain't,' answers the drunk, and just because no one knew the real bishop they had to let him vote."

At Police Headquarters we found Chief Devery presiding at the regular Thursday afternoon police trials. He was a big, red-faced man with a bull-neck, blue-gray eyes, and handle-bar moustaches, who obviously enjoyed the terrific tongue-lashings he administered to the cowering members of the force as they came before him, as well as the philosophical aphorisms about life in general he threw off for the benefit of the press. Just as we came in he was examining a policeman suspected of being drunk.

"Here you!" he ordered. "Open your mouth and breathe in my face!"

The cop protested that he ought not to be compelled to give evidence against himself. This seemed to please "Big Bill," for he grinned in our direction and winked.

"That's right, my man!" he cried. "Keep your mouth shut all the time! If you do that you won't get into trouble here!"

One patrolman was brought up charged with reckless shooting in the streets. Devery glared at him.

"Did you hit your man? No? Fined thirty days' pay for not hittin' him. Next time you hit him!"

Towards the end of the afternoon he became less good-natured and when a policeman who had been caught in a bawdy house was arraigned, he roared:

"When you're caught with the goods on you and you can't get away with it, you want to stand up and take your medicine! You don't know nothin' then! No matter under what circumstances, a man don't want to know nothin' when he's caught with the goods on him. You tell your lady friend to tip you off next time. Always get tipped off. You don't want to go blind into them places. You're a bum. I fine you fifteen days' pay. See if you can get that fine remitted—you loafer! Clear out of here and keep away from me!"

"And that, according to his honor the mayor," remarked Irv as we went out, "is the best chief of police New York has ever had!"

As I became more intimate with the machinery by which men were stamped as criminals and sent to prison I began to realize that the worst enemies of society were not those who were daily dragged to the bar before my eyes but those in power who profited by the alliance between politics and crime, vaguely known in New York at that time as "The System."

Based on the proposition that to the victors belonged the spoils, the party in power licensed the breaking of the laws under a regular tariff. Every saloon, disorderly house and gambling establishment paid so much per month to ply its trade undisturbed. So did every pimp, cadet, prostitute, fence, and petty gambler. The cop on the beat handed it to the roundsman, who turned it over to the captain, who delivered it to the inspector, who distributed it among the higher-ups. Any member of the force who refused to co-operate was broken, "framed" or sent on duty "out among the goats." The police were the protectors of crime, and the same unseen power that controlled their actions likewise controlled, either directly or indirectly, the administration of justice. Only those who worked with the System could successfully appeal to the police or magistrates' courts; and those who did were immune to arrest. Justice became simply a question of pull.

One day an indictment attracted my attention for the reason that the attorneys were Howe & Hummel and it had been eighteen times on the calendar for trial. The charge was attempted rape, and the defendant, a Tammany district leader, was not even present in court. Endorsed on the back of the indictment opposite the name Rebecca Levy, the complainant, were the words "House of Detention." There were two other witnesses, one of them Isaac Levy, obviously the father, the other an officer.

When the case was called a representative of Howe & Hummel requested a further adjournment on the plea that the senior member of the firm was busy in the trial of another case. The Judge was about to assent when I interrupted by inquiring what court the lawyer was in. The attorney hesitated and then replied: "In Part Three." I asked to have the case held, and sent Bonnie Doon to investigate. He presently returned with the information that Mr. Howe was neither in the General Sessions courts nor in the Supreme Court. Thereupon I had the Judge mark the case "Ready for trial."

The so-called "House of Detention" was really a prison to which a judge upon the application of the district attorney could commit vagrant or hostile witnesses in order to prevent their being tampered with by the defense. That a complainant should be incarcerated there seemed strange indeed. Turning the calendar over to my assistant I had the chief witness brought to my office. She was a haggard little creature of sixteen, so terrified that at first I could not persuade her to talk. "I want mein fader!" was all she would say. I sent for him and their meeting was pathetic, for, as I discovered, they had not seen each other for three and a half months.

Once satisfied that I had no evil intent, for he now trusted nobody, Levy told me what had happened. Hysterical with grief and anger he had sworn out a warrant and, although discouraged by the police, had had the defendant arrested. A mysterious and sinister sequence of circumstances ensued. At the hearing before the magistrate, Rebecca and her father having testified, the accused interposed no defense, was held for the Grand Jury and admitted to bail.

That same night the Levys were visited by an unknown person, representing himself as an employee of the district attorney, who threatened them with dire misfortune if they insisted on going on with the case. Levy, who was determined to bring the wrongdoer to justice, refused to have any dealings with him. After considerable delay the Grand Jury returned an indictment. Then, although the girl had a good home and her parents were respectable people, a policeman placed her under arrest, and took her to the House of Detention, where her family were refused access to her, and where she was daily subjected to pressure to "let up" on the defendant. Eighteen times she had been taken to court and put in the prisoners' pen along with handcuffed malefactors and vile women, being held there all day without anything to eat, until she now believed that every official was in a plot to keep her in jail for life.

When we went downstairs to the courtroom the defendant, a heavy-set, bleary eyed man of about fifty years of age, was already there. So was the white-haired Mr. Howe, who protested violently against his client being thus "railroaded." Only because I was supposed to be a protégé of Mr. Croker did I succeed in forcing the case to trial over his objections. Once at the bar of justice the defendant was convicted in seventeen minutes.

But that was only the half of it. Ten days later, in my absence and without my knowledge, he was surreptitiously brought up for sentence. A representative of Howe & Hummel produced a letter, addressed to the judge and bearing Rebecca's signature, stating that she was too ill to come to court and that she had been so unnerved at the trial she had not known what she was saying. His Honor, having read the letter, handed it back and promptly suspended sentence upon the defendant who was at once discharged.

Rebecca had neither known of nor signed the letter. When I summoned Howe's clerk before the Grand Jury he innocently explained that it had arrived through the mails enclosed in an envelope addressed to Howe & Hummel, who naturally supposed it had come from the girl herself. It was too late to do anything more about the matter. Colonel Gardiner, naturally, had never so much as heard of the case, and my inquiries regarding her committal to the House of Detention were met by vague explanations, such as "Why, we understood that this was a bad girl and that unless she were locked up the defendant might spirit her away." Rebecca Levy was the only person punished for the defendant's crime against her, and for her there was no redress.

I saw plenty of instances of what the System did to boys and girls. It was no fault of theirs that they could play only in the streets where they could not but make nuisances of themselves. A baseball would go astray and break a grocer's window, and—especially if it had happened before—the cop, who was grafting on the grocer, would arrest the nearest urchin for "malicious mischief"; the company which had insured the window naturally insisted on a conviction; the shyster lawyer assigned by the court wanted to squeeze all the money he could out of the boy's family; and, because the evidence was slight and the lawyer had a pull, the assistant in charge of the case, who took not the slightest interest, would keep postponing the trial. Meanwhile the boy would be locked up in the Tombs, perhaps for weeks, learning the habits of the criminals with whom he was confined. Finally, after the lawyer had sucked the family dry, he would plead his client guilty, the boy would go to the reformatory, and all the parties who "mattered" would be satisfied—including grocer, cop, insurance-adjuster, shyster, and deputy assistant district attorney.

In one case my suspicions became so aroused that I determined to get to the bottom of it. The defendant's name was Tony Bonico, a fatherless lad of sixteen years, his mother a sweatshop worker, the circumstances being almost identical with those I have described, except that in addition I felt morally certain that the cop had arrested the wrong boy. Tony was in fact a mere chip tossed aimlessly hither and yon by the eddies and crosscurrents of avarice. A shady lawyer named Kantor, who had been assigned as counsel to the defendant, managed by terrifying the mother as to the possible outcome of the case, to extort from her her entire savings amounting to four hundred and thirty-five dollars. Shea, the officer who had made the original arrest as a favor to Grossman the grocer, had expected that Kantor, once he had got his money, would keep on adjourning the case until

Tony pleaded guilty, but I sent Bonnie over to the Tombs to tell the boy, if he was innocent, to insist upon a trial. Hence Shea now found himself in the position of being obliged to swear through a doubtful case in order to protect Grossman from a possible suit for "false arrest."

When I moved the case Kantor arose and asked for another adjournment "at the request of his client." Much to his surprise and perturbation I called Tony to the bar and, when asked if he was ready to be tried, he answered "Yes." Getting cold feet, Kantor now tried to withdraw as counsel, but the judge refused to let him. Shea, the officer, fearful of a perjury charge, attempted to sneak out of the courtroom, was haled back, and when called to testify fainted from fright in the witness chair. Tony was acquitted and Shea, after being indicted for perjury, turned State's evidence against Kantor, who was indicted and convicted of extortion.

Although my entire time was devoted to what was euphemistically called "the administration of justice," I soon decided that there was little justice in it. While the police did a good enough job in rounding up professional criminals such as burglars, thieves, "moll buzzers" and confidence men, the majority of those arrested owed their plight to accident, ill luck, or the malevolence of their enemies. Technically guilty of some violation of law, they were morally no worse than most people and often better than those responsible for their arrest; while at Police Headquarters in the center of the legal web sat a foul-mouthed, low comedian, to whom Tammany had entrusted the decency, honesty and safety of New York's millions of inhabitants.

I perceived that, wholly apart from the matter of pull, one of the chief reasons why law was not justice was because law was a luxury which the poor could not afford. To enforce one's rights costs money, or its equivalent in working time. The poor man knows little or nothing of the complex system of statutes and ordinances hedging him about, and he has not the means to find out on the one hand whether he has actually broken some law, or on the other whether he has been wronged by someone else. Thus he is deprived of both his sword and his shield. The police court is his court of last resort. Small wonder the poor fear and shun "The Law" personified for them by the officer on the beat whose "G'wan!" or "Come here!" if disobeyed may bring the local gestapo swarming about their heads.

"So I returned, and considered all the oppressions that are done under the sun; and behold the tears of such as are oppressed, and they had no comforter; and on the side of the oppressors was power; but they had no comforter."

Since I have nothing to gain by these memoirs except a metaphorical kick in the pants, I have no desire that the kick should be harder than necessary. I was young and more intolerant in those days, and I want to give all my devils their just due. Colonel Gardiner, was undoubtedly a "nice gentleman," and the unfortunate slogan of "To Hell With Reform" which enshrines his name, may have been no more than an impulsive and sarcastic attack upon the hypocrisy of those who pretended to be desirous of improving conditions while secretly preferring the *status quo*; that "Boss" Croker had a kind heart is shown by what he went out of his way to do for me; even Devery was a good disciplinarian. But they all regarded the city government as essentially a political enterprise to be run for the benefit of Tammany Hall and its supporters. In those days—just as in the time of Julius Caesar and perhaps now as well—those who held office were supposed to feather their nests, the general attitude being well expressed by an old court officer when he said to me: "There'll always be graft, counsellor, and it don't make no difference who gets it."

I had just begun to appreciate the vital part which the office in which I was employed played in the Tammany scheme when the Legislature ordered an inquiry into the city's affairs. This was conducted by the famous Mazet Committee, whose report created a profound sensation. Its most picturesque exposure was that of the Ice Trust, in which it was established that the Croker Administration had given Charles W. Morse's American Ice

Company a practical monopoly of the sale of ice to the city in exchange for "gifts" of stock to almost every important Democratic politician, including 13,000 shares to Mayor Van Wyck and 5,000 shares to his brother Augustus.

It was publicly asserted * that a gambling syndicate composed of politicians took in annually $3,095,000 from poolrooms, crap games and gambling houses; that Croker had wrecked the Third Avenue Railway Company, driving its stock from $242 to $50, and finally forcing it into bankruptcy after he and his friends had presumably sold its stock short; that on the East Side an army of pimps—known as "cadets"—were given free rein to seduce and recruit young girls for the bawdy houses; that ten thousand protected gamblers were operating unmolested throughout the city; that positions on the police force and subsequent promotions were sold at fixed prices; and that "Big Bill" Devery openly flouted the laws he was paid to enforce.

It was the worst blow Tammany had suffered since the days of the Tweed Ring. Yet in spite of the proof of Tammany misrule, and Croker's barefaced admission upon the witness stand that, as dictator of the city's affairs, he was "working for his own pocket all the time," he won in the November 1900 elections by a handsome majority. The Republican legislature at Albany promptly legislated Devery out of office by abolishing the position of Chief of Police, a move which Mayor Van Wyck as promptly countered by appointing him "Deputy" Police Commissioner.

"Will dey put me out—dose fellers? G'wan! Never! Devery stays right here!" he boasted.

Then the Grand Jury indicted Devery for malfeasance at the elections, and when District Attorney Gardiner had the effrontery publicly to stigmatize its action as "an outrage," Governor Theodore Roosevelt, whose term still had a few days to run before he became Vice-President, removed Gardiner from office and appointed Eugene A. Philbin, an able and high-minded member of the bar, in his place.

* *New York Times,* March 9, 1900.

We on the professional staff waited in suspense to see where the ax would fall. It severed a good many necks but not mine, and although I had previously decided to resign, I hung on to see what would happen. That was how I came to meet Arthur Train, for he was among the first of Philbin's new appointees, and we soon became good friends. Even then Train was more interested in literature than in law. He would try cases all day and then go home and write stories all night. What I liked about his yarns was they showed the same sympathy for the underprivileged that I had myself. We have been pals now for nearly half a century. He has lost many of his sharp edges in the course of years, and although he is rather precise and dogmatic for my taste he is essentially a man of good will and a good companion in the woods.

Roosevelt's removal of District Attorney Gardiner and his appointment of Mr. Philbin gave the reformers their chance, for the gamblers and bawdy-house keepers were still openly doing business under the protection of the police. Working in conjunction with the new district attorney, Judge William Travers Jerome began a series of spectacular raids. Having appeared before him in many cases in the Court of Special Sessions I knew him well, so that when he asked me to join him in his crusade I was only too ready to go along. Wallace Irwin's verses satirizing the situation attained wide popularity:

> "Tut, tut!" said Jerome with a grin,
> "These games are disguised very thin;
>   When you hear a cop snore
>   By a strange-looking door
> It's a cinch there is gambling within."

The new Chief of Police was named McAdoo. Wallace wrote:

> A district attorney, who knew,
> Spoke of gamblers to Chief McAdoo.
>   Then to stir up his slumbers
>   He named streets and numbers
> So what could poor McAdoo do?

In the municipal campaign that autumn, Jerome, as candidate for district attorney, led the fusion forces to victory. He was a picturesque figure, alert, slender but muscular, brusque and by nature an aristocrat, but beneath his cavalier figure burned the wrath of a Hebrew prophet, and for the time being he became both the idol of the slums and the hero of Fifth Avenue. A "whirl-wind campaigner" his harsh voice would reduce an audience to tears or bring it to its feet with indignation.

Some of his stories became famous, in particular one to the effect that, during the investigation of the purchase of what appeared to be an inordinate weight of sponges for a public department, the inspector under fire plaintively inquired: "Hell! Do you think I weighed 'em *dry?*"

The day after Tammany's defeat and the election of the entire fusion ticket, Jerome sent for me.

"Eph," he said, "of course I shall make a clean sweep of the district attorney's old staff. I want my own men there, whom I can trust. You're one of them and I'm going to keep your friend Train, too. I'll be glad to make you first trial assistant at $7,500 per year. How about it?"

I hesitated. I was loyal to Jerome, but the fight for good government had been won. I had had enough of sending men to jail. I believed, with Bernard Shaw, that so long as we had prisons it made little difference who occupied the cells. Neither did I believe in the way justice was administered. It was entirely too hit or miss. I felt that if I were to practice at the criminal bar at all, and of that I was by no means sure, I would far rather act for the defense.

"Thank you very much, Judge," I said. "Of course I'm deeply grateful, but I think that for the present I've had enough of crime."

V

O N   M Y   O W N

IT TOOK some courage on my part to refuse Jerome's offer. Had I become his chief of staff I might have prosecuted Harry Thaw for killing Stanford White, Nan Patterson for the murder of Caesar Young, Albert T. Patrick for that of William T. Rice, and perhaps become as famous as James W. Osborne or De Lancey Nicoll. One kind of career was being offered me on a gold plate, and I had many misgivings before turning it down. But my heart was not on that side of the bar. I would have welcomed fame and money—not for myself, but for Esther whom, in spite of every obstacle, I hoped in some far-off day to marry.

Naturally I wrote asking her advice and her reply had much to do with my decision:

"Dear Ephraim," it read, "I wish I could help you, but I know so little about a legal career that I dare not express any opinion. I would far rather know that you were doing what you felt was most worth while both for yourself and others than to see your picture in the newspapers. The best advice I know is that of old Polonius—'To thine own self be true, and it must follow, as the night the day, thou canst not then be false to any man.' You'd know I was a school teacher, wouldn't you? But you also know that everything pertaining to you is close to my heart.

Esther Farr."

Her letter settled it for me. I no longer cared to earn a salary by putting in jail people whom fate had arbitrarily selected as its victims or to climb to fame over the bodies of those whom I had sent to the electric chair. There wasn't any highmindedness about it; I was merely too soft hearted. If I could have achieved justice under the laws of criminal procedure I'd have gladly given my life to it; but I knew that it was impossible. The antiquated machine was so cracked and out of gear that it simply didn't work. I had no desire to continue as a combination of detective, police officer and executioner, although my three years had given me invaluable experience, and I did not regret them.

I rented a small office on Franklin Street within a stone's throw of the Criminal Courts Building, hung out my shingle again and waited for clients. At first I was sadly disappointed by the result. I had assumed from occasionally having seen my name in print and having been treated with exaggerated deference by the hangers on of the criminal courts, that I was a person of distinction if not already famous, but I soon found that an ex-deputy-assistant-district-attorney was a dead dog so far as the general public was concerned. I was just another chap out of a job, and competing for a living with the rest of the criminal bar. My income dropped from several hundred dollars a month to practically nothing. I had no connections with Wall Street, no sources from which I might expect any business. Only the encouragement of Bonnie Doon, who had resigned his own position to join me and apparently had unbounded faith in my ability to reap success, enabled me to put on a brave front or prevent my reconsideration of Jerome's offer.

Yet now as I look back, I can see that this interim was one of the pleasanter periods of my life. I was absolutely my own master, beholden to no one for a salary. I needed to earn but ten dollars a week to live, and another ten for my office rent, since Bonnie had agreed to work for nothing provided he received half of the fees he might bring in, and before long he brought in plenty of them. I won't say it was the highest class of law practice, but it paid and sometimes paid well, for Bonnie, as a process server, had a wide acquaintance with the foreign born. He was a natural salesman with a ready tongue, and he lost no opportunity to advertise the fact that one of the greatest and most eloquent lawyers of all time was for the moment at liberty to accept retainers—provided they came quick enough.

Before long my office was crowded with Italians, Chinese, Greeks and Syrians. Each nationality had its own quarter—the Italians on Mulberry Street and its immediate neighborhood, the

Greeks and Syrians on lower Washington Street, the Chinese on Doyer and Pell Streets, and the Hungarians on Second Avenue. In these linguistic islands one heard no word of English. Each group kept to itself, adhering strictly to its own religious beliefs and traditions, preferring to settle their own difficulties among themselves. The Italians particularly had brought with them their inherited distrust of all government, and even the friends of a murdered man would shelter his assailant rather than have his guilt litigated in an American court of justice.

It was almost impossible to find anyone to testify in an Italian homicide case, and murders were of daily occurrence. Every participant and witness sedulously shielded himself behind the obligation of silence imposed by the *"omerta"* and, since the Mafia and Camorra both flourished in what was then called "Little Italy," the majority of homicides went unpunished save by the relatives of the victims. It is safe to say that in my day there was little or no administration of justice among the foreign born, who not only did not want it but whose divers languages and dialects rendered it practically impossible to find out where the truth lay. Usually no great attempt to do so was made, except when things got too bad to be overlooked.

Through the efforts of Bonnie Doon I was occasionally retained to defend some member of the On Leon Tong, a branch of the Three Brothers' Society, which had had a feud with the Hip Sing Tong originating in the days of Confucius, since when they had taken turns knocking each other off at the rate of about one a month. Because in a Chinese or Syrian murder trial no one is ever convicted, it loses the macabre quality of the ordinary homicide case and frequently turns into a side-splitting farce.

The first Chinaman I defended was named Mock Hen. He was charged with murdering one Sue Sing, and the chief witness against him was a Mr. Ah Fong. Each side insisted on having its own interpreter, so we ended by having three, the last to act as an umpire in the event of a disagreement between the other two. I suspect it was a put up job, since each received ten dollars a day for his services paid by the State. When this little matter had at last been settled the question arose as to how the witnesses should be sworn. I objected to having Ah Fong testify unless it appeared by preliminary inquiry that his religious beliefs were such as to obligate him to respect his oath.

"Mr. Ah Fong," I inquired, "do you believe in any god?"

The three interpreters gargled at Ah Fong and at each other for several minutes, after which one of them croaked:

"He say 'yes'."

"What god do you believe in?" I persisted.

Unexpectedly Mr. Fong made answer without benefit of interpretation.

"When I in this country," he replied complacently in English, "I b'lieve Gees Clist; when I in China I b'lieve Chinese God."

This obliging acquiescence in local theology did not seem to me to fulfill the necessary requirements.

"Ah Fong, do you think God will punish you if having taken an oath to tell the truth you break it and tell a lie?"

Fong looked blank. The interpreter fired a few salvos.

"He say it make difference what kind of oath."

"An oath before God."

"He ask what god you mean," countered the interpreter.

"Oh, any god!" I exploded.

The interpreter, after a long parley, made reply.

"Ah Fong say there is no binding oath except on a chicken's head."

This floored me.

"What kind of a chicken?" I stammered.

"A white rooster."

The Judge took a hand.

"Ask him if something else won't do—a big book, for instance."

Ah Fong shook his head. All the interpreters agreed that it was chicken or nothing.

Thereupon the Supreme Court of the State of New York, Criminal Trial Term, Part One, Catherwood, J., presiding, adjourned to find a white rooster. It was already the eighteenth day of the trial. It had taken us seventeen days to pick a jury, and not a witness had as yet been sworn. Three hours later the court officers reported that there wasn't a white rooster to be found in the entire city of New York. There were hens by the hundred, but roosters seemed to be extinct. At last a poultryman was discovered who agreed, for what advertising there was in it, to deliver a crate of white roosters, a hatchet and a headsman's block in the courthouse basement, and at ten o'clock next morning we all attended while from a melee of fluttering, squawking fowls one was finally caught and decapitated.

Once more we all ascended to the courtroom and Ah Fong resumed his place in the witness chair. The interpreter's blouse was covered with pin feathers and one of his thumbs was bleeding profusely.

"Ask the witness if the oath he has now taken will bind his conscience," directed the Judge.

There was a long interchange between Ah Fong and the interpreter.

"He say," translated the latter calmly, "that the chicken oath is okay in China but no good in United States."

The district attorney swore under his breath. The jury—at three dollars a day—were delighted.

Suddenly Ah Fong announced in English with an inscrutable age-long Oriental smile:

"Me tell truth allight. Go ahead! Shoot!"

The trial lasted six weeks. The prosecution produced several white witnesses who positively identified Mock Hen as having shot Sue Sing on the corner of Doyers and Pell Streets at precisely twenty-five minutes past one o'clock on a certain afternoon. Chinatown, according to them, had been practically deserted at the time. Its peace was like that of a New England Sabbath morning. In contradiction I introduced half a dozen dignified members of the On Leon Tong who testified that Mock Hen could not possibly have been there since he was with them in the stall of a fish-monger at Fulton Market a couple of miles distant. All had had watches and had carefully noted the time! Then the Hip Sings got busy. No less than twelve equally impressive Orientals swore that they had had a perfect view of the homicide, claiming variously to have been behind doors, peeking through shutters, from windows or roofs. They had all positively seen Mock Hen shoot Sue Sing with their own eyes, and none of them had ever heard of either the Hip Sing or On Leon Tong.

Re-enforcements began to arrive for both sides. They came by train-loads from Pittsburgh, Chicago, St. Louis, until the rotunda of the Criminal Courts Building was lined with a double row of blue-coated Chinese images, faces front, hands folded in laps, legs crossed beneath them, waiting to be called to testify to the truth, the whole truth and nothing but the truth. If anyone appeared in the offing a couple of hundred pairs of glinting eyes shifted automatically, following him until he disappeared, otherwise no muscle quivered. It was a bit uncanny at first, but I got used to it. Finally, after the trial had sunk into a dull, unbroken monotony, consisting, as Bonnie put it, of the "vain repetitions of the heathen," the Judge placed a limit to the number of witnesses to be allowed each side, otherwise the trial would still be going on today. As might have been expected, the jury disagreed.

Shortly afterwards, having thus become launched on a homicidal career, I defended a Syrian camel driver from Coney Island named Kasheed Hassoun, who in a burst of religious fanaticism had strangled one Sadi Babu for impiously remarking "I will spit on the beard of your bishop." The prosecution called as a witness one Halu Kahoots, a fat man with enormous paunch, curls and ring-laden fingers, who boasted that, although he came from Acre in Syria, he had lived in Augusta, Georgia, thirty years and could "spik Englees" as well as the next man.

I have the stenographer's minutes before me now, and reproduce his cross-examination verbatim.

Q. What's your business, Mr. Kahoots?
A. I have street fair and carnival of my own. I have electric

theatre, old plantation, Oriental show, snake exhibit and merry-go-round.

Q. Are you a citizen of the United States?

A. Me? No! Me no citizen. I go back sometime Acre and build moving picture garden and ice-cream palace.

Q. If you live in Augusta, Georgia, how did you happen to be in New York at precisely this time?

A. Just come.

Q. Why?

A. Just come.

Q. Just come to see the murder?

A. Just come to walk up and down on Washington Street. I rich man.

Q. How long did you stay at that time?

A. Tree day. Then I go back.

Q. Why did you go back?

A. Dunno. Just go back.

I took another tack.

Q. How many times have you gone over your story with the district attorney?

A. Nevvair see heem. I nevvair see no one.

Q. Then perhaps you'll be kind enough to tell these twelve gentlemen how the district attorney knew what you were going to testify to?

A. Dunno heem.

Q. Dunno who?

A. Dist' 'torney.

Q. Didn't you go before the Grand Jury and swear that Hassoun instead of strangling Babu, had stabbed him with a long knife?

A. I dunno heem.

Q. Who?

A. Gran' Jur'.

Q. Didn't you go into a big room and put your hand on a book and swear?

A. Me, swear? I no swear—nevvair!

I switched again.

Q. Now, Kahoots, isn't it a fact that you have been convicted of a crime yourself? Weren't you convicted of assault on Rafoul Rabyaz?

Mr. Kahoots swelled like a puff-adder.

A. Me? Look here, sir! I tell you 'bout dat. Dis Rafoul Rabyaz he my partner—in pool, billiard and cigar business on Greenwich Street. This long time ago, years ago, see? We split up. I sell heem my shares, see? I open next door—pool table, cafe and all. But I not get half the stock. He don't give me the table-cloth see? I was of the table cloth, you know, short. It don't be there. So I go back there that time and I see heem. I say, "We don't count dose table-cloth." He say, "Yes." I say, "No." He say, "Yes." I say "No." He say, "Yes." I say, "No—"

"We'll take your word for that part of it," I interrupted.

"Okay!" countered Mr. Kahoots. "I say, 'No.' I say, 'You look in the book." He say, 'No.' So we each take hold of the cloth. I have knife. I cut cloth in two. I give heem half. I take half. I say 'You take half—I take half.' He say, 'Go to Hell!' "

By this time the jury were rocking in their seats, effectively diverted from any thought of the electric chair.

The seat beside me at Mrs. Stevens' board was occupied by a Mrs. Atwood, a bird-like old lady, the only daughter of General Samuel Wilson, a multi-millionaire who after leaving the major part of his estate to charity had bequeathed the remainder of it to her. Years before, a fortune hunter had lured her into marriage, squandered her entire fortune, and so maltreated her that she had finally divorced him, with the result that she was now passing her declining years in genteel poverty, hardly able to scrape together the ten dollars a week payable for her hall bedroom.

Mrs. Stevens had a private parlor to which she invited favored guests to join her for coffee, and here one evening old Mrs. Atwood got talking about her childhood and youth in New York and the family estate on the East River. It had been one of the show places of the city, with stables, hothouses, and gardens, but her father having otherwise sufficiently provided for her as he supposed had left it for an old ladies' home. As such it was known as the "Wilson Home for Aged Gentlewomen." Suddenly

Mrs. Atwood burst into tears. She was, it appeared, nearly at the end of her resources, and could no longer afford to stay with Mrs. Stevens. She had applied by letter for admission to the Wilson Home, the house where she had been born, but had received a formal reply to the effect that it was full and that, in any event, a payment of $500 was required. She had only $170 in the world —only enough to keep her at Mrs. Stevens' for seventeen more weeks! Now she was trying to get into some other "home" in Jersey City where no such deposit was necessary.

The idea that Mrs. Atwood should be refused admittance to an institution which existed only by virtue of her own father's generosity seemed monstrous to me. The Registry of Social Services showed that it had been incorporated as "a home for aged women of good breeding and refinement who have fallen into adverse circumstances" and was located at Corndale, Westchester County, with a branch in New York City. An applicant was required to be over sixty-five years of age and to pay $500, besides making a transfer to the institution of all her property unless willed to relatives. While I knew this to be the common practice, the longer I mulled over the situation the more preposterous it all seemed.

One afternoon I put Mrs. Atwood in a cab and drove with her along a street in the West Fifties which ended in a sort of cul-de-sac marked "Wilson Place." Huge apartment houses surrounded what resembled an oasis in the congested city. Through the open ironwork of the gateway I could look out over a grassy lawn facing the river and planted with shade trees; at one end was a large brick Victorian mansion with a tennis court, and at the other flower and vegetable gardens. A well-dressed elderly lady was reading on a bench. Certainly it was a paradise for aged gentlewomen or for that matter anyone else! Mrs. Atwood mopped her eyes bravely.

"I'm silly, I know! Please forgive me! But as a young girl I used to drive through this gate every day in the C-Spring Victoria with Pompey, our old Negro coachman, on the box. My bedroom was right up there on the corner overlooking the greenhouse and stable;—I could hear the pigeons cooing from my window."

After considerable delay we were received by Mr. Otis Beckett, the superintendent, a pinkly bald, well-fleshed man with cold gray eyes. In answer to my plea that the usual requirements ought certainly to be waived in the case of the daughter of the founder of the charity, he deprecatingly stated that he had no authority to do so and in addition that there were no vacancies. I fancied that he seemed a trifle uneasy when I inquired as to the number of present inmates and he finally conceded that, in view of all the circumstances, he rather believed the matter might be arranged so that Mrs. Atwood could look forward to being received at "Corndale" in Westchester. Pressing my advantage I urged that my client, as I called her, should be admitted to the house in which her childhood and youth had been spent. At this he hardened, declaring it to be impossible, and we parted with the understanding that Mrs. Atwood should come a few days later, pay over her $170, and sign a deed to all her property, "both present and hereafter to be acquired."

Now, I happened to notice that the dining room table was laid for eight and that a game of mixed doubles was being played on the tennis court. Further, I learned from the servant who let us out that the lady reading on the lawn was Mrs. Freeman, Beckett's mother-in-law, and that the tennis party consisted of his daughters and secretaries. If this was an old ladies' home, I queried to myself, where were the old ladies?

Examining the will of Samuel Wilson I found that the devise of his house and lot to the "Home for Aged Gentlewomen, Incorporated," contained the provision "that the same be used for an old ladies' home, otherwise said house and land shall fall into and become a part of my residuary estate." Mrs. Atwood was the residuary legatee. I called upon Mr. John F. DePeyster,

Chairman of the Board of Trustees. He was a courteous and well-meaning gentleman, but so busy with his private art collections that he and his fellow trustees had for twenty-seven years left the actual conduct of the corporation's affairs entirely in the hands of a salaried superintendent, who in addition to $20,000 per annum, occupied the Wilson homestead, "for executive and administrative purposes." The investments of the corporation yielded an income of $250,000, the salaries paid amounted to over $80,000. The rest of the income went to keep up the "home" at Corndale, which housed but twenty-two inmates, maintained at a cost of approximately $8,000 per annum for each!

And Mr. DePeyster hadn't known anything about it! It was a glaring case of absentee landlordism. When I intimated that his corporation had forfeited ownership,* and that an action of ejectment would lie in Mrs. Atwood's favor, he was shocked and chagrined, furiously indignant at the man who had taken advantage of his position thus to feather his own nest. Mr. Beckett, his wife, daughters and secretaries were promptly thrown out bag and baggage, the entire executive staff at "Corndale" dismissed, and arrangements made for a complete audit of the corporation's books. The property which thus reverted to Mrs. Atwood had a value of several million dollars, but the good old soul had no use for money.

"My father wished his house to become a home for old ladies," she said simply. "I do not want it for myself. I shall be quite satisfied to deed over my interest provided I can live here quietly for the rest of my life."

So Sally Wilson went back to the home of her childhood and lived there peacefully for another fifteen years with a group of elderly ladies of her own choosing, and two additional wings each accommodating fifty new inmates were built at "Corndale," so that the institution instead of caring for but twenty-two beneficiaries, before long had two hundred and fifty; and incidentally I became counsel to the corporation.

* Green *vs.* Old Peoples Home of Chicago, 269 Illinois 134.

That I had in fact acquired some reputation as a trial lawyer seemed to be shown by my retainer in a curious case, with which or its ramifications I was involved for nearly twenty years.

I was lunching alone at Baracca's crowded restaurant one day when I heard myself being paged. Some one wanted me on the telephone. This, in itself, seemed strange, since no one at my office had known where I was going. I went to the booth, took up the instrument, and identified myself.

A gruff, unfamiliar voice accosted me.

"You are wanted at 23 West 86th Street," it said.

"Who is this speaking?" I asked.

"No matter," replied the voice. *"You are wanted at 23 West 86th Street."*

There was a click as the person speaking hung up.

I was bewildered. Was I being lured to my death? If my presence was honestly desired, why shouldn't I have been further enlightened? There was certainly something eery about it. However, I wasn't in a mood to let slip a possible client and about half past four I took the elevated uptown.

The gathering darkness, the stillness, the vacant streets combined to intensify the uncanny feeling which the mysterious telephone call had originally induced, as well as to challenge my curiosity and sense of adventure. The gloomy recesses of the areaways offered choice lurking places for footpads and no policeman was in sight. I reached No. 23, a large stone mansion with a curving double flight of steps, ascended them with some trepidation and rang the bell. Then I observed that both the outer and inner doors of the vestibule were standing wide open.

No one answered and I rang again. I could hear it buzzing in the rear somewhere, otherwise the silence remained unbroken— a silence of that peculiar quality which certifies that there is "nobody home."

"Hello!" I called. "Hello!"

Nothing happened.

I felt my way down the entrance hall to the pantry and looked in.

"Hello!" I repeated loudly. "Is there anybody here?" But there was no reply save the ticking of an alarm clock on a shelf by the ice-box.

Returning to the hallway I peered up the dimly lighted stairway, through the shaft of the high old-fashioned "well" that melted eventually into darkness and, having ascended to the second floor, found myself midway in another hall that ran through the house, upon which opened a series of unlighted and deserted rooms. I hesitated. If I wasn't deliberately murdered by some gangster whom I had sent to Sing Sing I might be mistakenly shot or killed for a burglar! No one would believe my story of the mysterious telephone call.

Then as I stood at the foot of the next flight meditating retreat I became conscious of a faint murmur.

"Some one's up there!" I concluded.

Four doors led off from the second hall. Three of them were ajar, but the fourth, that of the room in front, was closed. Placing my ear to the crack I could hear plainly an intermittent conversation carried on in subdued tones. I could make nothing of it and at the first pause I knocked. Eliciting no reply I knocked more loudly. The conversation started in again. Grasping the knob I opened the door.

In the center of the room an old woman, either dead or in a faint, lay upon a couch under an electric chandelier. Another old woman, in a red wig which had fallen askew over her right eye, stood at the head of the couch attempting to restore the first to her senses. A tall, sallow man dressed in black on the order of Simon Legree sat at the foot of the couch, and next him an ancient wearing a frock coat and string tie and holding an old chimney-pot hat between his knees, palpably a lawyer of a type supposedly long extinct. The curtains were close drawn, which accounted for the stuffy atmosphere of the room and for the absence of any visible light outside.

No one of the group so much as glanced in my direction. Then the old woman on the couch raised herself upon her elbow and said to Legree: "Go away, you wicked man! We shall have nothing to do with you—or them!"

The tall man arose.

"Very well!" he remarked. "Have it your own way. I came on a peaceful errand. Your blood is on your own head.—Good evening!"

He bowed sarcastically and stalked out without noticing me. Thereupon I slipped inside the room, found a chair and quietly seated myself in a corner.

The old lawyer, who had taken no part in the drama, got slowly to his feet.

"Well, I must be going along!" he quavered. "I'm afraid I can't do much good here. You ought to send for the police."

He tottered out, leaving me alone with the two old ladies who now, for the first time, appeared aware of my presence, which however, did not seem to occasion them the least surprise. It was as if, with so much going on, one person more or less made no difference.

The elder woman on the couch, whom the other addressed as "Eliza" had fine brown eyes, a strongly marked profile, and firm thin lips. Her silver black hair was piled on top of her head after the fashion of the last century and set with a huge tortoise-shell comb. On her breast she wore a large cameo pin.

"Are you the lawyer?" she asked.

"I am a lawyer," I equivocated.

"Will you get her back for us?" inquired the woman in the red wig.

"I will do my best!" I replied, although who "she" might be I had not the remotest idea.

"Then everything will be all right, Caroline!" sighed the woman on the couch. "Please bring her back right away!"

Evidently they assumed me to be fully aware of everything there was to know, and it was clear that, should I disabuse their minds, I might throw them into such a flutter that I would lose their confidence entirely and "Eliza" would probably go off into a faint again. She was all right now, and they were both quite calm. Better leave them so and trust to luck to solve the problem in some other way. So I smiled reassuringly, and, as if to carry out their mandate without more ado, got up, bowed and made my exit, in the hope that one of them might let fall some additional remark of an enlightening nature. But neither did so.

I closed the door behind me and descended to the entrance hall, which was littered with packing cases and pictures unhung and placed against the wall as if for removal. Through portieres of parti-colored glass beads I could look into a large drawing room crowded with heavily upholstered armchairs, sofas, gilt easels, vases filled with "cat tails," clocks in glass cases, "mosaic" tables and what were euphemistically known in the era of the Albert Memorial as *objets d'art*. Over the whole hung the odor of mothballs.

Should I go or stay? I sat down on a packing case and lit a stogy.

At that moment up the steps and into the hall breezed with an air of authority, if not of ownership, my friend Herbert Bayard Swope, then a reporter upon the New York *Morning World*.

"What are you doing here?" I asked.

"Just covering the case," he replied. "And you?"

"Oh, I've just been retained," I said. "But for heaven's sake, if you know, tell me what it's all about?"

Swope stalked into the parlor and snapped on the lights, revealing anew all the horrors of the early Victorian period.

"If you don't know, better make yourself comfortable!" he said, striking a match on a mahogany chairback. "There's dirty work at the crossroads, mate, and unless I'm much mistaken it's going to be a rough night. Those two old women upstairs, with their younger sister Marie Louise, have lived here alone for over fifty years without knowing a living male except the postman, the janitor and the clergyman of the church around the corner.

Look at this furniture! They haven't bought anything new since the Centennial Exposition.

"Ever hear of General John Ewen, a Civil War veteran? No? Well, he made a couple of millions, built this house, and died a widower, along in the early seventies, while his daughters were all infants. They've never married and they've hardly ever gone out of the house; they've oodles of money, have never spent any, wouldn't know how if you told 'em, and keep only a couple of old Negro servants. All three are interested in animals. Eliza likes birds, Caroline cats, and Marie Louise anything soft and furry.

"I got into it just by a crazy break. I happened to drop into Brown's Chop House for a highball one evening last November—and saw sitting by himself a young fellow in evening dress, quite blotto. Pretty soon he was telling me the story of his life, the upshot being that he was the scion of a noble Bavarian family—the Baron Boto von Koenitz—who had come to America to seek his fortune. He was pretty well down on his uppers, when he stumbled upon a fellow named Evans who had persuaded him that he had a drag with New York society. So they made an agreement. Evans was to act as the contact man and, if von Koenitz bagged an heiress, was to get fifty per cent of her bank account as rake-off."

"I shouldn't have believed it if the Baron hadn't kept referring to a written 'contract' with Evans, in a way that made me think he might have it on him. How to get it was the question, so I pretended I didn't believe there was any such contract and the next thing I knew he had it out on the table.

"By that time the Baron was so nearly comatose that it took only one more good slug of Bourbon to bury him. So I propped him up comfortably in a corner with his topper over his eyes, took the contract down to *The World* office, had it photographed, and carried it back to the restaurant and stuck it back in von Koenitz' pocket without his ever having missed it."

He pulled out a photostat.

"There it is. All I had to do was to pull it out of the morgue, and now *The World's* going to feature it tomorrow morning on the front page with the complete story of the elopement."

"Elopement!"

"Practically. Yesterday Marie Louise, who's nearly sixty—ran away with the Baron who is only twenty-six. It's an exclusive story with all the elements of high society, crime, money, and international romance."

"But how did Evans manage it? He didn't know the Ewen sisters, did he?"

"Rather cleverly! He organized what he called the 'Travel Club' and circularized the *Social Register*. The Baron was president, while Evans figured as secretary and general manager. Membership was free. The club met once a month at one of the big hotels, and for five dollars any lady could enjoy a nice lunch and listen to a lecture on 'A Journey to the Holy Land' or 'The Mysteries of Hidden India.' Imagine their excitement when the three old ladies received an invitation to hear all about the hidden mysteries of India for five dollars! None of 'em had been anywhere, except maybe to a church fair, since their father had taken 'em to the circus as little girls.

"Eliza and Caroline lost their nerve, but Marie Louise went and had a swell time. The Baron, who isn't a bad-looking fellow, naturally spotted Marie Louise as an easy mark. It ended, as you might suspect, in his escorting her home.

"Her sisters being older and steadier than Marie Louise, sensing something wrong about him, refused to have the Baron in the house. So after that she used to meet him in the park, and, being frightened to death of the other two, kept them in the dark until she had, as she supposed, solidly hooked the Baron and had given him $50,000, through mortgaging the house. This morning she went over to Jersey, was married to von Koenitz by a Justice of the Peace, and now thinks that she's a baroness. They need a lawyer, so let's pool our information and work together. The couple are honeymooning with one of the Baron's friends over in Lakewood Park. They'd like to come back and patch things up, but Eliza and Caroline say they'll never receive the Baron and that, if Marie Louise wants to come home, she'll have to come by herself."

"Their emissary of good will has just left. Eliza and Caroline kicked him out," I said.

"Naturally, I knew they would. What you've got to look out for is how to prevent the Baron bumping off his bride and grabbing her fortune. Of course, by this time he's got her to sign a will in his favor."

"But how am I to do it?"

"That's up to you. Hasn't he committed some crime you could arrest him for until we find out who exactly he is?"

"If we could prove he wasn't the Baron von Koenitz I suppose we could arrest him for obtaining the $50,000 mortgage money by false pretenses. But we can't. However—by the way, did you call me on the telephone today?"

"I did not."

"Why is the furniture all packed up?"

"Marie Louise gave it to the Baron and he's taking it away."

"And why is the front door open and nobody around?"

"The Negroes got scared and beat it this morning, leaving the two old women alone."

"Herbert!" I said earnestly. "We need each other!"

The fortune—and perhaps the life—of a delicate little old lady was at stake. I should have to act and act quickly, yet to act effectively I must spend money and plenty of it. I hadn't a thing on the Baron. Marie Louise had married him for love and since the house was hers had a perfect right to give him the $50,000. But, on the face of it, the fellow was a fortune-hunting crook and I felt justified in taking whatever steps were necessary to prevent his luring his bride away to some distant part of the world, where she would be helplessly in his hands. Once she had executed a will there was nothing to prevent his accidentally pushing her off a steamer or out of a window.

"Has the Baron announced any plans?" I asked Swope.

"He says that unless Eliza and Caroline change their attitud₁ he and Marie Louise are going to Florida. You've got to stop 'em I just dropped in to check up on the progress of affairs. It's exactly as I figured it would be. So I'll leave you to hold the fort. *The World* goes to press at one A.M. and I'll give you a ring just before midnight to hear what's doing. So long!"

Swope breezed off again, and I went back upstairs and asked Eliza and Caroline if they would authorize me to spend whatever sums might be necessary to get their sister back. They said yes, yes! any amount! Then I told them that I was going out to get some supper and would call again later in the evening.

Obviously the first step was to nail the Baron and Marie Louise's $50,000—or what was left of it. I telephoned the Pinkertons and directed them to surround the house at Lakewood Park and see to it that the Baron stayed where he was. Then I called up the Chief of Police of the town, explained what had happened and who I was, and intimated not only that the local jail was the safest place for the Baron von Koenitz, but that the Ewen family would be extremely gratified if he landed there. The chief said he understood the situation perfectly and would keep in touch with me. He added that he could easily manage to have the Baron—should he seek to escape—arrested on suspicion or for assault.

I then got in touch with the family clergyman, who was said to have some influence with Marie Louise, and arranged with him to go to New Jersey the following day, taking with us the other two sisters, in the hope of persuading the sixty-year-old bride to come home. But before we started something happened that put us in an immensely stronger position.

The World came out next morning with the von Koenitz case, including a reproduction of the marriage contract between Evans and the Baron, on the front page. I was mentioned as an attorney retained to represent the family. About ten o'clock I received a telephone call at my office from the Warden of the State Prison at Trenton. He had seen *The World's* story, he said, and had recognized the name "Boto von Koenitz" as that of a prisoner who had recently served two terms there—one for larceny and one for blackmail. He had also compared the signature on the contract with that in the prison files and found that they were the same! I told him to send me certified copies of von Koenitz' commitments and record.

Coincidentally I got another message that was not so good. It was from the Chief of Police who said that, although the Pinkertons had completely surrounded the house, which was located in the full glare of several electric lights, the Baron had climbed down a lightning rod and made his escape during the night—presumably taking, not his bride, but the $50,000 with him. However, we all felt that it was a cheap-enough price to pay for her safety and believed that of course she would at once, on learning the true character of her husband, return to her sisters' arms.

But we had counted without Marie Louise. I found her a tiny wisp of a woman with dyed hair, weighing not ninety pounds, and wearing a dress adorned with baby-blue ribbons. She received us politely, and although obviously somewhat disturbed to learn that she had married an ex-convict, positively refused to go home.

"I married him for better or for worse," she declared. "And just because it's a little worse I shan't leave him."

Boto had gone on ahead to Florida and she proposed to follow him as soon as he sent for her. She evidently enjoyed the excitement of being married and looked forward to her coming trip with eagerness. She insisted that she had not given him the money because he was a baron, or because she thought him a man of high character, but merely because she loved him—and with her statement any chance of a successful criminal prosecution against him vanished. All we could do was to arrange to have her protected as far as possible from physical violence and to seek for new evidences of the Baron's perfidy. These were easily obtained.

The local correspondent of *The World* in Munich cabled that he had located the only living representative of the von Koenitz family, who told him that he had received a letter from a "Boto von Koentiz," in which the latter stated that he was his cousin and enclosed a handkerchief embroidered with a "von K" below a coronet. Since there had been many cousins in various branches of the von Koenitz family and some of them had disappeared, the good Freiherr swallowed the story whole, accepting the handkerchief as proof positive, without being aware that the street address to which his reply was to be sent was in fact a euphemism for the New Jersey State's Prison. So he had cordially invited "Cousin Boto" to come over and visit him, and this Cousin Boto had done—as soon as he got his final discharge—making an excellent impression on the Freiherr and his attractive daughter, and securing from both of them all the data necessary to convince the world that he was a member of the German nobility and the owner of a castle in Thuringia, including photographs of same.

With this as a starter the detectives managed to trace the Baron from his place of origin in German South Africa to Texas, and thence to New York, where he had attained fame as a roistering wine agent on Broadway. It was only after having been jailed for blackmail that he had become a baron with a castle.

His fondness for women, together with his curious predilection for photographing them in various stages of undress, enabled me by a little judicious expenditure to secure incontrovertible evidence, not only of his tendencies but his acts, and within a month Bonnie Doon was on his way to Florida with a complete dossier of all the Baron's misdeeds and former romances.

The couple were registered as mother and son at a hotel in St. Augustine, and were having a swell time spending the $50,000. Marie Louise, in spite of her years, had enjoyed trying to learn how to ride horseback, drive a motor car, swim and dance. But she was highly religious and Bonnie managed to effect a meeting with her at the local rectory, having arranged that the Baron's motorboat should suddenly go out of commission while he was off tarpon fishing. Marie Louise, always polite, read the dossier and collapsed in a faint. But when restored she only repeated her former resolution. "I married him for better or for worse, and because it's a little worse I shan't leave him now!" I don't think she really wanted to—she was having too good a time and seeing so much of life.

Things continued about as they were, until the $50,000 was nearly exhausted, when the Baron began to be somewhat less attentive and drifted off with a couple of ladies belonging to a travelling revue. But Marie Louise still remained fanatically loyal.

Then something happened that started a chain of events that kept me busy for years. Boto, having cross-examined Marie Louise as to her further financial resources, made her kneel down on the floor and holding a pistol to her temple, swear upon "her mother's grave" that she would go to New York in company with a lady friend of his, procure her securities, valued at some $350,000, which were in a vault in the Fifth Avenue Bank, send them to him by express and then return herself to St. Augustine.

Locked in a compartment on an Atlantic Coast Line Pullman, poor little Marie Louise travelled back to New York, where her guardian again locked her in a room at the Hotel Martinique. She managed to extricate herself and knowing that I was anxious to protect her interests to telephone me. Her guardian was so delighted at being able to enjoy the pleasures of the Great White Way that it was easy for us to arrange a secret meeting at the Bar Association.

Her appearance was shocking. She had lost more weight and seemed on the verge both of a nervous breakdown and of physical collapse. What preyed upon her mind was the fact, not that she was married to a crook to whom she was afraid not to return, but that she had agreed to send him the fortune her father had left her.

"It doesn't seem right that I should give Boto, to spend as he pleases, all the money Father worked so hard to earn. I want you to think up some way so that, while I seem to want to carry out my promise to him, you can save my inheritance."

At the moment, it seemed a pretty large order. Then I took a bold step.

"Would you be willing to assign your fortune to me in trust until you secure a divorce or annulment of your marriage?"

"Yes, indeed."

"Then write a letter to the Fifth Avenue Bank telling them that, when you go there tomorrow morning at ten o'clock with your guard, and ask for your securities, they must invent some excuse for not giving them to you, but that later in the day you will call alone and receive them."

I wrote out a trust deed in longhand, which she duly signed and acknowledged; then she signed the letter to the bank; and I put her in a taxi and sent her back to the Martinique.

Early next morning I went to the bank where a directors' meeting was in progress, asked to be allowed to interrupt, and told them the story.

"Now, gentlemen," I asked, "will you stand back of me?"

There was a shout of assent.

I went down to the vault, put on an alpaca jacket to make myself look like an employee, and waited. Promptly at ten o'clock Marie Louise, accompanied by a flashily dressed young woman, appeared at the wicket. Marie Louise recognized me but gave no sign of it.

"I would like to open my safety box and get out some securities," she said.

The vault custodian retired for a moment and then returned.

"I am sorry, madam, but the lock seems to be out of order. You will have to come back tomorrow morning."

The harpy beside her turned purple with rage.

"What nonsense! What sort of a bank is this where you can't open your own safe!"

"I'm very sorry, madam, but the lock has evidently rusted."

Reluctantly, and with many unfavorable remarks as to the management, the two women departed. So far all had gone according to schedule, but how about the rest of the program? Could Marie Louise evade her guard long enough to come again that afternoon? Fortune favored us. The harpy wanted to see a musical show and locked her up once more. Again with the connivance of a room-waiter the little woman made her escape and joined me at the Fifth Avenue Bank, where this time she had no difficulty about the lock of her box. Without examining the contents, it was taken out, sealed and delivered by her direction to me. I had a car waiting at the entrance, the safe deposit box was placed on the floor under my feet, and with a loaded revolver in each hand I drove downtown to the New York Trust Company, then on Broad Street, where the president, Mr. Otto Bannard, was waiting for me (it was then after five o'clock) with the vault open. We shoved in the box, closed the door of the vault, and the fortune was safe.

But was Marie Louise? She had promised to send Boto her securities and, unless our ruse succeeded, she feared that he would take her life.

Next morning the two women reappeared at the Fifth Avenue Bank and Marie Louise demanded access to her box, only to be met with this extraordinary statement:

"We are sorry, madam, but yesterday afternoon your family's attorney came and took all your securities away!"

Marie Louise, in spite of her weakness, first pretended to faint and then staged an excellent imitation of outraged indignation. She was going to sue the bank, she declared. She would make them pay her half a million dollars. Her companion gave vent to a burst of profanity that shocked the attendants, but there was nothing she could do, except to keep the wires to St. Augustine hot trying to explain to Boto what had occurred.

I did my best to persuade Marie Louise not to return with her, but without avail, and back she went to make the best peace with the Baron that she could. Bonnie came home and for several months we heard nothing and feared for the worst. Then unexpectedly Marie Louise returned by herself to New York and came to see me. Boto, it seemed, had taken two young ladies on a trip to Havana and everything—including the $50,000—was finished.

At first Marie Louise would not consider having me attempt to secure an annulment of her marriage, but after a year, since Boto had not turned up, she rather reluctantly consented. I brought the action in Queens County and easily secured a decree on the ground that the defendant had concealed from her the fact that he was an ex-convict.

An interlocutory decree having been entered, and, the necessary three months interval having elapsed, I was about to have final judgment entered when unexpectedly Marie Louise eloped again—this time with a young clergyman only twenty-two years old. I say "eloped," for they travelled abroad together for nearly two years, he having resigned his curacy, although I believe they registered independently. Yet, however devoted he may have been, his path was not entirely strewn with roses, for his elderly companion was always having unexpected accidents. Twice she fractured a hip, the first time by falling out of an old-fashioned high bed in Munich, and the second by slipping off a camel in Syria.

"Marie Louise has broken her hip falling out of bed," he cabled. *"What shall I do?"*

"Send for a doctor," I wired in reply.

I had resigned as trustee of her estate early in the game and had her sisters appointed in my place. A furious legal contest resulted in her absence, during which she attempted to recapture her property, while they sought to have it sequestered on the ground that she was not able to look out for her own affairs. In the course of this I wrote a letter giving it as my opinion that she was mentally incompetent. Thereafter, for several years, the situation remained unchanged.

One day the Baron called at my office. He was dressed in a loudly checked suit with a red waistcoat, had on a gray Derby and carried a cane. He had come, he explained, just to let me know that there were no hard feelings and to ask if I could let him have ten dollars. I took a chance and gave it to him, then inquired how he lived.

"I'm really doing all right," he said. "You can see I look prosperous, although that's part of the game. I represent Doctor Blank, who runs an orthopœdic hospital in Harlem. I just sit in Peacock Alley up at the Waldorf and if anyone comes along limping I go up, touch him on the shoulder and say: 'I see you're a bit lame. I had the same trouble until I heard of Doctor Blank's Orthopœdic Hospital. He cured me in a week. I've been O.K. ever since. I'm so grateful to him I just want to pass the word along.' The doc and I go fifty-fifty."

The next legal event in the Ewen family was that Caroline died leaving practically all of her estate for the benefit of dumb animals—principally to cats. She bequeathed handsome legacies to animal rescue societies the world over, including those of Rome, Naples, London, and Madeira. Her will had been dictated by herself just before her death in the hospital and practically every legatee was misnamed. Thus she had designated "The Cat House of London" as an object of her benefaction, and London was full of "cat houses." The chief claimants to the legacy were The Royal Humane Society and The Islington Home for Lost and Starving Felines. Somehow, the Humane Society won, but I never thought it quite right.

Another equally large legacy was left to the cats of Madeira. There were, I was credibly informed, only nine cats in Madeira at the time—which would have made exactly $4000 per cat. Eventually an eminent lawyer, the father of John Dos Passos, the author, appeared for an organization called *La Sociedad Anonima Dos Animales de Funchal* or something on that order.

John Ewen, the nephew of the Misses Ewen—a most patient, long-suffering and fair-minded young lawyer—objected to his aunt leaving her entire fortune to cats, when she had grandnieces and nephews who needed the money, and contested the will on the ground of insanity. I was retained to defend it by Eliza. In the end a compromise was arranged whereby the cats got only half their money.

I always liked John Ewen and we remained friendly, in spite of the animosity exhibited against him by Eliza for contesting her sister's will. Later on both she and Marie Louise cut him off without a penny.

To return to Marie Louise. She and her youthful curate travelled abroad together for a couple of years and, although they were never married, finally returned to take up their joint abode in a West Side hotel in New York, where they lived in amity until she finally died, and he was received back into the bosom of the church. Every one naturally expected that she would have left her companion of the cloth her entire estate, amounting to some $300,000. But when the will was opened, behold she had left him only $10,000. Since, like Caroline, she had bequeathed all her money to charity to the exclusion of her family, John Ewen also promptly contested her will on the ground of mental incapacity.

On general principles it seemed that he had a pretty good case. But Marie Louise, in spite of her romantic tendencies, had shown herself a highly sensible person in her treatment of the curate and, in addition to a lengthy and entertaining correspondence with her sister, had kept a detailed, well-written, vivid and extremely witty diary of her trip abroad. During the last ten years.of her life she had been as sane as anybody and had efficiently managed her affairs. As usual, I was retained to defend the will and made a strong fight for the old lady's competency.

Unexpectedly, towards the end of the trial, John Ewen called me to the stand and handed me my long-forgotten letter, in which I said that in my opinion the old girl was obviously crazy.

"Did you write that letter?" he asked.

I flushed, but answered in the affirmative.

"Did you believe what you said?"

"I certainly did."

He grinned.

"That is all. You may step down!"

A hush fell over the courtroom and it was clear from the expression on John Ewen's face that he felt sure of a verdict.

I turned to the judge.

"One moment. I claim the right to cross-examine myself."

He nodded.

"Mr. Tutt," asked Mr. Tutt, "kindly state how you reconcile your present contention that the testatrix was competent with your former opinion, expressed in this letter, that she ought to be committed to an institution and her property sequestered?"

"I've simply changed my mind," I replied.

"Please tell the court and jury *how* you came to change your opinion as to Miss Marie Louise Ewen's mental competency."

"I will—gladly," answered Mr. Tutt, and turning to the jury I summed up the entire evidence—setting off, as against her peculiar marital adventures, her undoubted business acumen, her correspondence, her diary, and last but not least the fact that she had left her curate only $10,000, the equivalent of $2500 per year during their association.

The jury found unhesitatingly in favor of the will.

Eliza, the last of the three sisters, lived on for many years, alone save for a Negro servant or two, in a ramshackly old house near Spuyten Duyvil Creek. She was a beautiful character, although given to prejudices and of limited intelligence. She and both her sisters were gentlewomen of refinement and high principle. Toward the end Eliza heard voices and talked with Caroline and Marie Louise, who, she declared, told her to "trust Ephraim in everything." She wished to leave me her entire fortune. This I naturally refused to permit, accepting in lieu thereof the family portraits of herself and her two sisters—painted daguerreotypes on glass in oval gilded frames. They are hanging now on the wall of my library, three sweet-faced girls in charming old-fashioned frocks. John Ewen did not contest his Aunt Eliza's will in which she left her entire fortune to charity. To this day I have no idea who it was that sent the mysterious telephone call that called me into the strangest case in my professional experience.

Since I was a Democrat, although I had never joined Tammany Hall, I continued in excellent standing with the General Sessions judges and politicos of the Criminal Courts Building, who—the legend regarding my intimacy with Boss Croker still persisting—supposed that Jerome had kicked me out on account of my loyalty to the machine. In consequence they frequently assigned me to defend prisoners charged with homicide who could not afford to pay for counsel, and since each case entitled me to a fee of $500 from the county treasury I soon was making a sum equivalent to my former salary. Practicing criminal law proved easy money, for the fact that the burden of proof was upon the prosecution reduced the necessity for preparation on the part of the defense, and four out of every five of my clients were discharged in the magistrates' courts for lack of evidence.

Yet I knew that I was only marking time. Otto was already a junior leader of the New York bar. After his year as secretary to Chief Justice Oliver Wendell Holmes in Boston, he had accepted a position with Judge Isaac M. Furman, a well-known New York lawyer with a lucrative practice, whose partner he had in due course become, but success hadn't altered him in the least. He was the same old Ot. His hair was just as tousled, his clothes as unkempt, and he burned the midnight oil, often working sixteen hours a day. Already he had appeared a dozen or more times before the Supreme Court in Washington to which his former preceptor Holmes had just been translated.

By contrast what I was doing seemed small potatoes. Up to now I had not done so badly. I had worked my way through college and law school, had two degrees to my credit, had had four years of general practice in a country town, where I had done everything from invoking the XIVth Amendment to enjoining the sale of baby-diapers (patented), besides three strenuous years as a prosecutor, during which I had tried hundreds—nay, thousands—of cases. I was anxious to put my experience into practice. Yet I was still at loose ends, more or less a stranger in a strange land.

A lot had happened during those three years. The Spanish War was over, Cuba had been freed, the United States had taken over the Philippines; I had stood in the roaring crowd that watched Admiral Dewey ride under the white triumphal arch intended to be as imperishable as his fame but which had in fact withered overnight; Theodore Roosevelt whom Boss Platt had "kicked upstairs" into the vice-presidency—and into supposed political oblivion as well—now occupied the White House; we had become a world power. Yes, a lot had happened, and yet one might stand a whole afternoon on Fifth Avenue and not count over half a dozen motors—and those probably electrics— since the "automobubble" was regarded as a dangerous joke or at best an expensive toy. "Get a horse!"

Cal Coolidge shared the general skepticism as to automobiles. He had been appointed Clerk of Court for Hampshire County, Massachusetts, and took, I think, great, but secretive, pride in the fact as "a step in the right direction." At any rate he did something very unusual for him—invited me to come up to hear him make a speech at the Blandford Country Club. I hadn't seen him for ten years, but he looked just about the same—trim and dapper, with shrewd eyes, thin, dust-colored hair and sharp, intelligent face. He met me at the station with Fred Jager who owned the only automobile in Northampton. It was a rattlety-bang affair and every moment we were pitched half out of our seats. Cal preserved his usual silence until the agonizing experience was over, then remarked to me in a confidential tone:

"Of course it's a wonderful thing to ride in a horseless carriage, Eph—but it won't ever amount to much."

VI

WALL STREET LAW FACTORY

I KNEW that I was wasting my abilities in Franklin Street, and yet I hesitated to cut loose from the only clientele I had and try a hazard of new fortunes in Wall Street. Then out of a clear sky the well-publicized firm of Hotchkiss, Levy & Hogan invited me to join them as a junior partner at a salary of $5,000 a year. I felt greatly complimented that this celebrated firm had ever heard of me or that, with such an extensive and gilt-edged practice, they should have thought me worth their while, but my pride suffered a fall when I asked Otto's advice as to whether to accept their offer.

"It all depends on what you want, Eph," he replied making a wry face. "Hotchkiss, Levy & Hogan don't practice law; they conduct a business. Except for earning some money you'll gain nothing by your association with them—certainly not in reputation."

"I don't have to stay if I don't like it," I said, "and I'm sure that what I learn will help me later on."

"Well, don't say I didn't warn you!" he replied ominously. "And may God have mercy on your soul!"

It did not take me long to discover that Otto's strictures on the character of the firm had some basis in fact. Their outer office resembled the foyer of the Waldorf-Astoria, where clients came in, registered, and checked in or out. There was a reception clerk in a "dickey," striped trousers, and spats, and a row of messengers dressed like bell hops. You almost expected to hear someone call "Front!" Files of young men, bearing wire baskets piled high with papers, stalked back and forth on the horizon like caravans of laden camels.

Hotchkiss, Levy & Hogan was a typical Wall Street law factory, occupying two entire stories in a white-stone office building within spitting distance of J. P. Morgan & Co. There were fifteen full-fledged partners who shared a percentage in the profits and, in addition to twenty-eight juniors receiving regular salaries, there were thirty-five law clerks, forty stenographers, four cashiers, eight expert accountants, twelve office boys, a double-shift of telephone operators, a posse of process servers and detectives, a translator, a photographer, a real-estate expert, an architectural draftsman and two librarians. The plant was divided into a corporations department, a probate department, a patent department, a personal injuries and trial department, a divorce department, an international law department, and various others, while its total overhead was not far from half a million a year. Its filing system equalled that of Sears Roebuck, the lights burned all night long and luncheon was eaten off trays by all including the salaried partners, who came early, stayed late, and died young. Everything was done according to a highly perfected technique of written communications:

> Title: Smith *vs.* Jones
>   File No. 101,459
> From J.H.R. to E. Tutt:
> See Mr. Canthus before going to court. Send
> time charges and incidental ex. acc't to cashier.
>   J.H.R.

John Henry Hotchkiss, the head of the firm, widely known as a philanthropist and "friend of young men," wore a tall hat, mutton chop whiskers, and had a broadcloth covered paunch and liverspots. He looked a cross between a banker, an actor, and a sexton, and bore a strong legal family resemblance to the Mr. Curtis who had so nearly engaged my services in Boston. He spent his time commuting between New York, London, and Paris, ingratiating himself with wealthy passengers on the ocean liners and in addressing bar associations, Boost Clubs, Boards of Trade, Elks and Rotarians at their respective annual banquets.

Mr. Levy, the firm's heavy artillery, was a thickset man, with a clipped gray moustache and bulbous nose having a small drop of white flesh dependent between the nostrils. A brow-beater and bulldozer, he took savage delight in tearing out the entrails of helpless witnesses. Mr. Hotchkiss represented the firm's *suaviter in modo,* Mr. Levy its *fortiter in re.*

Mr. Hogan, the last triumvir, was a red-faced, white-thatched Irishman, a sachem of Tammany Hall, persona grata at the Cathedral, and a popular member of the Links Club, who spent most of his time playing golf with the Appellate Division.

The real brains of the office was the chief clerk, Mr. Canthus, a harassed little man with a bright red nose, who looked like Charles Dana Gibson's historic "Mr. Pipp." He lived in Flushing with a wife, five female offspring and a mother-in-law, neither smoked nor swore, acted as a lay reader in the Presbyterian Church, and received ten thousand dollars a year in return for his ability to maintain a perpetual and beatific calm. He had been with Hotchkiss, Levy & Hogan for nineteen years, and in a sense he *was* Hotchkiss, Levy & Hogan. "Ask Mr. Canthus." He was familiar with every point of pleading raised since 1735 and he knew the Civil and Criminal Procedure Reports by heart. He took nobody's word for anything and judges were no more to him than chattering monkeys. He smiled rarely, he never hurried. He spoke only to say "You've left out a comma there," or "You've forgotten the 'and' after 'damages,' " or "The clerk said that, did he? Well, tell him from me that he's a bonehead." He had made but one mistake in his career—in 1891, when in a moment of aphasia he had overlooked the "petition for further relief" in an equity order. He would sit unruffled at his desk amid a hurricane of questions, directions and objurgations, half snowed under with papers awaiting his signature, placidly studying some complaint, answer or judgment which must be filed at the County Court House in exactly nine minutes. In his heart he regarded the title members of the firm as ignorant and debased commercialists and his soul vomited at them and all their works. He had been born in Newburyport, Massachusetts.

It was Mr. Hotchkiss' custom annually to deliver a sort of

vade mecum to the neophytes in his office. He invariably commenced with an invocation to Justice, in which he referred
to the law as the noblest of all professions, a sacred calling of
which we were the priests in the temple. Here, having asserted
that it had numbered among its followers the greatest men of all
times, he would first glance up at the graven lineaments upon the
wall of Lord Eldon, Chief Justice Marshall, Chief Justice Shaw,
Daniel Webster, and Rufus Choate, then modestly allow his eyes
to fall upon his own stomach. Brightening visibly he would then
enunciate the general requirements for success, to wit:—the highest moral standards, unflagging industry and, of course, complete
sobriety. In a word, it was true in law as in everything else that
honesty was the best policy.

There were, however, a few other practical considerations
which were worth bearing in mind. You could not practice law
without clients, and the only way to get clients was to go out and
nab them. To do this a good impression was prerequisite. Hence,
"costly thy raiment as thy purse can buy." Next, one should af-
filiate himself with activities where he could meet people of
wealth and influence—a "good" church, a "good" club, a
"good" charity, a "good" fraternal organization—"good" meaning one having rich adherents who might logically some time become clients. "If you would have money, go where money is." He
also advised teaching a class in Sunday school, joining the
Knights of Columbus, the Y.M.C.A. or a Masonic lodge, and
accepting invitations to dinner. In this connection he recommended having half a dozen stories on tap and a funny speech
ready prepared in case one was unexpectedly called on for a few
remarks. Indeed, he could and did give instances where a young
man had landed a juicy piece of business simply by telling an
apropos Pat and Mike anecdote. He emphasized the fact that
elderly ladies like attention and are given to making wills, that
young ones are anxious to get married, and that anything in
trousers is socially eagerly sought after. However, he advised
going slow on marriage—unless the girl had money. He also

urged activity in politics, and contributing to campaign funds. The great thing was to get out, hustle, mix, attract favorable attention, and take advantage of one's opportunities.

When it came to starting out for oneself the best course was to organize a firm that would be "representative"; if you were a Protestant to select a Jew and an Irishman as partners, a method of which his own firm was a conspicuous example. But above all, you should be on the "right" side of everything, and studiously avoid socialists, laborites or any movement that would get people down on you. You should, in sum, seek to give the impression of being a serious-minded young man devoted to the welfare of your country, your city and your client's interests.

"And now," he would say arising and holding out a flabby hand as if in benediction to each of his audience as it shambled by, "I can only express the hope that with these ideals in mind you may all attain success. Good afternoon, gentlemen, good luck and may God bless you all!"

John Henry Hotchkiss, although I did not then realize it, was one of the protagonists of a hypocritical age of conventionality, euphemism, Sabbatarianism, and Comstockery, in which if one went to church, sang loudly and passed the plate, few questions were asked; an age of "front," in houses, clothes, and morals—but the fronts were false and it was not good form to look behind them. To be a senator was to be godly and to be a millionaire a favored of the Almighty. Thus while it was a matter of common knowledge that certain great philanthropists maintained dual households, the word "mistress" was socially taboo.

The firm of Hotchkiss, Levy & Hogan were famed as legal "go-getters." They never missed a trick. There was hardly a new organization that did not carry on its letter-head the motto: "Hotchkiss, Levy & Hogan, of Counsel" or "Hotchkiss, Levy & Hogan, Attorneys." Old-fashioned lawyers regarded them with annoyance, but treated them with respect. Every autumn ten thousand notices, engraved upon the costliest Tiffany stationery, flooded the mails, announcing that "Mr. John J. Smith (or whosoever) has this day become a member of our firm."

Mr. Hotchkiss was the chairman of the Committee on Legal Ethics of the Interstate Bar Association, Mr. Hogan a member of the Judiciary Committee of that same body; and if these professional plums had not fallen into their legal laps, they would simply have gone out and organized another association which should show better taste.

While the three title members of the firm were merely expert publicity men who devoted themselves to pulling in the business, the rest of the partners were capable, hard-working, high-minded attorneys who cringed at the antics of their masters, but who, for financial reasons, could not afford to sever their connection. New York is full of such. Nobody ever hears of them, for they sit in secluded offices looking up the law, preparing briefs and drafting papers which are later signed by the John Henry Hotchkisses of the bar. They are known only to the clients of the firm, to their professional associates, to the judges upon the bench, to the members of the law committees upon which they serve, and to their Father in Heaven.

There was one fly, however, in the amber of Hotchkiss, Levy & Hogan. They were successful, but they were not first class—and they knew it. At least, Mr. Hotchkiss knew it, and it hurt. For some reason, which he could not divine, people of established social position did not consult them.

Efficiency was the middle name of Hotchkiss, Levy & Hogan, who, while they naturally preferred corporate reorganizations, were prepared to undertake anything from a suit for damages for slipping on a banana peel to establishing a claim to the throne of Siam, or from floating a bond issue to securing an injunction to prevent repairs upon the White House. They had correspondents in every city in both the civilized and uncivilized world and numbered among their clients present and prospective foreign governments, railroad systems, banks, trust companies and defunct royal families. They were no respecters of persons, and they would stake you, break you, collect your alimony, buy your steamship tickets, or endeavor to keep you from being hanged, as might be necessary, and since it appeared that it was for this last, and in general for what they called "the criminal end" they chiefly required my services, I soon felt at home. In those days a life insurance official or banker who hadn't been indicted was like a dog without a tail. What was an indictment between friends? Hence my knowledge of the ins and outs of criminal practice gave me a peculiar standing in the office.

I lived in a cyclone of calendar calls, depositions, subpoenas, orders to show cause, motions to adjourn and to dismiss and for new trials. I interviewed bandaged victims in hospital wards, policemen, motormen, truck-drivers, and internes, dictated their statements to the peripatetic stenographer and notary who acted as my Sancho Panza, and I learned the difference between the pharynx and the larynx, the femur and the collar-bone. I shouted "Ready for trial," elbowing my way among the mobs of legal underlings smelling of damp rubber, acrid cigars, sweat, and wintergreen chewing-gum, who crowded into Part I of the Supreme Court, afterward herding my witnesses in the grimy corridors outside and trying to keep them in good humor, while I dashed frantically from one telephone-booth to another in an attempt to find such as had gone astray.

Thanks to my familiarity with jury trials I had such luck defending accident cases that I was soon promoted to the higher realms of civil litigation, thus escaping my repugnance at having to plead "the fellow servant rule" or the doctrine of "contributory negligence" in order that our corporate clients might escape financial responsibility for injuries sustained by their employees. I was heartily in favor of some sort of workmen's compensation law whereby the risk should be in part, at least, assumed by the employer; but up to that time wherever such legislation had been enacted it had been upset by the courts.

Until I joined Hotchkiss, Levy & Hogan my clients had all

been humble folk; now, and for the next five years, they were chiefly bankers, railroad presidents, mine owners or industrialists. Whatever wrongs they had suffered did not affect their personal lives; irrespective of the result of the cases they would be just as comfortable as before. They did not seem like real people, or their problems real problems. In a criminal trial one is fighting for a man's liberty or perhaps his life; in civil cases such as were now given me to try—even though they involved complicated questions of corporation law or had resulted in long-drawn-out litigations—I was just quarrelling over a wad of dough.

Our clients' troubles were not their own personal troubles but those of some class of which they were merely the representatives—associations, boards of directors, stockholders. If a machinist loses a finger it is his own finger and his own trouble; but, if a railroad mortgage has to be refinanced and the plan doesn't go through, it's the railroad's loss—not its officers'. It is the same difference as between taking a tramp into a cafeteria and filling him up with doughnuts and coffee and sitting in an office and directing a drive for the Red Cross. The Red Cross is more worth while, but one doesn't get half the kick out of it. I missed the little people who had lost their fingers or their jobs, or who had been personally wronged in some way. It made no difference to me how a couple of millionaires divided their loot.

But drama was not entirely lacking in the practice of Hotchkiss, Levy & Hogan. One of their clients was a genial old pirate known as "Wild Bill" Babson, president of the Great Western & Lone Star Oil Company. He was a big man, with a raucous voice, handle-bar moustaches and a six-shooter on his hip. He travelled in a private car with two young ladies euphemistically known as "nieces," or more carelessly as "wards," and he offered to take me out to the sage-brush and make a millionaire of me in no time.

It appeared that a villain by the name of Augustus K. Van Hamm was suing the Lone Star for an accounting, but when I hazarded to Mr. Canthus that, judging by the appearance of our client, Mr. Van Hamm was probably justified he explained that not "Wild Bill" but the Lone Star Corporation was our client. The distinction was in fact academic since Babson owned most of the stock, and it was easy to see that they were all a bunch of crooks, liars every mother's son of them—including Van Hamm's lawyer.

A civil case is easy going compared to a criminal trial. I romped all over the courtroom, and up to the last inning had things pretty much my own way. Then just as I thought I had my verdict in the bag Van Hamm was recalled to the stand and testified to a transparently false and obviously cooked up conversation with Babson in the back room of a saloon in Oklahoma City in July 1900, which if true would have changed the aspect of everything. I knew that it wasn't because Babson had been in St. Louis on that day and I could have proved it. All I had to do was to call him in rebuttal and have him deny that any such talk ever occurred. I was about to do this when I saw him in earnest conference with two pals in the back of the courtroom. Presently he signalled that he was ready to testify and took the chair just vacated by his opponent.

"Mr. Babson, were you in Oklahoma City on July 8, 1900?" I asked.

And then Wild Bill exploded the bomb that in his opinion was going to blow 'em all clean out of water.

"I was," he said innocently.

"You *were!*" I stammered.

"That's what I said."

"Did you have this talk with Mr. Van Hamm?"

"I did—only 'twasn't nuthin' like he said."

"Was anyone else present beside yourself and him?"

"Sure there was. Him, me, Jeff Dwyer and Tom Nason over there—four of us."

Obviously Wild Bill thought it better to admit that he had had such a conversation and twist it to his own advantage by calling two corroborating witnesses, than merely to deny it. Blundering old perjuror! I was too fresh from the criminal courts to consider any possible duty to my client.

"Your Honor," I cried, "I know that this witness is deliberately misstating the facts. He was not in Oklahoma on July 8, 1900, and the alleged conversation never took place. He is foolish enough to imagine that the best way to combat one lie is with another. I withdraw and disavow him. He ought to be indicted for perjury. I would abandon the case here and now were it not for the fact that the interests of other stockholders are involved. But this does not mean that I believe the plaintiff is entitled to a verdict—I think he is a bigger liar than Mr. Babson."

Judge Lemuel Saunders looked down at the witness.

"Do you wish to correct your testimony? Were you in Oklahoma City on July 8, 1900?"

Wild Bill twisted uneasily.

"Well, I thought I was, Judge," he said. "But if Mr. Tutt says I wasn't, I guess I must be mistaken."

The foreman winked at me.

"In that case, did you or did you not have the conversation testified to by Mr. Van Hamm?" I inquired.

"I did *not*!" declared Babson emphatically.

I turned to the jury.

"Gentlemen," I said, "The Ananias Club will now adjourn."

Two hours later they returned a verdict in favor of the Great Western & Lone Star Oil Company for three hundred and seventy-four thousand dollars. The first to congratulate me was Wild Bill.

"You're sure a crackerjack lawyer, son! That was a slick trick you pulled! At first I thought you was tryin' to doublecross me, but then I got onto it. You saved my bacon all right. Jake Van Hamm's waiting for me. Come along and have a drink with us?"

"With *Van Hamm*!"

"Why not? It's all in the day's work. Him and me is old pals. It's not the first time one of us has soaked the other and it won't be the last. Come along and show there's no hard feeling!"

The Lone Star case served me in similar good stead to that of the great wen trial before Squire Dow in Pottsville, and the next time I lunched with Otto at the Down Town Association a good many lawyers came up and congratulated me, including no less a personage than the Honorable Joseph H. Choate.

"It's not every lawyer who can call his witness a liar in open court and keep him as a client!" he smiled. "But be careful how you do it again!"

Mr. Choate was at this time the leading trial lawyer at the New York bar, which included James C. Carter, Elihu Root, John E. Parsons, John L. Cadwalader, William D. Guthrie, and John G. Milburn.

Mr. Carter was the Nestor of the group—to me a terrifying old gentleman with his beetle brows and gruff manner. While he did not resemble his contemporary, J. P. Morgan the elder, in appearance, he occupied a similar position of isolated grandeur to that of Morgan in finance, and like Morgan he had a human side, for I used to see him almost daily at the Hoffman House eating a lunch consisting of a dozen large oysters washed down with a pint of champagne. I wondered whether the time would ever come when Ephraim Tutt could afford that kind of a meal.

Although in due course I met and got to know more or less intimately all of these celebrated men, I was most drawn to Mr. Choate. He had already been Ambassador to the Court of St. James's, had won first rank in his profession, and was long past the age when most lawyers retire, but he kept on trying cases. One day I asked him why he did so.

"Because," he answered, "I don't know where so much fun is to be found as in court."

He had a dignified and beautiful face, prominent nose and chin, twinkling eyes, compressed lips, round shoulders and bushy hair. While he was, perhaps, a trifle conscious of his superior ability, he was immensely popular on account of his easy good nature and boyish gaiety, which combined an Olympian serenity with a devastating impishness. He was a Robin Goodfellow forever yanking out the stools from beneath fat judicial buttocks. Judges were afraid of him and hence allowed him free rein. His audacity sometimes approached effrontery.

I was once trying an accident case against him before Judge Freedman, who had a thick German accent. His Honor had allowed me to question a witness along a certain line against Mr. Choate's objection, saying in each instance, "Vell, I'll let it in for vat it's vorth." I closed my case and Choate immediately called a witness and asked him a palpably improper question. This time Judge Freedman promptly sustained my objection, upon which Choate with a bland and ingratiating smile, perfectly imitating his honor's accent, remarked, "Vell, I tho't you might let it in for vat it vas vorth."

In another case he said something reflecting upon the intelligence of the court.

"If you say that again, I'll commit you for contempt," shouted the judge.

"I've said it once," replied Mr. Choate coolly. "It's not necessary for me to say it again."

A clergyman, who had retained Mr. Choate to settle an involved estate but wished to sidestep the bill, called at his office.

"I always understood, Mr. Choate," he said, "that you gentlemen of the bar were not in the habit of charging clergymen for your services."

"That is an error," answered Choate solemnly. "You have your reward in the next world, but we lawyers have to get ours in this."

His urbanity masked a vitriolic sarcasm. Reverend Isaac K. Funk, D.D., had published an unauthorized edition of Dean Farrar's *Life of Christ,* as a result of which E. L. Godkin, of the *Evening Post,* had editorially attacked him as "a Methodist pirate." Funk brought an action for libel against Godkin, who retained Choate. In his address to the jury Choate said:

"The plaintiff, gentlemen, is a doctor of divinity. I am not a doctor of divinity. I cannot tell just how a doctor of divinity feels, but to me, an outsider and a layman, there is something incongruous in the idea of a doctor of divinity going into business for gain and beginning his operations by stealing the Life of his Saviour."

The jury returned a verdict for Mr. Godkin.

Probably his most important argument was made in the early Income Tax cases before the United States Supreme Court in 1894, by which he convinced a majority of the court that the tax was unconstitutional. It was widely compared to Daniel Webster's famous argument in the Dartmouth College case. Mr. Choate himself, however, told me that he considered his acquittal of General Fitzjohn Porter on the charge of treason committed during the Civil War as his greatest victory, since two prior courts martial had decided adversely to Porter and it was a Herculean task to reassemble the facts and present them after a lapse of fifteen years. In this case the Adjutant-General of the U. S. Army, appearing in full regimentals, made a forty-eight hour speech elucidating army regulations. When Choate arose to reply he began by saying:

"We have listened with patience to the remarks of the distinguished Adjutant-General of the United States Army. His long argument reminds me of the advice once given to the graduating class in the Theological Seminary of Tennessee: 'Now, boys, remember one thing; don't make long prayers; always bear in mind that the Lord knows something.' "

Mr. Choate was very kind to me and often invited me to dine at his house with other members of the bar. I had the greatest admiration for him and I have no doubt that my own indifference to judges as a class is due largely to his example.

Another of my seniors for whom I had a great admiration was Judge Isaac Furman, Otto's partner, whose office, while directly opposite Hotchkiss, Levy & Hogan, was so different that it might have been a thousand miles away. It was shabby and at first glance perhaps even a little gloomy, but there was a pleasing absence of small boys in buttons, potted palms, spruce young men, dinky girls with powdered noses, or any kind of "swank." In Judge Furman's office there was not even a railing. If you wanted to call upon him you just opened the door and, if you saw anybody around the offing, merely asked: "Judge in?"

In that atmosphere of leisurely good nature time did not seem of any particular importance, but a gray-haired woman known as "Nurse," who acted as Judge Furman's private secretary, kept track of his appointments and routed out clients or callers when they threatened to make him late. He had practiced in his native town of Buffalo until middle life when, having become an acknowledged authority upon constitutional questions, pressure of business had compelled his removal to New York, where he had instantly taken a commanding place at the bar. He was over seventy, craggy-faced, red-cheeked, clean-shaven, punctilious, good-natured, a brilliant raconteur, and a profound lawyer. He wrote most of his letters by hand and refused to have a telephone nearer his desk than the outer office. He rarely went out into society, but when he did so, was usually the life of the party. He was universally known among his brethren as "Uncle Isaac."

He was no respecter of persons and he had once bawled out the elder J. P. Morgan in front of his own office in tones audible all over Wall Street.

"I told you if you tried that monkey business you'd get your neck in a noose—and I'm glad you have!" he had shouted. "The only thing for you to do now is either to get out of it—if you can—or take up the whole damned bond issue. If you can't follow my advice what's the use of having a lawyer? Good day!"

The first time I encountered him I knew that I was in the presence of a great man.

"So you're Eph Tutt!" said Uncle Isaac. "I'm glad to see

you! Otto's gone to Albany, but come in. So you're the fellow who thinks that there's a higher law than the Constitution!"

While I had forgotten that I had ever hazarded any such opinion, I was flattered that Judge Furman should condescend to attribute it to me. I decided that he must have read one of my articles in the *Harvard Law Review,* and hastily endeavored to remember what I had once thought.

"You wrote those reviews of Reichel's *Gesetz und Richterspruch* and Cosentini's *Filosofia del Diritto,* didn't you?"

"I believe so, but that was over ten years ago," I hedged. "As far as I recall I really did nothing more than emphasize the point that any interpretation of the Constitution demands the following of some legal principle not contained in the instrument itself and hence in a sense superior to it. That has been the history of the law, hasn't it? The nature of the process that goes on, when a leading case is applied by analogy, or limited in its application, or distinguished, is more or less concealed. The law which enables this to be done must be higher or at least equivalent to that which, by a fiction, is said to be in process of 'interpretation.' "

"Why not come up and dine alone with me tonight and we can talk about it?" he said. I did so and we eventually became fast friends. It was another of those chance encounters which profoundly affected the course of my life.

I entered the office of Hotchkiss, Levy & Hogan on October 1, 1902, and I remained there with my nose flattened against the legal grindstone for five years. I had brought along with me Bonnie Doon, who acted as a sort of legal valet, running my errands, carrying my papers, and occasionally bringing in a worthwhile client. I had also been fortunate in finding a place in the office for Miss Wiggin, who had passed her examinations at about the time the firm had begun to place heavier responsibility on my shoulders, so that I was justified in asking for the services of a private secretary. She was not only a first-class lawyer but—what was rather unusual in those days for a woman —an expert stenographer and typist. Since we both still lived at

Mrs. Stevens' I had frequently called upon Minerva, even before her admission to the bar, to help me in running down decisions and briefing my cases for trial. Now she took charge of my office and to a certain extent of myself—and has done so ever since, acting as my guide, counsellor and friend as well as the keeper of my legal conscience.

VII

THE TRUTH ABOUT EXPERTS

WE both still lived with Mrs. Stevens. I had had no desire to change my boarding place and most of what social life I had centered about her dining room table. The standard of both guests and cuisine had noticeably improved during the years I had been there, and the price of board had gone up in proportion—it was now $12 per week instead of $10. The old-fashioned place enjoyed a certain vogue among the younger editors, writers and newspapermen, and in this way I met Ida Tarbell, S. S. McClure, Mark Sullivan, John S. Phillips, Lincoln Steffens and many others, while occasionally some author already celebrated or about to become so turned up there—including Rudyard Kipling, John Fox, Jr., Booth Tarkington or Jack London.

I had made a good many friends among my brethren in the Sacred Camels of King Menelik, joined the Harvard and the Salmagundi Club, the latter composed largely of artists and other supposed Bohemians, and was presently elected to "The Players" in nearby Gramercy Park where Edwin Booth had made his home until his death in 1895. I belonged to the Association of the Bar and the New York County Lawyers' Association, serving on committees in each, and one evening a week I taught a class in the boys' club organized by Richard Welling for whom I had a great admiration. Among my fellow boarders was a young dramatic critic named Walter Prichard Eaton, and with him I saw Richard Mansfield in "Dr. Jekyll and Mr. Hyde," Joseph Jefferson in "Rip Van Winkle," Maude Adams in "The Little Minister," Denman Thompson in "The Old Homestead" and Ethel Barrymore in "Trelawney of the Wells." I also from time to time would take Minerva to a lecture or concert.

But I was so driven at the office that, although I now had the money to enjoy myself, my time to do so was limited. Yet it was a good time to enjoy oneself, for a little money went a long way. Everything was cheap and plentiful, with sugar at four cents a pound, eggs a cent apiece, wheat seventy cents a bushel, and whiskey two dollars a gallon. You could get a full meal almost anywhere—a "Turkey Dinner"—for a quarter. Over on Broadway or even at the Waldorf-Astoria five dollars would buy a roast partridge with salad and champagne for two, while four dollars more secured the best seats at a theatre. A ten dollar bill would cover your expenses for an evening, including cab fare.

It is hard to believe now that in those comparatively recent days there were only horse-drawn vehicles on the streets, that for obvious reasons of propriety stenographers invariably were men, and that even in the largest law offices a single telephone apparatus hung on the wall like a sacred icon in some place mutually convenient to the heads of the firm who alone might use it. It is equally difficult to realize the heart burnings due to unsatisfied social ambition. Socially the conservative old Knickerbocker families had surrendered to the "Gold Rush" and the descendants of the Robber Barons of the late '60s and '70s were engaged in a contest of ostentatious extravagance, parodying the life of the English upper classes, and affecting a self-protective snobbery made necessary by the realization that their so-called "position" was merely a matter of money.

It was all buncombe, and that it should be openly caricatured by a great satirist, Charles Dana Gibson, himself a social favorite, made it the worse. Besides, since one gold plate was obviously as good as another a bitter sense of injustice rankled in those who did not make the grade. John Henry Hotchkiss had been left out and it had soured his life. Commodore Cornelius Vanderbilt had said "To hell with the law! Ain't I got the money?" and had got away with it. But for some reason John Henry was unable to say to Commodore Vanderbilt's grandson Cornelius: "To hell with Society! Ain't I got the money?" And what was fair about that? There were undoubtedly times when his five millions turned to gall and wormwood and he would have given them all for the privilege of kicking some Fish, Astor, or Vanderbilt in the face. I was innocently unaware of this. I only sensed that he was not wholly satisfied about something.

That I was regarded by my employer as a young man of promise was brought to, or rather forced upon, my attention when the great John Henry Hotchkiss, shortly after Mr. Choate had shaken hands with me at the Down Town Association, invited me to dinner—"just the family, you understand, my dear boy—my wife, myself and Emeline my daughter." I was naturally flattered to be, as I supposed, thus singled out.

Mr. Hotchkiss lived in a large, corner house on Park Avenue, ornately furnished with onyx mantlepieces, gilded mirrors, crystal chandeliers, bronze lamps and statuary, heavily stuffed furniture of vivid pinks and greens, paintings of langorous females by Bougereau and squadrons of cavalry by Detaille. It gave the impression, however, of being almost completely empty and, although luxurious, somehow lacking in comfort. There was nothing left lying about—no papers or magazines, no books except in exquisite tooled bindings arranged in neat piles on the marble-topped tables. Beneath the stairway, in what was known as a "well," a nude Grecian slave of white Carrara marble, her wrists manacled by a chain of real gold, peeked coyly from behind a potted palm.

An English butler conducted me to the drawing room where I was vociferously welcomed by J. H. who presented me to his wife, a timid little creature who never took her eyes off her husband, and to Emeline, a tall, awkward girl, who, although prettily dressed had evidently lost any ambition to make herself attractive, for having once said "How-do-you-do" she remained practically silent throughout dinner. Mrs. Hotchkiss was not much better, uttering only an occasional perfunctory "You don't say so, now!" J.H. did say so, loudly and aggresively, in a declamatory analysis of business and civic conditions in which I acted as interlocutor.

The meal was excellent, with sherry, claret and Rhine wine fol-

lowed by brandy and cigars. It then transpired that we were
going to make a night of it, for the butler presently announced
that the carriage was waiting. We went out and climbed into a
landau, with two men on the box, and drove across to Broadway
to the Empire Theater where Ethel Barrymore was playing in
"Captain Jinks" and for which J.H. had bought a box.

I had a wonderful time, since the taciturnity of the ladies rendered conversational effort unnecessary and, for the evening, I
fell head and heels in love with the beautiful Ethel. Had J.H.
had the sense to realize it he would have never taken a prospective suitor for his daughter's hand to a play where he could
observe her in juxtaposition to one of the most alluring of her sex.

Between the acts J.H. and I went out into the foyer where he
dropped hints, intended to put me in a proper frame of mind, to
the effect that every man wanted a hearth of his own, and a
good faithful wife to warm his slippers for him—not the flighty
kind, always trying to flirt and attract attention (he'd seen hundreds of marriages go on the rocks just for that reason) but a
virtuous, home-loving woman, whose price was above rubies—
he chuckled significantly—all the better if she had the rubies,
too, eh? What a man needed was a real help-meet, with connections if possible, who could aid him in his career—"Curtain's
up, is it? I don't know why I've been running on this way. Habit
of talking to the young men in my office, I suppose. Well, let's
go back." He hooked his arm in mine on the way.

We reached the Hotchkiss mansion a few minutes after eleven.
The lights were still burning in the drawing room and the
smaller library that opened off it.

"Well," said J.H. "it's time for old folks to go to bed. But
there's no reason why you two shouldn't go into my den and
have a glass of ginger ale and a chat. Peters will be on duty for
another hour."

I had no wish to spend an hour with Emeline, nor even another
ten minutes, but courtesy seemed to demand acceptance of the
suggestion, although in that era such a private conversation be-

tween a man and a girl without a chaperone was to say the least unconventional. Peters brought the refreshments and closed the door behind him. We were alone. I was embarrassed and annoyed but I resolved to make the best of it. For twenty minutes or so I poured forth a stream of anecdotes about my life in Pottsville and in the district attorney's office while Emeline listened politely and even laughed mildly a couple of times. Then, when I paused, she said unexpectedly:

"Don't bother about me, Mr. Tutt. You mustn't mind father."

"I don't understand," I said. "I—er—admire him very much."

"No, you don't," she cried fiercely. "No one could. I've been through this so many times I could kill myself. He doesn't think what a humiliation it is for me. Don't pretend you don't understand what I mean. I know, because some of the boys he's tried it on have told me about it afterwards. I bet he said exactly the same things to you—about a virtuous woman's price being above rubies, but that the rubies were worth having if you could get 'em thrown in. Maybe he told you that he was worth five million dollars and that I would inherit it? I only wish he'd leave me alone to lead my own life!"

She choked and began to sob softly. I was very sorry for her. She had precipitated an unnecessary situation but she had been goaded beyond endurance. I thought it fairer to her to meet it frankly.

"Miss Hotchkiss," I said, "I'll be just as honest as you have been. When your father asked me to dinner I had no suspicion there was anything else in his mind. Let me begin by saying that my affections are already engaged. Marriage is no doubt desirable for the majority of people, but it's not the only thing in life and it's by no means necessary to the happiness of everyone. If your father has the idea that I would make a suitable husband for a young woman of your culture and social status I am greatly honored."

"If you think I'd marry anyone when I'd been thrown at his head you're mistaken!" she sniffed.

"But I don't!" I laughed. "One of these days some nice chap will come along and camp on your doorstep and before you know it you'll be a married woman."

"No, I shan't!" she said. "Father never gives me a chance to meet anyone. He sent me to dancing school and all that and had a party for me when I came out, but he didn't like the people who came and now nobody asks me. I never go anywhere. Every few weeks he picks some one from the office and invites him up here and goes through the same old performance. None of them ever come back. I'm like a bird in a cage."

I was indignant—deeply touched by her predicament.

"I'll come back, Emeline—if I may call you Emeline," I said. "I'm glad we had this talk. If you'll have me for a friend I'll be glad to be one. Only I don't want to sail under false colors and we must arrange it so that your parents won't take it for granted that we are hurrying down the prim-path of matrimony. I'd love to take you to some concerts or plays. Maybe you've got some relative or acquaintance who can act as a chaperone, or I can get one of the ladies at my boarding house."

"Do you really mean it!" she cried.

"Of course I mean it. You can tell your father you don't think much of me as a matrimonial prospect, but that you like me as a friend—both of which statements I take to be true. By the way, how do you amuse yourself?"

She was a different Emeline already.

"I go shopping with Mama, and read and sew, and drive around the park, and sometimes look at pictures—if you call that amusement."

"Listen, Emeline," I said earnestly, "have you ever thought that you might get a lot of fun out of helping some of the down-and-outs? You could do a lot for the families of prisoners in the Tombs and even for some of the defendants themselves. There are so many people who are discouraged because they think no one cares about them."

"Don't I know that!" she exclaimed. "I'd love to try!"

"All right," I said. "Let's begin Saturday afternoon. I know a young woman about your age named Minerva Wiggin who's eminently respectable and on your father's payroll. She can go with us. Now I'd better leave, if we wish to avoid being found in what your parents may choose to regard as a compromising situation. Good night, Emeline!"

"Good night, Ephraim!" she replied, and her face wore an entirely new expression.

Our Saturday afternoon excursion was such a success that Emeline, now keenly interested in social service, became one of the first of the so-called "Tombs' Angels." Some years later she married a young clergyman, lived on the East Side with him at "Neighborhood House," and afterwards in Chicago with Jane Addams at "Hull House," making a notable career for herself among the poor. When at length John Henry Hotchkiss, having outlived his wife, was gathered to his fathers she inherited his fortune and devoted the millions he had accumulated to practical philanthropy.

Mr. Hotchkiss sent for me one day and introduced me to a young couple by the name of Jessup. The husband was a sturdy specimen who had rowed on the Harvard crew, the wife, hardly more than a girl, simple, direct and very pretty.

"Mr. and Mrs. Jessup are being blackmailed by Town Topics," explained J.H. "Please give them the best advice you can."

I conducted my new clients to my own office and listened to their story. Town Topics was what is now known as a "scandal sheet," owned and edited by a slithy rogue calling himself Colonel William D'Alton Mann, who may have been some sort of a colonel but who certainly was no man. This person lived on loans secured from people who feared that he might print in his columns matter to their discredit, whereas if they paid up he eulogized them and their families. Colonel Mann, who had a florid complexion and a sweeping white "ferry-slip," was both bankrupt and judgment proof. He was pompous and arrogant when he allowed himself to be seen in public, but most of the time he hid in a maze of offices having a secret exit. He had, however, devised a method of juxtaposing apparently unrelated items which rendered him immune from the law of either civil or criminal libel. It was done somewhat as follows:

A certain young married woman living not far from Thirty-second Street is frequently seen these days with a Spanish nobleman who has a torrid reputation for being irresistible to the ladies. It is fortunate that Mrs. —'s husband is at present shooting in South Carolina, for should he return home unexpectedly he might find his wife temporarily missing.

Mrs. Potter Smith-Jones of 37 East 37th Street, formerly Virginia Paxton, will join her husband shortly at Aiken. Potter Smith-Jones is quail shooting with a stag party near Charleston.

By this means and also under the guise of subscriptions to the expenses of an extravagantly sumptous book to be entitled "Fads and Fancies" in which their merits were to be extolled, he had extracted $25,000 from W. K. Vanderbilt, $6,500 from George and Howard Gould, $5,000 from Collis P. Huntington, $20,000 from John W. Gates, $10,000 from Charles M. Schwab, and $90,000 from James R. Keene.

Few dared to refuse, but when the Colonel had asked Mr. Jessup to subscribe $10,000 in return for favorable comment and the latter had told him to go to hell, a scandalous paragraph had immediately appeared in Town Topics, with the result that the innocent Mrs. Jessup was on the verge of a nervous breakdown and her husband determined to have Colonel Mann arrested for criminal libel.

When I explained that under the decisions it was unlikely that he could get any relief in the courts, he promptly announced that he would horse-whip the editor on sight. While sympathizing with him I advised against this course on the ground that it might lead to his own incarceration as well as to a great deal of undesirable publicity. For the first time the inadequacy of the common law rule that a wrong could be paid for in cash rather than, as under the Lex Talionis, in kind, was brought home to me. But here was a subtle variety of wrong for which not even cash could be collected. Justice demanded that something be done.

"I take it that what you want, Mr. Jessup," I said, "is that this rascal be made to suffer for his offenses?"

"Someone ought to thrash him," answered the oarsman. "And if no one else does, I shall!"

"Leave the matter to me," I suggested, "and don't say anything about it to Mr. Hotchkiss. I think I can satisfy you."

I went at noon to Tiffany's and bought two large envelopes of expensive stationery, one of which I addressed to Mrs. Philip Lydig, a famous society beauty of that day, and the other to Colonel Mann. On my most recent trip to Pottsville I had brought back Willie Toothaker whom I had managed to wangle into the office as a sort of page boy and bag-carrier for myself. He was a wiry, red-headed urchin, pugnacious and clever with his fists. I now sent for him.

"Willie," I said, "here are two letters and twenty-five dollars. Go out and hire some Western Union messenger boy's uniform and take these letters to the office of Town Topics. Its editor Colonel Mann has done a young woman I know a great injury. I am not asking you to do anything unlawful. Not for a minute! You understand that, Willie?"

Willie grinned.

"I want you to insist on seeing Colonel Mann personally. They will try to prevent you, but you can show them this letter and say you have been instructed to place it in his hands yourself. When and if you get into his presence hand him the one for Mrs. Lydig. Then as soon as he has read the address, say: 'I'm sorry, I've given you the wrong letter. Here's yours. Give me back the other.' "

I looked at Willie hard.

"Now, Willie," I said, "of course, if the old geezer does return to you the Lydig letter I suppose we're out of luck, but if he refuses, why then you are entitled to use all the force reasonably necessary to recover it—and you can interpret the phrase to suit yourself. In that case you may keep what is left of the twenty-five dollars."

Willie came back to the office about five o'clock that afternoon.

"O.K.," he said. "The uniform only cost me two dollars and I'm in twenty-three bucks. I did just as you said. They tried to head me off at first, but finally I got to him. The old guy was in the office at the end of a long corridor.

" 'Is this Colonel Mann?' I says. 'I've got a letter for him.'

" 'That's me,' he says. 'Give it here.'

"So I hands him the letter addressed to Mrs. Lydig and you ought to have seen his eyes bug out and his lips begin to drool.

" 'Sorry,' I says, 'you have to give that back. It ain't for you.'

" 'That's all right, my boy,' he says beginning to tear open the letter. "I'm going right up to Mrs. Lydig's, and I'll give it to her myself.'

" 'The hell you will!' I says, closing the door. And—well, I used whatever force was reasonably necessary to recover the property."

Colonel Mann did not appear for several weeks and when he did he looked as if he had been in a railroad accident. Mr. Jessup was delighted. The law, he declared, was a wonderful thing and I agreed with him. Hotchkiss, Levy & Hogan sent him a bill of $250 for "consultation and advice" which he cheerfully paid, but my own returns were far greater. Indeed they opened a new vista in my social and professional life and even led to a friendship with the President of the United States.

Some time later Jessup telephoned me asking if I could dine with him at the Racquet Club that evening. I found him in a private dining room with Robert Collier, Harry Payne Whitney, Charles Dana Gibson, Finley Peter Dunne, Norman Hapgood, Mark Sullivan and James W. Osborne, whom Jessup had invited to meet me for the reason that Collier's Weekly was itself engaged in a Mann-hunt and I had beaten them to the gun. Collier and

Whitney were two of the most charming men I had ever encountered; Dunne, of whom more hereafter, became one of my best friends; Hapgood, who had a profile like that of Dante, was an intellectual with a remarkable mental machine, while Mark Sullivan combined extraordinary literary ability with indefatigable thoroughness and integrity.

It appeared that Town Topics had printed a paragraph containing an outrageous innuendo about Alice Roosevelt, the daughter of the President. Editorially Hapgood had called it a "coarse and leering" act committed by a "degraded, sewer-like sheet," to which Collier had added a sentence to the effect that Mann's "standing among the people is somewhat worse than that of an ordinary forger, horse-thief, or second-story man." Of course Mann had at once brought an action for criminal libel against Hapgood, who was shortly to be tried before a jury. Osborne had been retained to defend him, and they wanted me to assist Osborne.

District Attorney Jerome, who was an intimate friend of Hapgood, turned the actual trial of the case over to Keyran O'Conner, a capable assistant with a flare for picturesque diction. Once when he was prosecuting a woman whom I was defending Keyran shouted at the jury: "Why, gentlemen, if you should tear the entrails from that woman's body and hurl them against the wall of this court room they would spell the word 'perjuress'!" But he didn't tear out Hapgood's entrails and the case resolved itself into a prosecution of Town Topics and of Colonel Mann himself rather than of the defendant, who was acquitted in seven minutes. The Town Topics suit made Collier's the most influential periodical in the country, and the associations I formed at that time led not only to lifelong friendships but to some important retainers.

I should doubtless have remained with Hotchkiss, Levy & Hogan indefinitely, and perhaps become a second John Henry Hotchkiss myself, had it not been for a litigation which unexpectedly revealed to me the dead men's bones hitherto more or less concealed in that whited legal sepulchre.

A Miss Susan Thorpe, an eccentric recluse reputed to be worth about three millions, had died leaving half of her fortune to charity and the other million and a half to her relatives, who regarded that sum as so beggarly a pittance as to be almost an insult. While most of the lawyers in New York seemed desirous of getting their fingers into the pie, Mr. Hotchkiss with his usual astute diplomacy had forestalled them, inducing the heirs and next-of-kin to forsake their personal legal advisers and to intrust to him the task of assuaging their injured feelings by breaking the will.

"This Thorpe case is a real plum!" he said to me. "It ought to mean a clear million to us. Naturally, in view of its importance, I shall take personal charge of the preparation myself, but you shall appear for the firm, conduct all the proceedings, and try the case. If there's a trial it will be a *cause célèbre* and you'll be famous, my boy—famous!"

"What will be the ground of our objections?" I inquired. "Was the testatrix insane?"

"Perhaps not exactly in the technical sense," he replied, "but she had a pronounced case of mysophobia, besides being seventy-nine years old. 'Senile dementia' will be our battle cry. It doesn't take much to persuade a jury of East Side peddlers that money ought to stay in the family. We can show that she'd been acting in an eccentric manner for years—was at times quite irrational, that she entertained all sorts of violent and totally unreasonable prejudices against people, and that while she had an enormous fortune she lived in a most miserly way. Why, she even used to go around the house after the servants, turning off the electric lights! And the way she'd quarrel with tradespeople over their bills was scandalous—go into regular paroxysms. During her lifetime she hardly gave away anything at all. Now she leaves half her fortune to charities in which she never showed the slightest interest while she was alive!"

"I've known that to happen even in the case of persons who were not mentally deficient," I remarked. "Was she able to manage her own affairs—make investments—run her domestic establishment?"

"Automatically, I suppose. She could have done all those things and still be incompetent to make a will. Even if she appeared competent, she was really incompetent. She never would have a telephone in the house, for one thing. You can see the effect of that on the jury! And she had delusions of poverty—was forever talking about having to go to the poorhouse!"

"Maybe she was joking!"

Mr. Hotchkiss looked pained.

"No, she wasn't! You may be quite sure of that! Another thing —she had a mania for cats! Her rooms were full of them. She even refused to sell the vacant lot next her own house, so that they could have a place to play in."

"Well," I commented, "I can't say that, so far, it seems to me to be a very strong case. The fact that an old lady of seventy-nine hates dirt, is fond of cats, lives economically, has occasional fits of temper, and leaves only half her fortune to relatives isn't, to my mind, much evidence of mental incapacity. Perhaps she didn't like them."

"That will be for the jury to say! Naturally I haven't had time to go over all the proofs with you, but you may take my word for it that when you talk to the witnesses you won't have the slightest doubt that Miss Thorpe was a 'senile dement.' And, of course, you won't have to rely merely upon your own opinion! We shall have at least half a dozen experts who will testify to that effect."

"Who are they?"

"I don't know yet, exactly," he answered. "Unfortunately most of our better-known New York psychiatrists have already been retained by the other side, so that we shall have to send away for ours—but we shall have no difficulty in getting 'em. I've made each of the contestants put up twenty-five thousand dollars for expenses, so that we shall have a war-chest of nearly a quarter of a million. What do you say to that!"

I was glad old Hotchkiss did not seem to expect an answer to his question. I suspected that he wasn't above bringing a strike suit, but I had no right to judge a case before I'd seen the witnesses and examined into its merits. Anyhow mysophobia sounded serious. As if to dissipate my doubts he laid his hand upon my shoulder.

"Don't forget that even if these people turn out not to have an overwhelmingly strong case, they're entitled to their day in court. You and I don't have to decide the issue. The jury does that. If we go into this crusade, it won't make the slightest difference whether you personally believe that the old girl was rational or irrational, sane or insane, competent or incompetent. Vulgarly speaking, nobody gives a damn what she was. The heirs have a right to object to the probate of the will and to break it if they can. We are their standard-bearers! Their cause is, for the time being, ours! We cannot shirk it or play the coward's part!"

The witnesses I interviewed during the next few weeks did not shed much light on Miss Thorpe's capacity to make a will; in fact, in spite of her peculiarities, it seemed to me that she had probably been a person of exceptional mental power and executive capacity. She had continued certain old-fashioned prejudices —which the next generation had outgrown and later ones had never heard of—such as that the outlets of bathtubs ought to be kept corked in order to prevent the escape of sewer-gas, and she had a habit after the departure of visitors of rubbing the knobs of doors and the arms of chairs with a damp cloth, in order to remove any contaminating germs they might have left behind them. She had a horror of soiled linen and dirty bills, and boiled all the metal money that came into her possession, before carrying it about with her. In short, she had what is technically known as mysophobia, but that it could affect, or had affected, her capacity to dispose of her estate seemed to me preposterous.

The fact, however, remained that each and every witness sent by Mr. Hotchkiss to my office—after describing some incident in which Miss Thorpe's fondness for cats or desire for cleanliness figured—unhesitatingly and emphatically affirmed that the conduct of the testatrix on such occasions impressed him or her as distinctly irrational.

Mr. Hotchkiss reported progress all along the line. The smaller charities were all anxious for their legacies, he said, and were exerting constant pressure on the larger and less needy ones to compromise in return for an immediate settlement. He himself would be responsible for the preparation of the hypothetical question to be submitted to the experts, and he assured me that it would be a "corker"! All you had to do was to find a witness to testify to some apparently irrational act on the testatrix's part, and you could put his whole story right into the hypothetical question, no matter how much it had been damaged by cross-examination. In a word, you could insert everything that any witness had testified to, whether you believed it or not, since, according to legal theory, it was the jury's business to decide what facts had been proved, and to give such weight to them as in their opinion these deserved.

"It's done and it's a lallapaloosa!" he exclaimed one morning, rubbing his hands as if to remove the liver spots. "It fills seventy pages, and by the time you get through reading it you'll have no doubt that the old woman was crazy as a bedbug."

"You've prepared this hypothetical question in advance of the trial?" I asked rather fatuously.

"Oh, sure! We have to get something ready for the experts to go on. They read the question and then say whether, provided the testimony in any way measures up to what's in it, they can testify that, in their opinion, the testatrix was mentally incompetent to make a will."

"And if they don't?"

Mr. Hotchkiss brushed a cigar ash off his abdomen.

"If the right sort of evidence isn't incorporated in the question, we do our best to supply the deficiency—get new witnesses, if necessary. Sometimes we have to get new experts."

"I see. Where do you find these experts?"

"Oh, everywhere! Of course, whenever possible, it's a good thing to get a man connected with some institution for the insane. It makes a better impression on the jury. I've got one from New Jersey, two from Pennsylvania, one from Cleveland, one from Washington, and one from Boston—Doctor Hunziker. He's a sort of 'bell-wether'—keeps the others in line and makes 'em toe the mark. We pay him something extra and call him our 'medical counsel.' I've had him in no end of cases. By the way, did you know that the executors have retained Judge Furman to represent them? That will make it much easier for us. He's a good friend of ours!"

A couple of days later Hotchkiss sent for me and said that Judge Furman wished a conference in the Thorpe case and that I had been elected to represent the firm.

"That means they want to settle, of course!" he declared excitedly. "But don't commit yourself to anything. Just feel him out. But be sure and give the impression that you have absolute confidence in the case. Tell him there isn't the slightest doubt, from what our experts tell us, that the testatrix had senile dementia."

"But they haven't had a chance to express any opinion on the evidence as yet, have they?" I asked.

"Oh, yes. Doctor Hunziker has given a preliminary diagnosis to that effect. I outlined the old lady's symptoms to him by letter. She was a 'senile dement' with an advanced case of mysophobia."

Judge Furman welcomed me genially.

"It's a relief to find you handling the case, instead of Hotchkiss or Levy, for we can talk to one another frankly," he said lighting his pipe. "I drew Miss Thorpe's will. In fact I've known her for over twenty years. You'll have to abandon this contest—she was absolutely competent—as competent as I am."

"I haven't gone very deeply into the matter as yet," I answered. "Didn't she have mysophobia?"

"What if she did!" he retorted. "So have thousands of old women! Every woman hates dirt! It has no bearing on her testamentary capacity. No one knows better than a woman's own lawyer whether she was sane or not. I give you my word, Ephraim, there is nothing whatever in the case."

"I'm credibly informed that she had senile dementia," I persisted.

"Senile dementia be damned!" exploded Judge Furman. "She was no more senile than you are! Who says so?"

I felt like crawling under the table.

"Our experts," I replied diffidently.

"Experts? Who in the name of Julius Caesar are they?" he roared.

"I haven't seen any of them myself, but Mr. Hotchkiss mentioned Doctor Hunziker—"

"Hunziker! That crook! You must have heard of Hunziker! He's notorious—one of the most dangerous men in the medical profession! So Hotchkiss has retained Hunziker! Well—that's—bad!"

The old man shook his head.

"He's retained others, also," I hastened to inform him.

"Naturally! Hunziker never goes on the stand without his bodyguard—Kelly, Tinker, Spinnelli, Rosenblum—I know 'em all! Well, my boy, if it has gone as far as that, it is useless for us to talk further. But it's a damn shame! Moreover, it's a greater shame for you to be connected with the case."

"I think that the heirs would consider favorably an offer of settlement," I hazarded, hardly knowing what else to say, since the interview had turned out so unexpectedly.

"Settlement? Compromise a baseless attempt to defeat the wishes of a gentle and charitable old lady who may have been slightly eccentric, but who was quite capable of carrying on her own affairs and of being a delightful social companion? If your friend Hotchkiss thinks he sees a chance of forcing us to buy off the heirs, he's mistaken! He'll not get a cent. I'd rather have my

clients lose their legacies than submit to blackmail. It wouldn't
be fair to Miss Thorpe. She wanted her charities to have the
money, and they have no right to share it with a lot of disgruntled
relatives who have received enough already. No, go back to your
office! Tell John Henry Hotchkiss that we have 'millions for defense, but not one cent for tribute'!"

"I'll report what you say to him," I said thoroughly uncom-
fortable, and reached for my hat. Judge Furman hesitated.

"I'm sorry I spoke so heatedly," he said. "After all, you're only
doing what you're told. But you're too good for that outfit. Let
me talk to you as a friend and then forget that I've said anything. Old Hotchkiss is a cross between a highwayman and a
mountebank. He's a superannuated jackass and a menace to the
bar. Of course they're glad to have you there, for, apart from
your abiilty, it lends respectability to their outfit. But you can't
stay there much longer without being contaminated yourself, or
at least falling under suspicion. If I were you I'd get out—no
matter what it cost!"

When I repeated Judge Furman's message to Mr. Hotchkiss,
the latter showed no sign of discouragement.

"Naturally he has to take that position at first!" he asserted
cheerfully. "He'll sing a different tune when the case gets on the
calendar for trial. The judge is a good bluffer!"

"But he says he knows Miss Thorpe was competent to make a
will. I should think any jury would be apt to sustain the will on
his testimony alone."

Mr. Hotchkiss leaned back in his chair.

"That's where we have him!" he chuckled. "No matter what
he knows, it won't do him a particle of good—for the law doesn't
permit him to testify! His lips are sealed by the doctrine of confidential communications!"

Judge Furman's unglossed indictment awakened me to the real
reputation of Hotchkiss, Levy & Hogan. Up to that time I had
had no evidence that my associates were willing to connive at
anything unprofessional. Their standing in the courts was excel-

lent. They rated as A1 in all "lawyers' lists" and "legal directories"—in which the firm name always appeared in bold-faced type. But I was aware that they were regarded by their fellow members of the bar as second-rate.

For one thing Hotchkiss, Levy & Hogan encouraged the idea that they had underground personal relations with politicians and advertised their friendliness with the bench. Mr. Hotchkiss' "law dinners" were famous, both for the distinction of those invited and the quality of the liquor served. At these little parties one was apt to meet an ex-governor or two, a State senator, a Federal district judge, a couple of Supreme Court justices, half a dozen prominent attorneys or city officials, and a leading Tammany Roman Catholic. Some of the judges, it is true, did not go to them; but, on the other hand, many did, both of which facts helped to diffuse a subtle impression that the firm had wires running to secret places.

And unexpected things did happen in litigations in which they were retained. They never appeared personally or as "attorneys of record" in criminal cases, but they were often found hovering in the immediate neighborhood, employing and paying the special trial counsel who actually conducted the defense. They were much too elegant to be referred to by the vulgar term of "fixers" —but they traded on the reputation of being such, and perhaps they were.

When I arrived at Mr. Hotchkiss' apartment for my first consultation with the experts in the Thorpe case, I found the party already on their second round of cocktails. Beside the host, Levy, and myself, there were present six others, of whom one, by virtue of his prophet-like whiskers, I spotted as undoubtedly Doctor Marcus Hunziker. Mr. Hotchkiss, white-waistecoated and odorously bay-rummed, was in an expansive mood. Leading me to the group about the sideboard, he heralded my arrival with:

"Gen-til-men! Permit me to introduce to you my—er—partner and friend, the Honorable Ephraim Tutt, erstwhile of Harvard and Boston, where the beans come from. That's why I have him

for a partner—on account of his bean! Ha! ha! Shake hands
with Mr. Tutt, gentlemen! 'The Six Little Bug Doctors,' I call
'em! 'The Six Little Bugsters!'"

The gentlemen in evening dress gathered about the cocktail
shaker turned toward me with an air of faintly amused tolerance
at their host's jocosity. I perceived that if the preponderance of
polished pink domes and carefully trimmed white beards were
any index to distinction I was in no ordinary company. These,
forsooth, were venerable men. Eminent, portly, and profound,
they suggested a meeting of the French Academy, with even a
touch of its elegance.

Doctor Hunziker detached himself from his fellows and shook
hands with me warmly.

"A pleasure to meet you, Mr. Tutt! Allow me to introduce
Doctor Rosenblum, at one time assistant physician at the Psychia-
trical Hospital at Prague, and now professor of neuropathology
at Durham University."

Doctor Rosenblum, who looked like the picture of a Prussian
field-marshal, clicked his heels.

"And my friend, Doctor Tinker," flowed on Doctor Hunziker, "professor of nervous and mental diseases at Kesaw Medical
College—Doctor Spinnelli, formerly of the University of Pisa
and now with the McGurk Colony for Epileptics—Doctor Fulham-Smith, consulting alienist to the Psychopathic Ward of the
Burlington State Hospital—and, last but not least, Doctor Hugo
Kelly, the chairman of the Interstate Lunacy Commission."

They all greeted me with the gravity appropriate to their importance in the world of medicine; so that I was a bit shocked at
Mr. Hotchkiss' levity.

" 'The Six Little Bungstarters,' I call 'em!" he carolled, seizing
the arm of Doctor Hunziker. "Now, boys, let's go in to dinner.
We've a long night before us! Tum-tum-te-tum! 'Here comes
the bride!' Wedding of law and medicine! Fall in, everybody!"

In spite of the ill-timed familiarity of their host, I could not but
be impressed by the distinguished appearance of his guests, par-

ticularly as no less than three of the six sported the red ribbon of the *Legion d'Honneur*. I began to wonder if, after all, Judge Furman could have been right. Surely, if these notable psychiatrists should agree that Miss Thorpe was incompetent to make a will there must be something in their opinion.

Mr. Hotchkiss' cook had prepared a meal befitting the importance of the occasion, and his supply of the best Scotch whiskey was apparently unlimited. As usual at men's dinner-parties, the conversation was sporadic, and, except for the host's noisy witticisms, carried on in low tones. All the *savants* evinced an extraordinary and almost unnecessary respect for one another. "Yes, doctor." "No, doctor." "Certainly, doctor." "I quite agree, doctor." They even occasionally conferred the title upon me, and I frankly found this excess of punctilio rather depressing.

According to Doctor Kelly, Hunziker was the ablest "expert" in the country, one of his chief claims to distinction being his dexterity in the invention of lawyer-baffling phrases.

Said Dr. Kelly:

"I regard Doctor Hunziker's invention of the term 'quasi-conscious knowledge,' for example, as a notable contribution to psychiatric terminology. As you are aware, the law holds every man responsible for his acts so long as he knows what he is doing and realizes it to be wrong. Such a definition amounts practically to holding every insane person responsible for his acts. The beauty of Doctor Hunziker's phrase is that while apparently accepting the law it nullifies it—'Confession and avoidance,' is I believe, the legal term. 'Why certainly,' says he, 'my patient had a quasi-knowledge of what he was doing when he killed his mistress, but it was not the kind of knowledge required by the law to make a man criminally responsible for his act, for—it was *an insane knowledge*'!"

Doctor Kelly smiled knowingly at me.

"Get the point?" Seemingly satisfied that I had, he continued with enthusiasm. "There's nobody quite like Hunziker. When it comes to paranoia, there isn't anyone who can touch him! I assure you it's a pure delight to hear him under cross-examination. He's done more to stabilize expert testimony than any man in the United States."

"Stabilize it?" I queried.

"Elevate it to its proper place in legal procedure, I mean. Why, I can remember the time when the public and even some of the judiciary were inclined to make small of experts. In those days, if a lawyer wanted to break a will, he simply sent over to the nearest insane pavilion and hired the first attendant or interne he could find, and paid him a measly *per diem*—fifty dollars or so—to testify. Any roughneck would do. The result was that expert medical testimony fell into disrepute. It opened the door to all sorts of abuses. But now, largely due to Hunziker, the expert is accorded the weight that he deserves. The courts recognize that the intricacies of the human mind can only be grasped after years of study, and the lawyer regards the psychiatrist as a worthy and necessary ally."

All the experts present, he confided to me, were constantly called upon to assist the courts in the decision of difficult cases. I was at first puzzled by the recurrence of the word "we" throughout his remarks.

"But," I hazarded innocently, "suppose you gentlemen don't agree—"

"We never disagree!" interrupted Doctor Kelly naïvely. "We take the position that on a given state of facts there can be but one opinion. If, in rare instances, one of us finds himself opposed to the rest of us, he merely drops out. We never testify against one another. In union is strength."

It dawned on me that these "experts" were, in fact, a psychiatrists' union, with Hunziker as their neurological boss.

Mr. Hotchkiss pushed back his chair and tossed his napkin upon the table.

"Let's have coffee in the library. We might as well be comfortable."

He thrust his arms through those of Doctors Kelly and Spinnelli, and strolled across the hall, where a circle of heavy arm-chairs upholstered in brown leather was grouped about the fire-place.

"Shall we begin?" he asked, when they had all lighted the cigars and drunk the coffee they prohibited to their patients. "I've prepared a hypothetical question which sooner or later, I suppose, it'll be necessary for you to read. It's rather long—perhaps first we'd better discuss terms?"

"That is always in order," smiled Doctor Hunziker. "May I inquire the size of the estate?"

"About three mililons."

"In that case, from what I know of the fees in similar cases, I suppose you lawyers will get something like a million dollars for yourselves?"

"We shall make an adequate charge for our services, natu-rally," temporized his host who did not regard it as out of place for the experts to wish to know the general amount involved.

Doctor Hunziker turned to his colleague from Prague.

"What do you think, Doctor Rosenblum?"

"Dere must be no *per diem* pishness!" growled the Von Hin-denburg of psychiatry. "Oddervise we leave de amount to you."

"There is no suggestion of a *per diem*," hastily conciliated Mr. Hotchkiss. "We shall expect to compensate you adequately—by a lump sum. How much do you feel that you should receive? Speak up, gentlemen. The heirs, I'm sure, will be inclined to be generous—they'll surely agree to anything we advise."

"What did you pay us in the Watts case?" inquired Doctor Hunziker. "That was the last we had for you here in New York, wasn't it?"

"Yes. There was a million dollars involved. And if I recall correctly, we paid each of the experts five thousand dollars, with seventy-five hundred to you individually, as medical counsel. As this is a somewhat larger case, although it will involve no more work on your part, I had in mind to suggest a fee of ten thousand each and fifteen to Doctor Hunziker. Is that satisfactory?"

I was startled at the amount offered. I had supposed that insanity experts received from fifty to a couple of hundred dollars per day for each day that they actually appeared in court, with perhaps something additional for working time. But ten thousand dollars each, with five thousand extra to Hunziker, would make sixty-five thousand dollars!

The "Stabilizer of Medical Testimony" looked around the circle of graybeards—at Doctor Kelly sprawling on his chair with his feet crossed on the fender, at the sardonic, begoggled Doctor Spinnelli, at Doctor Tinker's double storied pink skull, at the melancholy Fulham-Smith—at Rosenblum again.

"How does Mr. Hotchkiss' offer strike you, gentlemen?"

The question hung in air.

"I'm of the opinion that the whole system is wrong!" volunteered Doctor Spinnelli.

"Good!" I thought. "I'm with you on that!"

"How do you mean?" asked Hotchkiss. "What's the matter with it?"

"We should receive a percentage of the amount recovered," said Doctor Spinnelli. "That's the only logical way. Why should you lawyers get a million dollars and we doctors get only sixty-five thousand?"

Mr. Hotchkiss focussed an opaque oyster-like eye as sternly as he could upon the psychiatrist. I could see that in his opinion the fellow was getting too obstreperous. After he'd given him such a good dinner, too! That extra five thousand to Hunziker ought to insure his co-operation, else why pay it?

"It is unnecessary to discuss the equities between us," he said in a tone of reproval. "We got the case. We're responsible for it. If we see fit to retain you gentlemen as experts, the only question is what shall be the size of your fees. Am I not right, Doctor Hunziker?" he added hopefully.

Doctor Hunziker ran his fingers through his white beard.

"I confess, Mr. Hotchkiss," he answered, "that, in a general way, I incline to the view expressed by Doctor Spinnelli."

"I'm by no means sure that the courts would regard such an arrangement as ethical!" declared Mr. Hotchkiss impatiently. "The committee of which I am chairman—"

"Say, what are you fellows up to?" Levy pushed his way between the chairs toward the fireplace. "This is something new, eh?"

Hunziker made a palliating gesture. It was clear to me he had more respect for Levy than for Hotchkiss, whom he probably regarded as a windy jackass.

"It's merely a question of how we should be compensated, Mr. Levy. Mr. Hotchkiss brought it up himself. You may recall that you agreed with me, when we abolished the old *per diem* system, that the only thing to be considered was that the evidence given had directly contributed to the result. We merely claim now that, in a difficult or delicate case, what we've been getting in the past is not enough in proportion to what the lawyers expect to receive. The laborer is worthy of his hire. If we're willing to take a flier and receive nothing in the event of the case being lost, we see no reason why we shouldn't split fifty-fifty."

Levy's leathery countenance turned purple.

"Have you actually got the nerve to say that if—huh!—we pull down a million dollars we should give you five hundred thousand of it?" he barked.

Hunziker looked Levy squarely in the eye.

"Why not? You wouldn't get anywhere without our help."

"But you wouldn't—huh!—be here but for us!" shouted Levy. "It's our case!"

"We wouldn't be here, if you hadn't needed us!"

"We could have got plenty of others."

Doctor Hunziker smiled with patient sarcasm.

"Try it!"

Levy hurled his cigar butt into the fire.

"If we split with you—huh!—they'd have us up before the Grievance Committee of the Bar Association!"

"I don't see why it's any worse in principle for us than for you," retorted Hunziker coolly. "If it's ethical for a lawyer to take a contingent fee, why shouldn't it be for a doctor?"

"May I say a word?" intervened Doctor Kelly, removing his legs from the fender. "We don't want to crowd the mourners. We're trying to establish a principle. We recognize the importance of getting the business in the first place—don't we, doctor?"

"Of course," conceded Hunziker. "Let's not get excited over nothing. Let's just try and accustom ourselves to the idea of being partners in a common enterprise, the proceeds of which we expect to share between us. Have you any counter-proposition to make to us?"

A silence, significant and ominous, followed his words. Messrs. Hotchkiss and Levy exchanged glances.

"Pardon us a moment," said Mr. Hotchkiss. "Just step out into the hall with me, Levy—and you, Tutt!"

I followed them out of the room.

"It's—huh—an outrage!" growled Levy hoarsely, shaking his fist toward the library. "They've got the expert market cornered and they know it! But don't pay 'em a cent—huh—more than you have to—eh?"

I was not consulted. I clearly had been invited only in order to give an impression of a deployment in force. With dignity we returned to the library.

"Well, gentlemen," said Mr. Hotchkiss, "we have talked your suggestion over, and if you wish to be paid on a contingent basis and are fully prepared to take nothing in the event of failure, we're willing to double the amount I offered you in cash—that is to say, in the event of success we'll increase your fees from ten to twenty thousand each, and Doctor Hunziker's from fifteen to thirty thousand."

To my surprise Doctor Hunziker exhibited no pleasure at this proposal.

"I think we should have at least twenty-five per cent of your fees," he said evenly. "Most of my associates feel we should get fifty."

Mr. Hotchkiss shook his head definitely.

"Out of the question. We're surrendering thirty-five per cent of our take already to an outsider in return for the business. If we gave you twenty it wouldn't leave us half. We'll give you fifteen flat. That's the best we can do."

Doctor Hunziker glanced at Doctor Kelly, who nodded.

"All right, doctor—let it go at that! Are you satisfied, gentlemen?"

Hunziker turned to Hotchkiss and Levy.

"It's agreed, then, that if the will is denied probate, we are to receive collectively a sum equal to fifteen per cent of your gross fee, without any deductions for expenses?"

"Correct!" replied Mr. Hotchkiss. "It's a bargain!"

I had been growing more and more restive. Doctor Hunziker helped himself to a fresh cigar, lighted it, stroked his whiskers, and turned his chair so as to face his fellow bugsters.

"Want to look at the hypothetical?" inquired Mr. Hotchkiss, patting his breast-pocket.

"No, not now!" Hunziker waved the suggestion aside as unimportant. "Well, gentlemen, we all know why we're here! Our host has told me that, if this will is going to be broken at all, it must be on the ground of senile dementia. We've a pretty good basis for such a claim already—complication of chronic diseases, mysophobia, delusions of poverty and persecution, general irascibility and sudden outbursts of temper, antipathy to old friends and relatives, and an insane fondness for cats—the latter, of course, most important. Senile dementia's sufficiently vague to let in almost everything. I don't think the evidence is picturesque enough for paranoia or dementia praecox, but if you gentlemen have any suggestions to make I shall be glad to hear them. No? Well, then! Assuming that the testatrix had senile dementia, it's up to us to tell our legal friends here exactly what sort of evidence they should look for to support that theory. Suppose I describe for the benefit of us all what I would regard as a typical case—"

I could not believe that I had heard truly. Was this freebooter in broadcloth and white linen, who had just sold himself and his band for a contingent interest in the swag, about to instruct them how to perpetrate the crime and dispose of the body? In what way did the present proceeding differ from the hiring of a mob of gangsters to commit a robbery? In none, essentially, save that these were soft-voiced crooks who took no chances of putting their heads in a noose, and, instead of wearing black masks, disguised themselves as learned men. What was this but one more instance of the universal truth that what passes for respectability is often nothing but crime in a clean collar?

"One moment, Doctor Hunziker!" I said. "Am I to understand that you are prepared to diagnose the testatrix's condition without reading the hypothetical question?"

"I am prepared to state here and now that, from what Mr. Hotchkiss has told me, the testatrix must have been a senile dement," replied Hunziker tartly.

"Wouldn't a perusal of the question—provided it was based on the evidence—be of any value to you in coming to your conclusion?" I persisted.

Doctor Hunziker munched his moustache.

"My dear Mr. Tutt—that's the name, isn't it?—you do not quite get my position! My associates and I have come here at your request to help you prepare your campaign. We must assume that we have not been summoned without reason, that the case is an honest case, and that you gentlemen are sincere in your contentions. That being so, we must, merely in the interest of time if of nothing else, eliminate from our investigation all forms of insanity which on their face are improbable; and, conversely, we should select tentatively some form of insanity as being supposedly what she did have and test our hypothesis as we go along. I hope I make myself clear?"

"In other words," I answered, "you are prepared to decide upon what kind of insanity the testatrix had before you know whether or not she was insane!"

"Come, come, Tutt!" interrupted Hotchkiss. "That is a gross distortion of Dr. Hunziker's remarks."

"The young man deliberately ignores the fact that our diagnosis is purely tentative," said Hunziker icily.

"Diagnosis?" I retorted. "How can you diagnose a case when you aren't willing to listen even to supposititious facts which may never be proved?"

"That's enough, Tutt!" snapped Levy. "My partner and I are conducting this conference. Your attitude towards these distinguished gentlemen is extremely impertinent. Just keep out of it."

"What he says is pure pettifogery!" affirmed Hunziker.

"You are dodging the issue," I replied. "There is more involved here than the mere haggling over the price to be paid for expert testimony. It is a question of common honesty."

"Do you dare to suggest that I am not honest?" demanded Hunziker.

"Pay no attention to him, my dear doctor!" protested Hotchkiss. "I don't know what has got into the fellow. I suggest, Tutt, that you go walk around the block and leave this matter to Mr. Levy and myself. It's not your affair."

"Not my affair?" I returned. "You expect me to try the case and my professional honor is involved." I faced Hunziker. "My clear understanding is that you and your associates, without knowing anything of the actual evidence, are prepared to swear to the opinion that this old lady had senile dementia and hence was incompetent to make a will!"

"Tentatively! Only tentatively!" repeated Hunziker.

"That is mere subterfuge!" I replied. "You have just agreed, in return for a contingent fee of one hundred and fifty thousand dollars, to tell us what evidence we should get, and to sell us your assistance, including your testimony under oath, to help break this will—provided, I suppose, that the case turns out to be not too raw."

"Shut up!" roared Levy. "Get out of here!"

"I intend to!" I answered. "Dr. Hunziker and his friends may be willing to practice medicine that way, but—I'm not willing to practice law that way. If you try to break this will you'll have to do it without my help." I tossed my copy of the hypothetical question into the fire. "I retire. To hell with all of you!"

That finished my connection with Hotchkiss, Levy & Hogan, and, in spite of its unpleasantness I was glad it had ended that way. Someone had at last told Hotchkiss and Levy what he thought of them.

I wrote Esther about it and received a letter of unqualified approval of what I had done. Then, after I had informed Otto of my experience, Uncle Isaac invited us both to dinner and opened a bottle of champagne in celebration of the event.

"Of course Hotchkiss will think you sold out to us," he remarked. "They won't be able to understand your conduct otherwise. But the scalawags won't dare peep. Well, son, I congratulate you!"

My satisfaction was complete when three months later my former firm withdrew its objections to Miss Thorpe's will, which was duly admitted to probate.

Again I was adrift. Just as I had seen how faultily the legal machine worked in the administration of criminal justice, so I had now had an illustration of its abuse in civil litigation. I had been sadly disillusioned. I was tired, I needed a vacation, and I wanted a chance to think things over quietly, take an account of stock and decide what to do with my life. So, having retrieved my few personal effects from the temple of Baal, I packed my fishing things and went back to Pottsville for a month or two.

Nothing had changed during my eight years' absence. No one seemed any older. Mose Higgins, now sheriff, Toggery Bill Gookin, and Cap Barrows met me at the deppo; Ma Best clasped me to her ample bosom and installed me in my old room at the Phoenix; and the following Friday evening I was joyously welcomed by my brethren of the Sacred Camels of King Menelik.

The only faces missing were those of Judge Tompkins and of Esther; otherwise I could hardly realize that I had been away.

Yet whenever I looked across the road at the little Grecian temple which had been my former law office I felt an unutterable desolation at Esther's absence. We still corresponded regularly. She had moved with her husband to Iowa where she now held the chair of modern history in the State University, had written a couple of widely used textbooks and had attained considerable scholastic distinction. Farr's health had continued to improve, although he was not able to do any regular work. Apparently he was going to live forever. Dependent upon her as he was, that she should divorce him was inconceivable. Friendship was all that remained to us, friendship and a distant hope that perhaps some time we might be united. Nature was my only solace. Every morning I put on my waders and, accompanied by Mose Higgins, revisited my old haunts, Chasm Brook and Turtle Pond, and the remoter streams hidden in the Broadalbin Hills, including the pool where I had caught "Wasgatt's Cow."

While thus reliving the days of my legal youth, I received a letter from Otto saying that Judge Furman had decided to retire and suggesting that we form a partnership to be known as Wiegand & Tutt, to take over the business with the Judge acting as counsel in important cases. It looked like the opportunity of a lifetime. Not only was Uncle Isaac's practice large and lucrative, but since no one at the bar had a higher standing than he, I should, by accepting his offer, be publicly absolved from any contamination due to my former connection with Hotchkiss, Levy & Hogan. I wired my acceptance at once.

VIII

I ACQUIRE A DOG — AND A HOUSE

I was delighted to be associated with Otto again and to settle down into an old-fashioned law office with its smell of sea-coal and old leather, its easy-going friendly atmosphere and its absence of pretense and bunkum. Beside the backlog of Judge Furman's established clientele, family estates, banks and trust companies, Otto had his own personal clients and I mine. My reputation as a criminal lawyer still clung to me and, although I dodged the necessity of so doing when I could, I frequently appeared in the General Sessions.

The platitude that trifles can alter the whole course of a man's life is well illustrated in my own case. Suppose I hadn't roomed at Harvard opposite Angus McGillicuddy? Or Hi Watkins hadn't had that wen on his forehead? Or Boss Croker hadn't slipped on the curb in front of me?

When I refused Jerome's offer to become his chief trial assistant I had firmly made up my mind that I was through with sending people to jail. To that I stuck; but the fact that I was familiar with a branch of the law which most Wall Street attorneys are careful to avoid often led these to send for me when their clients got into trouble. If the accused was a multi-millionaire they hired Sam Untermyer or DeLancy Nicoll, if he was sufficiently scared they retained John B. Stanchfield or Max Steuer, but I got a substantial proportion of the others; and since I was always ready to try a case and Otto enjoyed drawing the fine distinctions possible in criminal law, we were frequently called in to handle that end of important litigations.

Waiting in Part I of the General Sessions to argue a "plea in abatement" * before my friend Judge Foster, I noticed in the line

---

* Abolished by statute in 1790, but (according to Otto) still available as a defense.

of prisoners a freckled lad with pale blue eyes, wide mouth, big ears, and a pineapple haircut. In appearance he was neither unprepossessing nor vicious—just a common or garden boy. Finally he reached the bar.

"Augustus Menken, you have been indicted for the crime of burglary in the first, second and third degrees, grand larceny in the first and second degrees, assault in the second degree, and illegal entry. Do you plead guilty or not guilty?"

He did not answer.

"Got a lawyer?"

The boy shook his head.

"Ain't got no money."

I had often asserted that, instead of assigning shysters to the defense of poverty-stricken prisoners, the judges ought to delegate for that duty well-known members of the bar, and now Judge Foster glanced around the courtroom until his eye fell on me. With a slightly malicious smile he said:

"I will assign you as counsel in this case, Mr. Tutt."

I was caught—"estopped" as the legal phrase is. The defendant's mother, a gray-headed woman in a knitted shawl, explained that Gussie, her only son, had done nothing but step inside a store the door of which happened to be unlatched, yet because he had been in trouble once before the Grand Jury had indicted him on seven counts. I did my best to reassure her and went over to the Tombs to confer with my client. His story—a familiar one—was that, after his discharge from the reformatory, the police—including Grady, the policeman who had originally arrested him—had tried systematically to hound him off the streets.

On the night of his alleged offense, and wholly without evil intent, he had caught sight of Grady coming down the block, and, in order to avoid a possible beating up, had ducked into the portal of a grocery store and, finding the door providentially unlatched, had taken refuge inside, where unfortunately the officer had discovered him. His eyes were so honest and the ring in his voice so truthful that I almost believed him. Anyhow he was entitled by law to the benefit of the doubt. Would the jury give it to him? There was no evidence to support the first six counts, but they could, if they saw fit, properly convict him of illegal entry, in which case he might be sent back to the reformatory and, as his mother feared, started on a criminal career. It was clearly a case for an *argumentum ad hominem,* as we lawyers say.

Walking back to my office I happened to see some boys chasing a dog. It gave me an idea.

"Bonnie," I said on my return, "I want you to go up to the Animal Rescue League and pick out the measliest little tyke you can find. Smuggle him into the rear of Part I tomorrow, and when I give the signal let him loose."

"Okay," answered Bonnie. "I'll get one at the city pound."

Next day, when Gussie was put on trial, I baited the assistant district attorney to such an extent that he withdrew all the counts in the indictment save that for illegal entry, upon which he pressed for a conviction. He was so manifestly fair that I could see the jury was with him. They had a perfect right to discount Gussie's story and I feared that they would do so.

"Gentlemen," I said when I arose to sum up. "Officer Grady testifies that he caught Gussie Menken in the commission of a crime. The boy denies it. It is word against word. Grady, an official of the State, comes before you backed by the prestige and majesty of the law. Gussie, on the other hand, is a half-starved guttersnipe. Even so, under the influence of his mother he has in him the makings of a man. If you send him to the reformatory he will be contaminated and demoralized by association with criminally minded boys."

At that instant there was a faint scuffle followed by a subdued yelp and a small dog of obviously miscellaneous parentage trotted inside the rail. Nothing of the sort had ever happened before and the court officers were taken completely by surprise. Having sniffed around the enclosure the little animal sprawled on its forelegs, lifted its muzzle towards the judge, and uttered a feeble but cordial demand for recognition.

"Woof!" it said playfully. "Woof! Woof!"

"Where did that dog come from?" angrily demanded His Honor. "Why did you let him in, officer?"

"I didn't let in no dog," replied the door-keeper. "I only seen him this minute!"

"Well, remove him!" ordered the Judge. "Take him away!"

But the little dog, who was clearly enjoying what he regarded as a game, squirmed out of his reach. Reinforced by two other cops, Gallagher was about to reduce his victim to captivity when I asked respectfully:

"Your Honor, may I inquire what you propose doing with this dog?"

"What does one do with lost dogs?" inquired Foster. "Send him to the pound, I suppose."

It was the chance I had been playing for.

"I beg Your Honor to reconsider sending this little animal to that dirty contagious kennel known as the public pound. He seems like a nice dog and, unless he is thrown with a lot of disreputable curs will probably remain one. Why not give him a chance?"

"But what can one do with such a dog?" he persisted.

"Give him a good home!" I replied.

"Where?"

"Well," I said, caught again, "rather than have him sent to the pound I'll take him myself."

"All right, Mr. Tutt," said His Honor. "Gallagher, put the dog in my cloak room.—Proceed with the case, gentlemen. Do you wish to sum up?"

Neither of us did and the Judge charged.

"You may retire, gentlemen," he said to the jury.

A smothered whine came from the judicial chamber. The jury hesitated, then collected around the foreman.

"I don't think we need to go out," he said. "We're already agreed. Our verdict is not guilty."

Judge Foster beckoned to me from the bench.

"Say, Eph," he whispered. "Where did you get that dog?"

"From the pound," I said.

"I shall hold you to your word," he chuckled.

Well, I'd won my case and acquired a dog—the filthiest and most olfactory, yet most affectionate and obedient little beast I'd ever laid eyes on. But what was I going to do with it?

"What's that?" demanded Mrs. Stevens when I brought it into the boarding-house parlor.

"I—suppose—it's a—dog," I answered apologetically.

"What are you going to do with it?"

"I don't know," I said. "I thought maybe I could keep it up in my room—"

"There'll be no dogs in this house as long as I run it!" she declared.

"But Mrs. Stevens—" I pleaded.

"No buts about it. I won't have that dog here."

I was more than disconcerted, I was shocked. I had been on fairly intimate terms with Mrs. Stevens for eight years and had grown very fond of her: I knew that she liked me in return; yet when it came to having a dog around she was adamant. "No dogs, peddlers, vagabonds or musicians allowed." Friendship was all right so long as it did not affect one's business.

"You mean it is him or me?"

"Exactly that!" she declared stiffly.

At this point the yellow object on the rug between us, evidently sensing that I needed moral support, wriggled over on his belly and thrust his cold little nose into my hand. Clearly he was a one man dog, and I was that man.

"I shall be sorry to leave you, Mrs. Stevens," I said finally, "but if that is your ultimatum, I—I should say we—will go."

We went. That night we spent at the Lafayette Hotel on University Place, whose French proprietor had the continental attitude towards dogs and raised no objection to mine.

I called my new acquisition "The Chief Justice"—the "C. J."

for short—although he was a biological curiosity whose ancestry would have stumped a canine college of heraldry. For the most part "plain dog"—as Mark Twain, and perhaps others before him, might have said—he showed definite traces of fox-terrier, bull, collie, Manchester and bloodhound, and I suspect some stravagling dachshund had once got at least as far as his mother's front door. His hindquarters, legs, and paws were much too large for the rest of him, so that he "gallumphed" rather than walked, but he had a beautiful head, ears like sensitive plants, with a black mark between them down his muzzle, liquid brown eyes that would melt your heart, a white ruff, three white paws, and a flag on the end of an intelligent tail fully as long as his body which could both act as a semaphore or broadcast on any wave length. He was what I call a real dog—a compact, muscular, little bastard, of a vitality inexhaustible. What he lacked in education he more than made up in dog sense, following me everywhere without a leash, even to the door of the courthouse where he would wait for hours until I came out, and where, his manners being perfect, he would occasionally slip into a corner, ruling with his tail on the various points of law as they arose. Frequently in the office I held long arguments with him—literally trying them "on the dog."

"What do you think of that, Your Honor?" I'd ask, and first putting his head on one side with a look of meditation, the C. J. would thump the floor either doubtfully or in definite agreement.

It had never occurred to me to set up an establishment of my own, but I had accumulated several thousand books which overflowed both my bedroom and my office. I was tired of having to go to the Salmagundi Club or the Society Library on Lafayette Street when I needed works of reference, and I wanted a place where I could entertain my friends without taking them to a restaurant or having to play second-fiddle at Mrs. Stevens'. Once the idea had suggested itself I became all for it. I did not wish—indeed I could not afford—a fashionable neighborhood. What I was looking for was quiet and independence, where I could shuffle around in carpet slippers if I felt like it, and there was a yard for the "C. J." to smell about in.

One afternoon with the Chief Justice trotting along behind me I had searched all around University Place, Union Square and Greenwich Village without finding anything, when walking north on Eighth Avenue, I turned into Twenty-third. Unexpectedly the Chief Justice disappeared. I stopped and looked about. A row of old-fashioned houses stood some distance back from the street, the peeling stucco of their white façades faintly pink in the setting sun—"London Terrace." A gnarled old plane tree topped the nearest roof while a giant wisteria vine had entangled itself about the ironwork of the window balcony. It was homelike, cozy and inviting. Evidently the Chief Justice thought so too, for he stood between the pillars of the doorway, looking towards me and wagging his tail. "This is it!" he seemed to be saying.

I pushed open the gate and followed the brick path leading across the grass. Sure enough, a printed sign hung in one of the lower windows, reading "For Sale or To Rent." Inside, a narrow staircase led up one flight to a front room running the width of the house, which would serve excellently for a library. The dining room was on the ground floor, slightly below the level of the yard, and connected directly with the kitchen in the rear. There was one double and one single bedroom and a couple of baths. It looked ideal and the years proved it to be so.

The house needed little done to it, and as soon as the lease was signed I had shelves built for the library, and took possession. I put a faded Turkey-red carpet upon the floor and between the two windows an old-fashioned mahogany escritoire, behind whose covered doors I housed a collection of bottles, the drawers beneath being filled with boxes of vintage Havana cigars for my guests and of stogies for myself. The crowded book-shelves ran half way to the twelve foot ceiling, the tops lined with busts of Grecian philosophers, the Founding Fathers, and of Lincoln, Webster and Rufus Choate. In one corner stood a round card-table and in another my roll-topped writing desk over which, side by side, have always hung the photographs of the only women I have really loved—my mother and Esther Farr. A few engravings in heavy gilt frames which I had picked up from time to time completed the decorations. From the day that I moved in a sea-coal fire always burned in the iron basket beneath the Adam fireplace, an eternal flame upon the altar of bachelor comfort—my slippers toasting before it on the hook rug I brought from Pottsville, and opposite them the "C.J's" basket.

I once had a college friend who, after having been given a position in the family bank, overheard his father, who was showing a visitor his private office, assert with some pride that he had spent thirty years of his life there—upon which the son incontinently fled and never returned. Quite to the contrary I spent the better part of thirty years in my Twenty-third Street library and I would be glad to do so all over again. I have never kept a diary, but I could easily reconstruct my life from the diplomas, pictures, photographs and mementoes upon the walls. That room is part of me—perhaps the best part. There I have laughed and occasionally—when alone—have wept; there I have planned my court-room strategies and examined in secret my witnesses; there have I heard confessions of everything from infidelity to murder; there I have seen husbands and wives reconciled, repentant daughters and sons forgiven, restitutions made after many years; and there in my low, sway-backed, horse-hair covered armchair, with my feet crossed upon the fire dogs and a bottle of Burgundy upon the hearth beside me I have enjoyed the intellectual companionship of saints, philosophers, historians, poets, and lovers.

I was lucky not only in my house but in my cook, for the day after my arrival there appeared at my front door a smiling Negress, weighing at least three hundred pounds, with excellent references, and unhesitatingly asserted that I was the one pussun she'd been lookin' for: "Sho' Ah'll take care of you, Mister Tutt!" she declared. "An' I doan' wan' no one else botherin' 'roun' me neither. Ah's movin' right in!"

Mandy must have been sent from heaven. She had been born

in New Orleans and knew how to prepare all the succulent Creole dishes—such as the eggs *St. Dennis,* chicken *papilotte,* oysters *François,* trout *Margery,* shrimp *Remonlade,* frogs' legs *en Casserole Vieux Carré,* and *Crépes Suzette,* which have made Begue's and Antoine's famous. She had worked for Antoine, the elder Alciatore, and afterwards for his son Roy, the present proprietor, and could prepare Oysters Rockefeller as well as he. In fact I have more than once served them at my own table to John D. Jr. and Abby, his charming wife.

Luckily Mandy liked dogs, for the C.J., in spite of his intelligence, loyalty and other endearing qualities, involved us in continuous excitement. Life on 23rd Street was never dull when he was around. Having acted as my agent, so to speak, in discovering the house he had a tremendous sense of proprietorship in it. This extended over the front grass plot as far as the sidewalk. Dogs might come and dogs might go beyond the iron fence that separated what was his from the public right of way, but no one of them might place a paw inside it. He would attack dogs ten times his own size and, perhaps because his heart was pure, usually drive them away with their tails between their legs. He obviously did this only from a sense of duty, for under all other circumstances he was the friendliest and most amiable of animals. I never knew him to bite a human being but once.

Mr. Pawling, the corner druggist, owned a large black French poodle, named "Pierre de Bonton," of whom he was very proud. It appeared that, before we had moved in and while the property was vacant, Pierre had formed at attachment for the plane tree in the front yard. So irresistible a compulsion did it exert upon him that he could not pass without at least a sniff. The afternoon of our arrival, and unaware of the C.J.'s presence, Pierre stepped daintily across the border to pay his customary tribute. Suddenly arose the noise of a mêlée such as the neighborhood had never known. One would have thought that not only two, but at least a dozen dogs were involved, and I rushed out to find Pierre and the C.J. in bloody conflict, with the C.J. solidly attached to the ear of Pierre who was uttering shrieks of pain and terror. Coincidently Mr. Pawling appeared panting.

"Call off your dog!" he cried frantically.

Since I was unable to exact obedience, he proceeded to attempt to separate the two animals by grasping—not his own dog—but mine, by the tail, whereupon the C.J. promptly bit him in the hand and refused to let go until Mandy drenched them both with a pail of water. I never was sure whether it was the indignity of his rescue or the injury to his hand that led Mr. Pawling to take legal action, but next day he sued me for $500 damages.

At the trial I claimed that Pawling had contributed to the unfortunate result by his own negligence through seizing a strange dog by the tail. He replied that since the C.J. was at the moment minus a collar there was nowhere else to grab him. I argued that he should have grabbed his own dog, citing as an authority Raymond *vs.* Hodgeson, 161 Mass. 184, which holds that before you mix up in a dog fight the circumstances must warrant your interference, in which case you must exercise due care, or, the other way round, must not be negligent; that it is not negligence contributing to one's injury if you, being the lawful custodian of a dog, for the purpose of rescuing it and preserving the public peace, grab its opponent by the collar, but it may be negligence if, under precisely similar circumstances, you mix into the rumpus and, the winning dog having no collar on, you grab it by the tail and get bitten. The jury found in my favor after listening to an exhaustive and exhausting charge from the judge, who had taken the opportunity—being a dog owner himself—to make a thorough study of the law of dogs—their rights and duties and the liability of their owners.

There seems to be something in dog cases that incites every judge who tries one to mad waggery or maudlin sentimentality. There is more gush from the bench over dead dogs, and more asinine humor over live ones, than is ever wasted on either the deceased or the defendant in a murder case. Few judges can resist quoting "Old Dog Tray," Goldsmith's "Elegy on the Death of a

Mad Dog," and Byron's epitaph to his dead St. Bernard, to say nothing of the inevitable references to Cerberus, Landseer, and the joy of following the hounds, on the part of legal luminaries who never got nearer to a fox hunt than a barroom sporting print. Such literary efforts usually begin with a barefaced allegation that it is customary to despise the dog as a mean, cowardly creature, fit only to be kicked about, to have a can tied to its tail, or at best suffered to shiver in a corner beyond the heat of the fire. The heroic expounder of canine merits then boldly declares that the time at last has come to stand up for the poor downtrodden brute, and proceeds to picture him as the friend of man from the time of the Pyramids to the present day, from the frozen pole to the torrid zone. Self-respecting dogs are entitled to resent the levity which the mere mention of the canine breed seems to arouse in the judicial breast.

Originally the common law was loath to regard dogs as property and recognized only four varieties—"the mastiff, hound, spaniel, and tumbler." Moreover it was not a crime to steal one. The reason for the disinclination of English judges to regard dogs as subjects of larceny lay in the fact that all felonies were punishable in England by hanging, and larceny was a felony. Even a hanging judge, though he might hang a man for stealing a sheep, could not bring himself to hang him for stealing a dog. Thus it was said: "The taking . . . of any creatures whatsoever which are *domitae naturae* and fit for food, as ducks, hens, geese . . . may be felony"; but subjects of larceny "ought not to be things of a base nature, as dogs, cats, bears, foxes, monkeys, ferrets, and the like, which, however they may be valued by the owner shall never be so highly regarded by the law, that for their sakes a man shall die." (1 Hawk. P.C., Ch. 33.)

It is, of course, today well established in most jurisdictions that the owner of a dog has the same right of property in it as in anything else, which he can defend in equal fashion, and for damage to which he can sue in the courts. But this is not so everywhere, and the courts were for a long time slow in adopting the view that a dog could have any particular value or that the owner of a dog run over by a wagon, trolley car or train, or otherwise injured carelessly, could successfully maintain an action.

Dogs can be the subject of larceny, of conversion, and for damages when killed or injured through the fault or intention of others. Any animal which has escaped from its owner can be followed and recaptured, or replevied from the possession of another, no matter how long a time has elapsed since its escape or how great a distance has been covered in its flight, unless it is a tamed wild animal which has succeeded in regaining its native habitat *"sine animo revertendi"*—that is to say, "without the intention of returning." This principle works both ways, for so long as a beast's owner can still claim it as his, he is naturally liable for any damage it may have done up to the moment when it has regained its natural habitat and became legally wild again.

Today, as everybody of course knows, under no theory of jurisprudence can an animal be made a plaintiff or a defendant in a litigation except by special provision of law. If beasts have any rights or duties of their own they are merged in those of the owner, whose property they are, or, if not owned by anybody, they are protected from cruelty or destruction only by statutes which, as in the case of migratory birds, are concerned less with the rights of the animals themselves than with those of the public. It might almost be fairly said that an animal had no rights and no duties, save when by special legislation it has been made individually liable for offenses, in which case it should be entitled to all the rights of any accused.

But the idea that animals should not be held responsible for their acts would have been greeted with derision in former times. In mediaeval Europe, on the theory that they had consciousness and hence will and intent, dogs and other animals were held criminally liable and subject to public prosecution, their right to counsel being recognized centuries before such privilege was extended to human defendants in the English courts. We have records of the trials of mules, bulls, cows, mares, pigs, dogs, goats, cocks, turtle-doves, swallows, eels, caterpillars, flies, locusts, weevils, worms, leeches and snails. The ecclesiastical authorities of the Middle Ages were ready to prosecute pigs and sows not only for what they did but also because they were suspected of being possessed by devils, as in the case of the Gadarene swine.

Anything "in motion" which caused the death of a human being was "*deodand*" and forfeited to the crown. A horse which kicked a man to death was *deodand,* and so might be a knife, an axe, a stove, a cart, a millwheel—or, I doubt not—a dog. There is a recorded case in which a man having fallen from a millwheel into the race and been drowned, the whole works were declared *deodand* because the mill was in operation at the time. Even as late as the reign of Queen Victoria a locomotive which ran over a man was convicted and forfeited. In my opinion this might well still be the law—if the locomotive ran over a dog.

IX

THE FIRST ROOSEVELT ERA

THE business of Wiegand & Tutt expanded rapidly and we were obliged within a year to enlarge our office force. We had a diverse practice. Reference to my files discloses that in addition to run-of-mine accident, landlord and tenant cases, libel suits, probate matters, and general advice to banks, business corporations and private clients, we acted as attorneys or advisory counsel in several litigations of major importance which it would be neither profitable nor interesting to enumerate.

The Omega Trust Company gave us constant employment: from time to time old established private banks sought our advice as to the certification of corporate securities; we acted as counsel to the Stock Exchange and to reorganization committees and receiverships, in some of which it was necessary to maintain foreclosure proceedings in eleven States; while on the lighter side I note that we appeared for the defense in United States vs. One Thousand Barrels of Rye Whiskey, in Bump (sic) vs. the New York Central Railroad, and in Livitsky vs. The Sweet Smelling Geranium Window Cleaning Company. In addition I was retained as trial counsel by other lawyers and argued appeals in decisions which had gone against us.

I was thirty-nine years old and by way of becoming a confirmed bachelor. I was absorbed in the problems of the law and its philosophy, I was happy in my little stucco house and in my library with its shelves of well worn books, and after a hard day's work in court I was more than content to spend the evening before the fire, with a box of stogies and a bottle of Burgundy beside me, drowsing over the classics or tying salmon flies to use when the ice should break in the Canadian streams.

For years I had missed the fun of my Saturday night poker games in Judge Wynkoop's office in Pottsville and I now revived them on Twenty-third Street. I called my little group somewhat irreverently the "Bible Class." Among the regulars were William Travers Jerome, Walter Damrosch, Robert Collier, Finley Peter Dunne, Charles Dana Gibson, Richard Harding Davis, and Arthur Train, while occasionally John Drew or William Gillette would drop in. The stakes were small, but there was plenty of good talk, stories and swapping of ideas between jack pots. Later the "Bible Class" moved to the Colophon Club where I am glad to say it still functions. Few of the original members remain, but the memories of those who have gone are very much alive, and often as I sit alone before my sea-coal fire I hear the echo of jovial laughter and seem to see through the drifting smoke of my stogy the cluster of kindly faces that did so much to console me for my loss of Esther.

There are even more vivid memories, however, of those who came to consult me there, of aged men and women cheated out of their savings, of young men and women faced with difficult problems, of parents whose sons and daughters were in trouble, of persons unjustly accused of crime, and of more than one fugitive to whom I gave lodging for the night.

It is today hard to realize the change that has come over New York City in thirty-five years. It was really like a town then. When I moved into London Terrace the grounds were embowered with vines and foliage, and the side streets of the city were still lined with the maple, willow and ailanthus trees that gave some of them the aspect of a village. Most of those trees have died, but I am glad to say that in many parts of the city others have been planted in their place. Horse-drawn stages still ran up and down Fifth Avenue, although not upon the Sabbath, due to the religious propensities of Elliott F. Shepard, the owner of the line, which had given rise to the jingle:

> "No longer on Sundays the stages do run,
> For our Good Shepard has bought every one,
> He thinks that the earth is his own heritage
> Since Shakespeare has said that the world is a stage."

Indeed, Sunday in those days was a reflection of that former period when heavy iron chains were hung across the streets to prevent secular traffic. It was the decade of "best clothes"— "dudes" and "belles." There being no golf or motoring worthy of the name, the gallants perforce donned their silk hats and Prince Alberts and submitted to being led to church, after which, having paraded up and down Fifth Avenue, they returned home to a heavy meal of roast beef, horse radish and brown potatoes, followed by ice cream, sleeping or smoking it off in the afternoon.

It was a period of clubs and heavy drinking, it being the custom for businessmen to walk uptown, stopping by the way at the Holland House and other places of entertainment for liquid refreshment, until they reached their favorite rendezvous and with an introductory "Take the orders" joined the group inevitably to be found gathered about some raconteur. At that time the fruit of the vine, except at dinner parties, where the tradition of hospitality still required a fleet of wine glasses at every place, was reserved to the male, and it was not unusual for a gentleman to arrive at his domicile in a state of alcoholic exhilaration due to seven or more assorted cocktails or whiskies and sodas.

Those were the days of propriety in speech. No gentleman referred in the presence of a lady to any major part of the human anatomy below the neck, "damn" was printed "——" or "dash," used vocally it was good for a sure-fire, if nervous, laugh at anytime on the theatrical stage, while "a good goddamn" would have brought the police.*

Among my close friends was Finley Peter Dunne—better known as "Mr. Dooley"—whom I had met through Sam Jessup, at the time of the prosecution of Norman Hapgood by Colonel Mann. He was stocky, with a plump, shrewd, kindly face, but beneath his wit, good nature and warm humanistic philosophy was hidden a characteristic racial sadness. A great reader and truly erudite, he would drift in to my West 23rd Street

* Goddamn was first heard on the American stage in Clyde Fitch's "The City" in 1909.

library after an evening at The Links or Meeting House and, sinking into one of my swaybacked horsehair covered chairs, stay "just for a gab" until two or three in the morning discussing books and politics. He was interested in my explanation of the difference between law and justice, which he had sensed but never clarified in his mind. Our talks regarding the struggle of labor for recognition and the ease with which beneficial legislation could at that time be defeated resulted in his famous line "I do not care who makes the laws in a nation if I can get out an injunction."

Fond of the good things of life and popular with the wealthy and influential, he was a democrat to the bone. He believed all men were fundamentally alike. "I, miself, an ivry man barrin' iddycation an' th' business we're in, is all out iv th' same peck measure," he made Mr. Dooley say. "If I know mesilf, I know thim all. King, Czar . . . they're all me with better or worse clothes."

Dunne hated demagoguery and the masquerading of selfish interest as altruism, religion or patriotism. He saw red at any American claim of national and racial superiority. "We're a great people," says Mr. Hennessey earnestly. "We are," says Mr. Dooley. "We are that. An' th' best iv it is, we know we are." He was a master debunker of sham and pretense, but he was always so good-natured and so fair to his victim that the latter could never complain. Undoubtedly Peter was a political force.

As my friend Charles A. Beard says, Dunne "relaxed the tension of the moral overstrain" of public controversy. He would have made a wise and upright judge. He believed, according to Elmer Ellis, his biographer, that "the system of organizing economic and political society (i.e., the laws), was not of primary importance. The motives of people, the standards of value by which the great mass approved or disapproved of action, these were the important things. Only as the individual was improved, as his understanding of society was sharpened, as his love of decency was deepened, as his sympathy for the distressed was quickened, as his consciousness of duty to his fellow men was made more acute, would society make real improvements." * No wonder that I loved him and that we remained friends until he died.

One day in 1908, Peter telephoned to ask if I could go down with him to lunch with President Roosevelt at Oyster Bay. He said that T.R. had expressed a desire to make my acquaintance and to hear the story of Doc. Robinson's Old Gray Mare. We were met at the station by an ancient darky who drove us in a ricketty trap up to the big, sprawling house at Sagamore Hill, where the President welcomed us on the veranda in riding breeches and soft shirt. It was a family affair, save for ourselves, Mark Sullivan and Gifford Pinchot, then Chief Forester. I sat between Mrs. Roosevelt and Ethel, a radiant vivacious girl who had just made her debut. Across the table from us was an intimate friend of hers, named Helen Coster, who years afterwards married Arthur Train. Everyone talked at once including Teddy, Jr., Kermit, Archie and Quentin, the youngest—the President loudest of all. Then the host banged on the table with a pewter beer mug and announced that Eph Tutt was going to tell a story about a horse-trade in the upper part of the State. They were an appreciative audience and shouted for more.

"Well," I said, "when I was an assistant district attorney under Asa Bird Gardiner—"

"You!" cried the President incredulously. "You—a Tammany man!"

"No, sir," I explained. "I helped Boss Croker one night after he'd fallen into the gutter and he gave me a $3,500 job in return."

"O.K.!" grinned the President. "At least he made one good appointment. Go on!"

My story was this: There used to be an old court officer in General Sessions named Michael Fenton, who was an ardent Roman Catholic. One of his duties was to help take each pris-

* Mr. Dooley's America, pp. 296–7.

oner's pedigree, after conviction. Fenton would ask him a set form of questions and relay the answers to the clerk, who thereupon would endorse them upon the back of the indictment. The first question always was:

"Are you temperate or intemperate?"

If the prisoner hesitated Fenton would help him out with: "Do yez iver take a drink?"

"Sure!" the defendant would answer.

Whereupon Fenton would turn to the clerk and remark with an air of gratification: "Temperate!"

One day I overheard the following (here I attempted to take the parts of both Fenton and prisoner):

Fenton: "Where were ye born?"

Prisoner: "Lowell, Mass."

Fenton: "He says 'Lowell, Mass.' Where do yez hang out?"

Defendant: "Nowhere."

Fenton to Clerk: "Ain't got none. Phwat do yez do fer a livin'?"

Defendant: "Nothin'."

Fenton to Clerk: "Ain't got none. Are yez married?"

Defendant: "No—thank God!"

Fenton to Clerk: "He says, 'No, thank God!' Did yez iver receive any previous religious instruction?"

Defendant: "How's that?"

Fenton (explaining): "What's yer religion?"

Defendant: "Ain't got none."

Fenton to Clerk (loudly): "Protestant!"

The general laughter was drowned in the Presidential guffaws. T.R. literally almost rolled on the floor and kicked his heels with delight. It was, he vowed, the best story he had ever heard, and I believe he thought so too, for I heard him tell it that autumn at the White House and on other occasions afterwards. That is the only reason why I repeat it here.

Theodore Roosevelt was the most dynamic and stimulating human being I have ever met. Whatever his political mistakes may have been—and of that I am no judge—he was a perfect father, his home life with his wife and children one of singular intimacy and tenderness. He spent the afternoon taking Pinchot, Sullivan, Dunne and myself on a long walk through the woods and around the beaches, talking politics most of the time. Anyone could see that he loved Pinchot deeply, admired and trusted Sullivan, and had the greatest respect for Dunne—was perhaps the least bit afraid of him, for he never disagreed with what he said as he repeatedly did with the others. His plans were already well advanced for his African trip and we discussed the "Pig Skin Library." I could not but feel that he regarded the foregone occupancy of the White House by William Howard Taft as merely a sort of *ad interim* tenure, until he should return. We were all liberals—Sullivan at that time being regarded as a semi-socialist. As Roosevelt shook hands in goodbye he said:

"Boys, this man Eph Tutt is one of us. He ought to be put to active use. I shall see that something is done about it when I come home."

Going back on the train to the city I happened to mention to Pinchot how much I enjoyed fishing and he suggested that I come up to Milford, Pennsylvania for the week end where his father had a country place. I was glad to go for I had been singularly attracted by him. I have rarely, if ever, met a man of such distinguished appearance. Slender and tall, he had finely etched delicate features and luminous eyes like those of an ascetic. There was something mystical about him. He was an excellent fisherman and he taught me for the first time how to use a dry fly. A stream, full of German trout, crossed his father's property and before flowing into the Delaware formed a waterfall composed of a series of terraces ending in a deep pool not far from the house. At the conclusion of our day's fishing Gifford and I would take off our clothes at the top fall and lying flat on our bellies allow the stream to sweep us over the edge to the next below, where we repeated the process until we slid finally into the pool. It was exciting fun but I lost most of my abdominal epidermis and felt as if I had an extremely sore throat on the outside of my stomach.

My connection with the Collier crowd led to all sorts of other contacts. One of these was with Mark Twain, of whom Norman Hapgood, Bob Collier and Peter Dunne were intimate friends. Collier took me one noon to call on "Old Mark" on lower Fifth Avenue. We found him in bed, smoking a pipe, writing pad on his knees. Twain got talking and continued for several hours, oblivious to the necessity of sustenance. It appeared that some time before Mark, who had taken a fancy to Collier, had offered if he panned out sufficiently well on further acquaintance to take him into his club. Collier wanted to know the name of it, but Twain refused to tell him until he was satisfied of his qualifications, except that it was the G.D.H.R. Club. Collier, who belonged to every desirable club in New York and Long Island, was rather piqued at not being taken in at once, and on the occasion of our visit frankly asked the author if it wasn't time for him to make up his mind about his candidacy. Mark took a couple of solemn puffs:

"Well, Bob," he said, "I know I've kept you on the waiting list quite a while, but one has to be careful about these matters. On the whole I think you'll do. You're elected. Welcome to the G.D.H.R. Club!"

"I'm very much complimented!" beamed Collier. "Now you can tell me the full name of it."

"It's 'The God Damned Human Race,'" said Mark.

Bob Collier was one of the most charming of that race. He was tall, with blue-black hair and deep blue twinkling Irish eyes. He was a great polo player, had been educated at Oxford, moved in English literary circles and had excellent taste in books and art. His old father, Peter Fenelon Collier (or "Pete" as he was called by his contemporaries) had come to America with twenty-five cents in his pocket, driven a street car, and hawked Bibles from house to house.

Out of this had grown an enormous subscription business, distributing three million books a year. He loved to entertain and he had thousands of friends. Young Bob was the passion of his life and he poured all his financial resources into the magazine which his son was conducting so brilliantly yet so lavishly.

Norman Hapgood, the editor of *Colliers,* was the most perfect example of highbrow I ever encountered. He could "harness a team with a logical chain," and granted his premises there was no escaping his conclusions. Unfortunately his premises, although usually so, were not always sound. He lacked spontaneity and his humor was purely cerebral. When his mind told him that something was amusing he would laugh, but it was never what Broadway calls a "belly laugh."

I still taught my class at Dick Welling's Boys' Club and through either him or Hapgood I met the sister of John L. Cadwalader, Mrs. Cadwalader Jones, whose house was a center for writers and artists. Her Sunday luncheons were famous, and at one time or another I met at her table Edith Wharton, Henry James, John Singer Sargent, F. Marion Crawford, William Dean Howells, Henry van Dyke, John La Farge, Brander Matthews, Richard Watson Gilder, Henry Adams, Booth Tarkington, and Winston Churchill the novelist. I particularly remember on one occasion there collecting five dollars from "Tark," who had taken me up when I offered to bet that Ethel Barrymore's name would not be found in the social register. It wasn't, although no one ever registered socially with more success than she. Our local Debrett has never admitted to its pages the name of anyone directly connected with the stage.

What little I saw of smart New York social life was due to my friendship with Richard Harding Davis, then at the height of his popularity who occasionally visited the criminal courts in quest of material. He may have regarded me as quaint, just as I looked upon him as a dashing man of the world. No two people could have been more unlike, but for some reason we hit it off together, and through him I met his comrade and illustrator Charles Dana Gibson.

Davis was a big, handsome, ruddy fellow, generous and at times childishly sentimental. His books and plays had made him famous at an early age, he had travelled all over the world and been petted by the great, and to the debutante he personified romance. But he stood for clean living, courage, and what a gentleman did and did not do. He was vain, something of a poseur and at times a bit "high hat," but as a writer of tales he deserved every bit of his popular reputation.

Dana Gibson was his complement. Taller, equally handsome and masculine, but far more engaging on account of his modesty and warmth, his mind and wit were sharper than his friend's. A marvelous draughtsman in pen and ink he could satirize a current trend or foible with devastating irony. Tawdry ambition, sham and venality in social aspirants—plotting dowagers and calculating millionaires sacrificing youth and love to wealth—were Gibson's particular aversions. The moral impact of his work upon his generation was, in my opinion, far greater than Davis's. Each an artist in his own right, as a team they were unsurpassed, exerting a pronounced influence upon American ideas and ideals. Between them they popularized as a national hero, a clean shaven, square-jawed and square-shouldered young Galahad, who, as drawn by Gibson, strangely resembled Davis; and as the ideal of American womanhood, a balloon-sleeved, wasp-waisted Venus in a rakish straw hat, easily recognizable as Irene Langhorne, the artist's beautiful wife.

Whenever Davis sold a story he gave a party, not a fancy party, but a good one, with champagne—which cost then less than gin does now. Sometimes it would be in his rooms, sometimes at Delmonico's or Martin's, sometimes at McGowan's Pass Tavern in Central Park, the guests arriving on horse-back, by Victoria, or in the case of Helen Hastings by coach and four. He was kind enough to invite me on a few of these, always insisting that I should tell the story of The Great Wen Case or Doc Robinson's Old Gray Mare.

These parties invariably included Ethel Barrymore and Maude

Adams, Elsie Clews, Helen (Mrs. Thomas) Hastings, Peter Dunne, John Fox, Lloyd Griscom, Gouverneur Morris, Duer Irving, Alice Green, Virginia Harned, Sally Fairchild of Boston, Arthur Pollen, Herbert Satterlee, Ed and Sam Sothern, Arthur Brisbane, and Charles Belmont Davis, Dick's brother.

They were a gay, witty and decorative group. I was proud to be occasionally one of their number and through them I became acquainted with a world of which I had read but of whose existence I had entertained some doubt. Presently I began to receive invitations from young ladies whom I had met in this way and before long was asked to attend a dinner given by one of the prominent hostesses on Fifth Avenue where I, Eph. Tutt of Leeds, Town of Plymouth, Vermont, actually sat down with forty other guests at a table laden with orchids, rose trees and a service of solid gold, while a famous organist warbled over the keys a potpouri of classic and popular airs. After a couple of hours at the table we returned to the drawing room and for our entertainment the Kneisel Quartette was led in from the pantry where they had been held *incommunicado* amid the dishes most of the evening. Later I heard that our hostess when engaging a celebrated virtuoso to sing at one of these soirees had protested at the three thousand dollars he asked for his services.

"I think it's very high," she hesitated, "but I suppose I shall have to pay it. Of course, you understand, M'sieu, that you are not under any conditions to mingle with the guests?"

"In that case, Madam," he replied, "the price will be only two thousand."

The story may be apocryphal, but it is none the less possible and typifies the feeling of insecurity among New York plutocrats as to their social position, which led them to an excess of self-protective snobbery. Although themselves in trade they pretended that trade was vulgar, that artists were immoral Bohemians, that to be a gentleman a man had to own a smart Victoria with two men on the box, and that two young people who loved one another could not possibly marry on an income of less than fifteen thousand a year. Yet they were not like that when you got to know them individually. It was part of the collective hypocritic shell. They were in fact kindly, well intentioned, otherwise sensible people, afraid to admit that they were so and worried lest they should make some social or grammatical slip. I found that if I made no pretenses they were quite willing to welcome me for what I was. Doc Robinson's Old Gray Mare proved an open sesame to Fifth Avenue houses, and in 1909 there was a brief Ephraim Tutt social season, before I retired to my former obscurity with a substantial number of my new friends as clients.

The reader may wonder why in a serious autobiography I take the time or trouble to mention what may appear such an ephemeral and unimportant aspect of New York life. The answer is that it was not unimportant either to me or to the country at large. This ostentatious luxury had a great deal to do with the growing antagonism to great wealth. Personally what I saw of society strongly influenced my subsequent career; for I knew at first hand what life meant to the great bulk of the people who had to work for their living.

I had come to New York at a time when materialism held full sway—a period of gorgeous fancy dress balls, of licentious and reckless rich men, of immense concentrations of wealth. The phrase "corporate abuse" represented no imaginative idea. It was not just talk. Alexander Agassiz—the brother-in-law of Henry Higginson, head of the great banking house of Lee, Higginson & Co., founder of the Boston Symphony Orchestra, and Boston's leading citizen—was a large owner in Calumet & Hecla, the bonanza copper mine of that day. He said: "If it were a question of bribing a State Legislature, I should regard it in the same light as the removal of a bank of sand." And this in God-fearing New England! Mr. Higginson himself had no doubt in his mind but that he represented the highest product of social evolution. When asked if he proposed to give orders to the members of his orchestra as to how to vote at election time, he replied that he certainly should.*

The root of the trouble lay in the fact that a corporation was not a human being, nobody being responsible for its actions, since responsibility, spread over a score of officers and directors, could be easily evaded. There was no ethical restraint upon it whatsoever and not much legal restraint either. The deluge of immigration during the nineties had brought many socialistic theories along with it. Municipal politics had always been the most corrupt phase of American life, and the alleged relationship of corruption to corporate privilege became a favorite subject of periodical literature.

Sam McClure, Ida Tarbell, Ray Stannard Baker and Lincoln Steffens started a reform wave over the country that played a large part in landing Colonel Roosevelt in the White House. McClure's Magazine shook the temple of American self-confidence to its foundations; Ida Tarbell published her epoch-making but perfectly documented exposure of American business fascism, the "History of the Standard Oil Company"; while Steffens and Baker attacked corruption in city politics, the railroads and industry generally in a way to shock the ordinary citizen and fire his indignation. The muckraker had not only appeared but had proved that the muck was there.

In 1901, in the midst of all this excitement about the power of money, J. P. Morgan & Co. conceived and gave birth to the Steel Trust, and Mr. Andrew Carnegie was observed hurrying from the bedside with a bag containing a quarter of a billion dollars which he had received as his share of the payment made for the Carnegie Iron Works—the largest sum up to that time ever held in the hands of a single individual.

Four years later Charles Evans Hughes appeared in the limelight as Counsel for the Armstrong Insurance Committee of Investigation, disclosing just enough of the iniquities of the life

* M. A. DeWolfe Howe's *"John Jay Chapman and His Letters,"* pp. 198–9.

insurance companies to shake the nation-wide popularity of District Attorney Jerome who found it impossible to find any punishments to fit their crimes. Roosevelt threw his sombrero into the ring, and went after "the wicked trusts" with his big stick, challenging the "malefactors of great wealth" in shrill but stentorian tones. The working man was told that the "vested interests" were his enemies and that nothing good could come out of Wall Street.

The panic of 1907, one of the worst in financial history, seemed convincing evidence of this. It was reaching its height in October and November of that year. The Knickerbocker Trust Company failed on October 22. Nine banking institutions closed their doors, and call money rose to 125 percent. If it hadn't been for the calmness and sanity of J. P. Morgan, Senior, the whole financial structure of the country might have collapsed like a house of cards.

Hotchkiss, Levy & Hogan had represented one of the banks involved and I was sent up one evening with some papers to deliver to Mr. Morgan personally. The marvelous Morgan library was full of desperate and bewildered New York lawyers who had just held one of their nightly meetings there. An attendant admitted me to a small adjoining room where Mr. Morgan was seated alone, apparently oblivious to the tension outside, smoking a long black cigar, and playing a game of Patience. An hour's delay might bring disaster to the business world. He looked up, nodded and I handed him the papers. "Thank you," he said and went on with his game. I shall never forget the impression of imperturbability, courage and integrity that he made upon me.

On January 31, 1908, Roosevelt sent a special message to Congress in which he said: "Everyone must feel the keenest sympathy for the large body of honest business men, of honest investors, of honest wage earners, who suffer because involved in a crash for which they are in no way responsible. . . . Our main quarrel is not with the representatives of the interests. They derive their chief power from the great sinister figures who stand behind them. They are but puppets who move as the strings are pulled. It is not the puppets, but the strong cunning men and the mighty forces working for evil behind and through the puppets, with whom we have to deal. We seek to control law-defying wealth."

By February the panic was over, but some sort of transitional adjustment from an archaic economic and social condition to modern requirements had obviously become indispensable if not inevitable.

And now T.R. had gone to Africa to shoot elephants, leaving the benevolent Taft to carry on where he had temporarily left off. The new president was not the type to handle successfully the Pandora's box of troubles which had been handed to him, and his misery was humorously pictured by Timothy Hays in the San Francisco *Bulletin*.

> "Dear Teddy, I need you; come home to me quick,
>   I am worried and weary and worn.
> And as hope long deferred only makes the heart sick,
> I am sadly in need of your potent 'Big Stick';
>   So, Teddy, please haste your return."

One of these miseries was the famous Glavis-Ballinger controversy in which, owing to my friendship with Gifford Pinchot, I was asked to assist Louis D. Brandeis, later a justice of the Supreme Court of the United States, as counsel for Glavis before the Congressional Investigating Committee.

As soon as I had freed myself of the incubus of Hotchkiss, Levy & Hogan and was master of my own time I became, largely through my admiration of Clarence Darrow, deeply interested in the cause of labor and active in the defense of free speech.

One of my most stimulating acquaintances was Lincoln Steffens, whom I had first met at Mrs. Steven's boarding house and later while defending a man charged with "inciting to riot," as a result of a speech in Union Square. "Link," who never betrayed a confidence, was an ideal reporter and investigator. He loathed cant and, much as he hated corruption, preferred a frankly crooked politician to most types of reformers, so that, being both engaging and plausible, he could get almost any tycoon to give up his guts to him. One of his favorite comments was, "If only the good people were as good as the bad people." As a friend he was erratic, as a conversationalist "paradoxical, lively and incalculable as quicksilver." His autobiography * is an invaluable historical and human document.

It is difficult to realize today the fear of capital for labor, the animosity existing at that time between them, or that industrial conditions could have been as bad as they actually were; but it was inevitable that my sympathies should have been with the workers and that I should have joined the Labor Defense Committee and later should have been one of the organizers of the Civil Liberties Union. In 1912, when twenty thousand employees of the Pacific Mills at Lawrence, Massachusetts, walked out in protest against a wage cut, 35 per cent of them, including women and children, were earning less than $7 for a fifty-four hour week. Yet the mills, capitalized at $2,000,000 paid 12 per cent regularly, had declared 36 per cent in extra dividends between 1905–12, and had accumulated a surplus of over $6,000,000 in addition to sinking fund and depreciation. More than thirty-three thousand people were concentrated in stinking, unhygienic squalor on three hundred acres. The death rate for children under five years was 176 per 1,000—20 per cent, due to tuberculosis, while the owners, it was said, deliberately stimulated excess immigration in order to depress wages so that men competed for children's jobs.

At Steffens' suggestion I took the train for Lawrence and offered my legal services to the strikers, but on my arrival I found that martial law had been declared, that no meeting or "congregating" was allowed and that strikers who wished to send their children away from the scene of the disturbance were prevented from doing so. That afternoon a white-haired old farmer, who

* "The Autobiography of Lincoln Steffens," Harcourt, Brace & Co, 1931.

had come all the way from my native State of Vermont, tried to read the Declaration of Independence to a group of workers. He had no sooner started than a policeman grabbed him by the collar and choked him off. When I protested we were both seized, my hat was jammed over my eyes, and we were hustled roughly down the street. Resistance was useless. I confess that when I compared one of these drab women who worked in a mill fifty-four hours a week and slept in what was little better than a sty, with one of the pink-skinned, pearl-encrusted dowagers I had taken into dinner on Fifth Avenue my blood boiled. I could do no good in Lawrence, so I went back to New York.

Calvin Coolidge, who had been elected in 1907 and 1908 to the Massachusetts House of Representatives and in 1910 and 1911 as Mayor of Northampton, was now a State Senator, and although I wrote to him during the Lawrence strike urging a legislative investigation, he voted against it. It was then I saw that Cal and I no longer looked at the world from the same viewpoint. It was not that he did not desire the best for the people and the country; it was just that he didn't want to rock the boat. He believed in the *status quo*. As at Amherst he had sought election to a fraternity, so he had aligned himself with the Massachusetts feudal aristocracy whose power was based on the ownership of mines, mills and factories. To quote William Allen White, his "reverence for the dignity of wealth amounted to belief in the existence of a wise overlordship of the affluent; under the kindly guidance of an intelligent government, justice and mercy and peace would bless its subject classes. This involved a faith in a moral government of the universe." *

Perhaps a majority of the electorate—at that political moment—had that same faith. Ten years after being chosen a State senator in accordance with a local party rule of political rotation, he became President of the United States.

---

* William Allen White's *A Puritan in Babylon*, a masterly analysis of politico-social conditions in the United States during the Coolidge period, pp. 81, et seq.

After Roosevelt returned from his African hunting trip and his triumphal progress across Europe the rift between him and Taft became an unbridgeable chasm. The nation was treated to the pitiful spectacle of two former friends accusing each other of disloyalty and falsehood. In that disastrous fight Collier and Mark Sullivan were on the Roosevelt side, but Hapgood was for Wilson and, when Roosevelt was shot at Milwaukee on October 14, wrote an editorial so detached in attitude that Collier ordered it taken off the presses and one of his own substituted. This ended in the resignation of Hapgood and a quarrel in which each attacked the other in the public press in a way utterly humiliating to their associates. It broke up forever what was known as "the Collier crowd."

The year 1912 stands in my memory as a sort of mile stone. I had reached certain definite conclusions respecting the limitations of my profession; vast social and economic forces were in motion; T.R. having failed to secure the Republican nomination at Chicago, had bolted the convention, organized the Progressive Party and lost the election to Woodrow Wilson; Germany was arming; there was a general feeling of uncertainty.

But the greatest shock of all had been the sinking of the *Titanic* with the loss of 1635 lives. Not even the torpedoing of the *Lusitania* or the treacherous attack by the Japanese on Pearl Harbor thirty years later gave me the same feeling of horrified bewilderment, for these were within the realms of possibility. But that the *Titanic*, the latest product of man's invention and skill supposedly unsinkable, in touch with the land by radio and guided by the most experienced ship's officers should, on her maiden voyage and on a smooth, still sea, have crashed into an iceberg and plunged to her doom shattered the sense of security in which America had been living for nearly half a century. To "cross the pond" had come to be regarded as no more hazardous than to cross the street. The giant leviathans of the Cunard and White Star lines with their ballrooms and swimming pools, their barber and florist shops, their squash courts and French restaurants seemed but an extension of one of the piers upon which one could stroll to Europe.

And now that illusion was destroyed. There was no such thing as safety on sea—or land. It marked the end of the period of self-complacency, of confidence in the *status quo*—a harbinger perhaps of what might come in politics, in Wall Street or in world affairs.

X

THE RIGHT TO REBEL

MY experience in Lawrence did not make me a socialist, but it led me to do a lot of thinking. As a former prosecutor when I had heard it said that the law was "at the end of a policeman's night-stick" I had not taken the statement seriously. Now that the shoe was on the other foot I realized just what it meant. "Where law ends," Pitt had said, "tyranny begins." There was no difference in theory between a thug who hit you on the head and a cop who took advantage of his uniform to jam your hat over your eyes. The worst tyranny of all was that which was disguised under the form of law. What should one do about it?

Shortly after my return from Lawrence I was assigned to a case where the defendant, a truck driver named Ivan Zalinski was accused of shooting Michael Kelly, an East Side politician. Zalinski had previously been sentenced to prison for an alleged assault in connection with a labor picket row, in which Kelly had figured in some vague way. Shortly after his discharge he had met the deceased face to face opposite the mouth of an alley, and although it was quite dark several witnesses, who had been on the opposite side of the street, swore that they had heard the report and seen a flash at Zalinski's right side. He had made no effort to escape and submitted quietly to arrest, but a revolver, which could not be identified as his, was found a short distance up the alley where he might have thrown it. Because of the dead man's local prominence the homicide had attracted much attention in the newspapers and the district attorney was hell-bent on a conviction. He sincerely believed Zalinski to be guilty and flatly refused the adjournment which I naturally desired in order to secure evidence regarding the actual ownership of the revolver. If I could show that it belonged to someone else it would have greatly weakened the People's case.

Zalinski, who denied ever having possessed a gun of any kind, claimed that he was walking home without suspecting that his so-called enemy was in the neighborhood, when suddenly there was an explosion in the mouth of the alley and a man fell prostrate in front of him. He had, he said, been scared nearly out of his wits. A guilty man would doubtless have made an equally convincing claim, but there was one fact, to which he did not allude but which I learned from his wife, that inclined me strongly towards belief in his innocence—he was on his way home to celebrate the birthday of his two-year-old child. When searched by the police a woolly rabbit, which he had purchased at the Five & Ten as a present for the baby, had been found in his pocket. In pleading for delay I urged that no man—not even a hardened criminal —would select that moment to perpetrate a murder. But Assistant District Attorney O'Brien did not see it that way. It was all baloney he said and he was going to make an example of Zalinski and send him to the hot-squat, as he called it, in the shortest possible time.

My own theory was that some enemy of Kelly's, knowing that he usually passed the spot, had hidden in the alley, shot him, and escaped by way of the other end, dropping the gun in his flight. There was in fact an empty barrel just inside the opening behind which he could have crouched. But this was hypothesis only. If I had been given a reasonable chance to find out who really owned the pistol, to prove that Zalinski was on his way home to his baby's birthday party, to explain that Kelly's connection with the strike case was remote, that the deceased had many enemies in the underworld, I should not have so much to fear. But Babcock the presiding judge was an old bloodhound, who hunted in the same leash with O'Brien and was absolutely under his control, and from the opening of the trial poor Zalinski wasn't given a single break. Besides excluding everything in his favor, including the fact that it was his baby's birthday, O'Brien deliberately created out of whole cloth the impression that Zalinski was a Communist, that he and his wife were not legally married, that the child was illegitimate, and that during the defendant's term in prison Kelly had been intimate with her. It was tantamount to Zalinski's being gagged, with his hands tied behind his back, while O'Brien slugged him at will.

The night before the summing up I knew that it was all over. Zalinski was practically in the chair already—as a result of the false atmosphere the prosecutor had managed to interject into the case. It was an unparalleled example of official despotism. I decided that my only hope lay in making O'Brien's conduct of the case so obviously unfair and prejudicial that it would prove a boomerang. The more vindictive he was the better! That trial was going to be so raw that the jury wouldn't stand for it, even if I had to make it so myself. And I did. I accused Babcock and O'Brien of bias, I deliberately violated all the rules of procedure, in short I raised the devil—just how, the court record demonstrates.

I harped on the woolly rabbit that Zalinski had had in his pocket at the time of the arrest. Was that, I demanded, a murderous weapon with which he had planned to choke Kelly to death, perhaps?

"Was he meditating murder, within less than fifteen minutes before, when he went into the Five & Ten and bought this childish toy? Was his heart curdled with venom and hatred as he walked along the street? Rather on the contrary was it not filled with love for his wife and the baby she had born him during his imprisonment?

"The law," I continued, "is supposed to be impartial, to give every man an equal chance. The Goddess of Justice is pictured as holding evenly balanced scales. It is a pretty picture, but a misleading one. The scales are not even. What chance has this poverty stricken defendant against the power of the State? The district attorney has ten thousand police officers and detectives at his beck and call, while my client has not enough money to feed his family. Why has not the District Attorney—in mere fairness to this defendant—traced the ownership of that revolver?"

"We can't divert the entire police force of the City of New York to one case," interrupted O'Brien. "They have other important matters—"

"Not more important than the result of this case is to my client," I retorted. "The cards are stacked on your side. It is as absurd to claim that the pauper, shivering without a coat, is as warm as the rich man in his furs, as that he has equal advantages before the law. Even so, gentlemen, substantial justice might be done if the law were fairly administered and the poison gas of prejudice were not allowed—nay often invited—to creep into a case. This, gentlemen, has not been a trial by law, but trial by prejudice. It is not the sort of trial guaranteed to American citizens under the Bill of Rights. The personal safety of each and every one of you depends upon the preservation of the inviolability of due legal process, uninfluenced by any sort of pressure, official or unofficial—"

"I object!" shouted O'Brien. "This sort of stump speech has nothing to do with the case."

"The galled jade will wince!" I retaliated. "You gentlemen of the jury are the sole judges of the evidence. While His Honor may comment upon the testimony, even he cannot substitute himself for you in determining what the testimony may or may not establish. Much more then is it beyond the right of the District Attorney to attempt to sway your judgment by false innuendo or prejudice."

Bang! went Babcock's gavel.

"That will be enough!" he shouted. "It is within my judicial discretion to limit the speeches of counsel. Get off generalities. Come down to business!"

"Very good, Your Honor," I replied. "I will come down to my business. You gentlemen have taken a solemn oath to a true deliverance make between the State and Ivan Zalinski. The Judge and the District Attorney are sworn to uphold the Constitution of the United States and of the State of New York, both of which under the Bill of Rights guarantee an impartial trial to

My father

Enoch Tutt.

My mother

Margaret O'Conner Tutt.

Ephraim Tutt at age of five years.

On a fishing trip while at college.

Pottsville, New York, 1895.
Showing Phoenix Hotel.

Esther

Ephraim Tutt at twenty-seven.

My home in London Terrace.
"A row of old-fashioned houses stood back from the street, homelike,
cozy and inviting."

My portrait by Arthur William Brown by which
I am best known to the public.

every defendant accused of crime. This is the charter of American liberty, our priceless heritage. But do not forget that a democratic form of government does not guarantee liberty. The words in which laws are drawn are of little importance unless they are fairly administered. Any law can be used to strangle freedom in the hands of those who scoff at civil rights. It is not the law so much as the man behind it. I claim that Ivan Zalinski has been denied the right to a fair and impartial trial!"

"I am the sole judge as to whether or not the defendant has had a fair trial," roared Babcock. "You are reflecting upon this court. You may sum up your case, but within proper bounds."

"How can I tell what Your Honor may regard as proper bounds when you have such strange ideas of what constitutes an impartial trial?" I demanded. "I shall ask Your Honor to charge that if, in the jury's opinion, the defendant has not received a fair trial, it will be their duty to acquit him."

"Stop!" ordered Babcock. "I've had enough of this!"

But I paid no attention to him.

"I shall ask Your Honor to charge the jury," I went on, "that it is more important to preserve the integrity of the administration of criminal justice than that a particular defendant be acquitted or convicted. That—in the language of the Declaration of Independence—'all men are endowed by their Creator with certain inalienable rights, that to secure these rights, governments are instituted among men, and that whenever any form of government becomes destructive of these ends, it is the right of the People to alter or abolish it.' That, in the words of Thomas Jefferson, 'rebellion to tyrants is obedience to God'!"

"Sit down!" ordered Babcock, his face purple. "The jury will entirely disregard this stump speech of counsel."

But I did not sit down. I wanted one thing more to make my defense a success. Turning to the jury I said:

"We live under a government of laws and not of men, but even a democratic form of government can become a despotism when administered unfairly by those in power—as in this case."

Babcock had turned from red to white.

"I declare you in contempt of this court. I order the sheriff to place you under arrest."

"As you choose!" I answered. "And if this defendant is convicted of murder may his blood be upon your head!"

I had accomplished my purpose. I had made it clear to the jury that I was prepared to face fine and imprisonment rather than to see my client unfairly convicted without protest. The sheriff conducted me to one of the two vacant jury rooms, then the jury, bell-weathered by Callahan, the court officer, filed out and retired into the other directly opposite. My own door was wide open and several of them had looked at me curiously as they passed by.

"If you want anything," said Callahan to the foreman, "knock on the door. I'll be outside."

"How about a pitcher of ice water?" asked a juror.

"Or a case of beer?" suggested another. "Say, Callahan, couldn't you smuggle in a bottle of Scotch and some ice?"

Callahan grinned.

"Sorry. It's agin' the rules," he said. "But here's water and some glasses."

"Okay! I've got the fixings," added the first juror.

There was a gurgling sound followed by "Here's how!" and "Happy days!" "That's the real stuff." "Lookin' at you!" "Here's luck!"

Callahan had almost closed the door.

"Do we get any dinner?" asked someone.

"Not until siven o'clock—if you ain't agreed by then."

"We'll agree all right," declared another.

Callahan closed and locked the door and returned to the courtroom leaving me to my thoughts. I could hear everything that was said in the jury room, and having developed by that time my own peculiar form of shorthand I took down the debate. Minus some of the obscenity I reproduce it here.

Various voices: You'd think we was a bunch of jail birds.—--

Phew! It's hot in here.—Why not open the window.—That's an idea. Gees! You can't hear yourself think. Put her down a few inches.

The foreman: We might as well get busy, boys.

A voice: The sooner we fix the sonofabitch the better.

Another voice: Which sonofabitch?

First voice: The defendant—of course.

Second voice: I thought you might 'a' meant the District Attorney.

Another voice: I thought they were all sonsofbitches.

Still another: God! Didn't the Judge give Tutt hell.

First voice: Didn't he give the Judge hell! I guess it'll cost him a good five hundred bucks.

Foreman: We might as well take a ballot and get out of this pest house.

(Foreman tears off sheets and shoves them around.)

Foreman: H'm! Eleven to one for conviction. —Who's the only wise man?

An irate juror: Yeah! Who's the Know-It-All?

A new voice: If you mean who voted to acquit—I did.

Another: But the Judge practically told us to convict.

The new voice: Babcock had no right to try to dictate our verdict. We're the only judges of the defendant's guilt or innocence.

A voice: But the bastard's as guilty as hell.

Another: Sure he is!

The foreman (politely): Mr. Calkins, suppose you give us your reasons for thinking this man innocent.

Juror Calkins: It would have been a crazy thing for him to do.

A juror: Are you going to believe a goddam Communist?

Calkins: He denied he was a Communist.

Another juror: Of course he'd deny it. I don't care what they say they're both of 'em Communists.

A juror: Naturally he ain't goin' to admit anything. Of course he's guilty. He's an ex-convict besides.

A juror: You can't consider that. I agree with Mr. Calkins. The evidence isn't enough to electrocute a man.

A juror: But six witnesses saw Zalinski shoot him.

A juror: Nobody saw a gun. I don't believe any of 'em saw a goddamned thing—a lot of Yids and Wops.

A voice (angrily): *Sapristi!* What you mean "Wops"?

A voice in reply: Well, a lot of Yids then.

A juror: As I see it it's as plain as the nose on your face. This feller was a first class trouble maker. Maybe he was a gangster too—they found a gun, didn't they? Kelly was after his girl while he was in Sing Sing. So the first chance after he comes out Zalinski drills him.

Another juror: That's the picture as I see it.

A new voice: There's no such thing in the case. That girl is straight.

Juror: The hell she is. Was she goin' to wait two years?

The new voice: Maybe not the kind of girls you know.

There are sounds of a scuffle.

Foreman: Order! Order! Put your hands down.—Now suppose all who think the evidence isn't enough stand up.

Sound of chairs being pushed back.

Foreman: Three wise guys!

Juror Calkins: May I say a word? Let's admit for the sake of argument that there' is technically enough evidence upon which some of you might be willing to convict this defendant. Didn't you hear Mr. Tutt say that it was more important to preserve the integrity of the administration of criminal justice than that any particular defendant should be acquitted or convicted?

A juror: Yeah, I did. And I heard the Judge send him to the hoose-gow.

Calkins: I'm coming to that. What right did the Judge have to arrest him for quoting the Declaration of Independence?

A juror: Gees! Was that the Declaration of Independence?

Calkins: The whole trial was rotten. A man's political opinions have nothing to do with his guilt or innocence of a particular crime. The fact that he has served a term in jail doesn't mean anything. As for the District Attorney, trying to make him out a Communist, it was a lousy trick.

A juror: I thought the D.A. was pretty slick. He might have fooled him into admitting something.

Another juror: Yeah, it was a damn smart trick.

Foreman: I don't approve of all the District Attorney did but that has nothing to do with the defendant's guilt or innocence.

Calkins: It has a great deal, in my opinion, to do with whether or not we should convict him. Let me ask a simple question. How many of you honestly think this defendant had a fair trial?

There was a silence for perhaps a quarter of a minute.

A juror: Well, they did seem to be giving him the bum's rush.

Calkins: Suppose you got the same kind of bum's rush.

The juror: That's right, too.

Calkins: Now as to the evidence. No one on his way home to celebrate his baby's birthday, and had just bought him a toy at the Five & Ten, would have selected that moment to kill a man. They never even tried to pin the gun on him. If it was his, why didn't they prove it? What's the detective bureau for anyhow? They had ten thousand cops and no need to hurry. The fellow who killed Kelly made his get-away up the alley and threw the gun away.

A juror: You said a mouthful.

A juror: Let's take another ballot.

Foreman (disgustedly): Seven for conviction—five for not guilty.

Loud argument followed amid cries of "Aw, hell!" "You're the nuts!"—"No such evidence!" "That's a goddam lie!"— "Bugs!" "You're kidding yourself!"—"You're crazy!"

Foreman: Now look here, you guys, we swore to find a true verdict on the evidence.

Calkins: But the Judge and District Attorney are under oath to uphold the Constitution and the Bill of Rights. If they don't, that releases us. They can't force us to be parties to a miscarriage of justice.

A juror: I agree with Mr. Calkins. We're here to see that the defendant gets a fair trial.

Foreman: But the Judge decides whether the trial is fair or not.

A juror: Not much he don't! We do.

Calkins: I tell you we were under pressure from the moment the trial started. Look at the tactics O'Brien used in cross-examining Zalinski. There's nothing he wouldn't do to get a conviction.

A juror: He's a louse, all right.

A juror: I'll change my vote. I'm for acquittal.

Another juror: So am I.

Another juror: That makes it ten to two. Say Joe, if you'll vote to acquit, I will. No use staying here all night.

A juror: That leaves only one. How about it, Old Socks?

Last juror: Oh, well, if you all feel that way.

The jurors (variously): All up! Seventh inning!—Put your coats on!

After the jury had acquitted, I was arraigned at the bar, and Judge Babcock fined me five hundred dollars for contempt of court—the exact amount allowed me by the State for my services. *"Fiat justitia ruat coelum!"*

XI

THE HIGHER LAW

I F one has the right to defy the law when it is but a cloak for tyranny, is this not also true when it runs counter to one's moral principles?

Among our clients was a Miss Althea Beekman, an elderly lady who devoted her life to good works and whose family numbered among its members many famous divines and jurists as well as a Signer of the Declaration of Independence. One day she came into my office in a highly indignant state. A young girl with a tendency towards kleptomania named Katherine Holahan, in whom she was interested, had been arrested for shoplifting and indicted for grand larceny. Miss Beekman had gone at once to visit her in the Tombs where under the assurance of secrecy the girl had confessed her guilt.

The case was a pitiful one, for should she be sent to a reformatory her life would doubtless be hopelessly wrecked. Nevertheless, the agent of the department store where she had been picked up was determined that she be convicted, and the assistant district attorney was anxious to keep his good will. But the evidence was slim, and hearing that Miss Beekman had had a talk with the defendant the assistant sent for her and, after beating about the bush, ended by asking her to tell him what Katy had said. This the outraged lady had refused to do. Now she had been subpoenaed to appear next day as a witness in the General Sessions. What should she do?

"You'll have to go, Miss Beekman," I said. "And if called as a witness, you'll have to take the stand. You will be put on oath to tell the truth, the whole truth and nothing but the truth."

"Suppose they ask me what Katy said and I refuse to tell them?"

"They can lock you up."

Miss Beekman compressed her lips.

"Let them try!" she answered!

The following morning Katy Holahan was brought to the bar, and the evidence against her—legally insufficient—was introduced by the prosecutor. Unless he could furnish more the judge would be obliged to direct a verdict of acquittal.

"Althea Beekman," he called. "Kindly take the stand."

Miss Beekman arose, walked composedly to the witness chair and bowed to the bench. I have always liked old women, but this one inspired my admiration.

"I do not wish to testify against this defendant," she said with the dignity befitting her long line of distinguished forebears.

"I am sorry but your wishes cannot be allowed to control this proceeding," replied the Judge. "Let the witness be sworn."

"Do you swear to tell the truth, the whole truth and nothing but the truth?" intoned the clerk.

"I do—if I tell anything," she replied defiantly.

It was not a proper answer, but His Honor let it pass. Better wait and see what developed.

"Miss Beekman," said the District Attorney, "did you have a conversation with Kate Holahan, the defendant, on Friday of last week?"

"I did."

"Kindly tell His Honor and the jury what it was."

Miss Beekman looked at the judge.

"I promised Miss Holahan not to divulge anything she told me. What she said was in confidence."

The Judge smiled with a certain condescension.

"The law," he explained, "recognizes as privileged only confidential communications between husband and wife or such as are made to a physician, to an attorney or to a clergyman in his professional capacity—nothing else."

"But I gave her my word!"

"I absolve you from the obligation of secrecy."

Miss Beekman stared at him.

"*You* absolve me!"

"Yes, I—as the representative of the law."

"Surely the law, which I have always been taught to respect, does not demand that I break my word!"

His Honor did not reply.

"Answer the question!" he directed. Miss Beekman's blue blood turned to scarlet in her cheeks.

"My conscience will not permit me to betray a confidence!" she informed him.

"But I instruct you to answer!"

There was no reply. The wheels of justice hung on dead center.

"Miss Beekman," said the Judge, "as a loyal citizen of the State of New York, having due regard for its institutions and its statutes, you cannot be allowed to set up your own ideas of what the law might or, from your point of view, ought to be in defiance of the law as it stands. You are not responsible for our statutes. Neither are you responsible in any way for the consequences to this defendant of your testimony. The matter is out of your hands. I order you to answer. If you refuse I shall be obliged to take steps to compel you to do so."

"I am sorry," she replied, "but my own self-respect will not permit me to answer."

"In that case I shall be obliged to commit you for contempt."

Miss Beekman drew herself up stiffly.

"Very well. Do your duty as your own conscience and sense of honor demand."

His Honor twisted uneasily. He had no wish to figure as a Jeffreys:

"Look here, Miss Beekman," he said bending towards her and lowering his voice. "Don't you see that, if the law permitted any discretion on the part of witnesses as to what they would and would not say, the most atrocious crimes would go unpunished? Its requirements are merely for the good of society. Please answer the question."

But Miss Beekman's dander was up.

"I shall not change my mind," she retorted. "You can do anything you like with me, but it will make no difference. I refuse to answer the question."

This time His Honor lost all patience.

"Do you understand that you are in contempt of this court?" he cried. "Do you intend to show contempt for this court?"

"On the contrary," she retorted, "I'm doing my best to conceal it!"

Someone in the rear of the courtroom clapped his hands and the officer pounded for silence. The Judge beckoned to the District Attorney and the two conferred. Obviously the old girl ought to be sent to jail, but you couldn't send a woman to jail who had given away three million dollars and founded a home for friendless girls.

"The witness stands committed for contempt," said the Judge shortly. "I fine you two hundred and fifty dollars."

Miss Beekman removed a roll of bills from her bag, counted off two hundred and fifty dollars and laid it on the edge of the dais.

"If this is contempt," she remarked disdainfully, "make the most of it!"

There is more behind this incident than may at first meet the eye. Law and honor are no more nearly related to one another than are law and justice. They are but distant cousins stemming from different ancestors and connected only by marriage. Law is the creation of man, while conscience is assumed to be implanted in us by the Creator. While the state naturally cannot tolerate an appeal to any other authority, this does not excuse the individual for abandoning his own inner standards of what is right and wrong. This is the problem of the conscientious objector. "Render unto Caesar the things that are Caesar's, but to God the things that are God's."

The antiquity of the law, the enormous power behind it, and the great reverence in which it is held have resulted in the supposition that it is a substitute for morals and the equivalent of justice. When it came into being there was no such thing as ethics.

but only brute force. Its sole purpose was to make people behave themselves quietly enough to live together in reasonable harmony. In general, except where possible disorder was involved, it has not primarily concerned itself with morality, which has been left to the church and to the home. The result is that the law, since it does not pretend to tell us what we ought to do, but only what we must not do, is no adequate guide to conduct. To be a good citizen it is not enough simply to obey the letter of the statutes, for these merely set a minimum standard of decency. Some of the most despicable things a man can do are not crimes at all. The law usually deals only with acts and rarely with omissions. Thus, you can sit still and allow a child to be run over by a motor car, or a blind man to stumble over a cliff, or a woman to drown, when by stretching out your hand you could have saved any one of them, and still be guiltless before the law.

Conversely there is no sanctity in a law just because a legislature has enacted it. No State legislature—even the Congress of the United States—is either inspired or inevitably righteous in its edicts, which are often passed for selfish ends. The worst dictators accomplish their most barbaric purposes under cover of law. Even Hitler is meticulous about the "legality" of everything he does. There is nothing sacred in the legal process or in a law merely as such. A law may be morally right or quite the opposite, and what is right each individual must decide for himself. One's private honor is in one's own keeping.*

The conflict between law and morals often places the lawyer in an ambiguous position. He may well have to elect between retaining his client and his self-respect. Supposedly high-minded advice—like the loan in old Polonius' speech in *Hamlet*—"oft loses both itself and friend." Also it may turn out to be wrong!

Although the counsel I gave my clients was often based quite as much upon ethics as upon law, I cannot claim that it was al-

* "The Court can't determine what is honor," Chief Baron Bowes, 1743.
"I know what my code of honor is, my lord, and I intend to adhere to it," John O'Conner, in the Parnell Proceedings.

ways justified by the result. A young man, Payson Clifford, Jr.,
called upon me one evening about the will of his father, who
had left him his entire estate amounting to $25,000. A few
months after I had drawn the will, the testator, who was a
widower, had asked me to place an envelope with it. I had done
so under the impression that it was merely an inventory, but the
document having been opened, the envelope was found to contain an undated slip, reading: "In case of my sudden death I wish
my executor to give $25,000 to my very dear friend Sadie Burch
of Hoboken, N. J.—Payson Clifford." The son was both executor
and residuary legatee, and the paper not being attested had no
legal validity. If he carried out his father's legally inadequate
instructions, there would be nothing left for himself.

At first Payson Clifford, Jr., was disinclined to obey his
father's direction, on the ground that, had the latter really
wanted his friend Miss Burch to have his entire estate, he would
have, or at least should have, executed a proper instrument to
that effect. Moreover, he suspected that Miss Burch might be a
lady of doubtful virtue who would waste the money in riotous
living. The direction seemed unjust, unwise, at best the result of
momentary impulse or possibly the fear of blackmail.

I can see the youth now as he sat there opposite me, his forehead wrinkled, his straw-colored hair in disarray, his face pale
and distressed, debating the question from every angle. Common
sense seemed to justify his doing nothing about that miserable
slip of paper. But suppose his father had really wanted Miss
Burch to have the money? If ever a nice young fellow found himself on the spot it was Payson Clifford, Jr., and he wanted my
advice not as a client but as a man.

In spite of the danger inherent in attempting to mix law and
morals, this seemed an excellent chance to stress the duty of
filial piety. So I opened a bottle of Burgundy and delivered a
lecture on honor as opposed to statute. Perhaps I was too eloquent. But I took it upon myself to point out to him that, had his
father made a similar request orally on his deathbed, he would

undoubtedly have respected it, and finally—after a second bottle—he decided to carry out the supposed parental wishes even though it left him penniless. That night I made a prayer of thanks for Payson Clifford, Jr.

Sadie Burch proved a curiously elusive person. There were no Burches in the directory or telephone book, and no response came to my advertisements in the newspapers. At length after three months had passed I received a letter from a small town in central New Jersey, saying that she had just learned that she was an object of my professional interest, but regretting her inability to come to the city. So I took the train to Newark, hired a motor and drove eight miles into the country to a small farmhouse where I found a kindly-faced, white haired woman knitting a baby-jacket on the piazza. When I told her that Payson Clifford, Sr., was dead the tears came into her faded blue eyes and she fumbled for her handkerchief.

"Mr. Clifford was the best friend I ever had except my husband," she said. "If it hadn't been for him, I don't know what would have become of me. Now that John is gone and I'm all alone in the world, this little place with the flowers and the bees is all I've got."

"No," I said. "It isn't all. Mr. Clifford left a letter in his will instructing his son to pay you twenty-five thousand dollars. I have a check for it here in my pocket."

A puzzled look came over her face. Then she shook her head.

"That was just like him," she said. "But it's all a mistake. He paid me back that money over a year ago. You see, he persuaded John to go into some kind of business scheme with him and they lost all they put into it—twenty-five thousand dollars apiece. It was all we had, and after John died, Mr. Clifford, although it wasn't his fault, insisted on giving me back the money. He must have written the letter before he did so and forgotten all about it."

I had discovered three good people—Payson Clifford, Jr., Payson Clifford, Sr., and Sadie Burch; but I should not have known about the last had I not given the first some rather bad advice. That it was exactly such I now see. The son's argument to the effect that, had his father expected him to carry out so important a direction, he would have incorporated it in his will, and not left him in doubt as to its validity had been sound. Since I personally knew that Mr. Clifford had placed the envelope with the will after its execution, I was doubtless justified in advising his son that loyalty required that the matter be looked into. But suppose, as occurred in another case in my office, a similar paper, also undated, had been found loose in the testator's general files, so that no one could tell or even guess when, or under what circumstances, he had written it? Or suppose Miss Burch had not been the honest woman that she was?

There are countless similar situations, each posing its own ethical problem. Young Mr. Clifford's high-mindedness is in marked contrast with the conduct of families who suppress wills, prejudicial to their interest, which happen to be in their possession. I have known of several such criminal acts and suspected many more. Many an old lady, who has left the major part of her property to persons other than her immediate next of kin, while trustingly retaining the document in her cupboard to which the latter had access, must have turned in her grave at its unaccountable disappearance. I have even heard of supposedly reputable people, who did not scruple to erase damaging annotations in a will showing the testator to have changed his mind since making it, or even to "strengthen the signature" by an artistic touch, on the theory that they were "merely guiding the testator's hand" —although doing so after his death.

Anyhow Payson Clifford, Jr., is one of my pleasant memories, even if I did rather unwisely presume to direct his conscience.

The ideas of gentlemen and sportsmen as to what is right and fair, or—if one prefers to put it that way—as to what "is done" or "isn't done," have not changed since Fabius Tullius caught snipe in the Pontine marshes. Of course, if a man holds you at arm's length, and is obviously conducting a transaction from a strictly legal aspect, including the requirements of the Statute of Frauds, etc., he has a right to claim that by mutual consent any other standard than that of technical legality has been waived between you. Yet such is rarely the situation among plain people, who usually do not know what is legally binding and what is not.

"*Caveat emptor*" is a time-honored legal doctrine, meaning "let the buyer beware." The attitude of the law seems to be that a purchaser ought to conduct himself in general on the theory that all men are at least moderate liars. But an honorable man does not lie; and he keeps his word irrespective of the consequences to himself. Despite the presence or absence of what is called "a legal consideration" a promise is a promise and if relied upon in good faith should be honored in spirit as well as in letter.

If one makes a definite verbal agreement with another to sell him a piece of land at a given price, everything being above board, the fact that the contract is not in writing and duly acknowledged, or in some other manner technically defective, should not excuse either from the obligation of carrying it out. Contrariwise, where a contract has been induced by false representations the maker should be no more bound to respect it than if it had been extorted by force, and he is justified in doing his best to get out of it.

I had such a case during the early years of Wiegand & Tutt while vacationing in Pottsville.

An elderly widow, by the name of Mrs. Clara Pulaski, had found among her husband's effects a deed for some oil land in Texas which he had bought as a speculation many years before. The territory was remote, no oil had been found in the neighborhood up to the time of his death, and it was assessed at practically nothing. One day a well-mannered stranger, calling himself Dr. Rufus M. Blake, drew up at the Pulaski farmhouse and stated that he was a cattleman buying up Texas property for a range. He offered her fifty dollars for an option on her land at $5,000 to be exercised within six months. She asked him if any oil had been struck in that part of Texas and he assured her that any day-dream about oil in that part of the State had long since evaporated. Five thousand dollars was like a million to Mrs. Pulaski, and the fifty she received for signing her option like finding money. In point of fact oil had already been struck in the neighborhood and shortly after signing the option she received an offer of $20,000 for the property. Then a gusher was brought in a hundred and fifty feet just beyond her boundary line and she had another offer for $250,000.

At this point Doctor Blake, who had been gallivanting round the State looking for suckers, turned up to exercise his option which would expire at noon on June 6, 1923. Mrs. Pulaski came to the Phoenix Hotel where I was staying and tearfully inquired what she could do. I examined the option and, finding that it was iron-clad, advised her that she would have no choice but to deed over the property in receipt of the purchase price. Blake had retained Hezekiah Mason to prepare the papers and handle the title clearing which was to take place at the Pulaski farmhouse, and on Saturday we all drove out there together, arriving a little after ten o'clock.

According to my instructions the old lady apologized for appearing in her everyday working clothes and offered us a large decanter full of elderberry wine. I lit a stogy, spread the deed upon the table, adjusted my spectacles, and studied it minutely. This took about ten minutes, during which Squire Mason and his client emptied most of the decanter.

"Well," I said finally, "the deed seems to be in proper form— how about payment?"

Doctor Blake took from his wallet a certified check for $5,000 drawn on the Pottsville National Bank to his own order.

"There you are!" he said.

"I'm sorry," I replied. "The option calls for cash. The easiest thing for us to do is to take Mrs. Pulaski down to Squire Mason's office and, while she is signing and acknowledging the deed, you can go across to the bank and turn the check into money."

It was now nearly eleven o'clock and by the time Mrs. Pulaski had changed her dress and we had reached Pottsville it was twenty-five minutes to twelve. Doctor Blake stopped off at the bank and a couple of minutes later joined us in Mason's office with a package of fifty of the one hundred dollar bank notes then in general circulation issued by the National City Bank of New York.

"Here's your money," he said tossing them over to me.

I counted them carefully.

"National bank notes," I remarked, "are legal tender only for obligations owed to and payments due from the United States Government. I cannot accept them. My client will lose a fortune if this option is taken up. I insist on legal payment. If you want to make a legal tender with national bank notes that's up to you."

Seventeen minutes to twelve!

"What is legal tender, anyhow?" demanded Blake of Mason. "You're a lawyer. You ought to know."

The Squire squirmed uneasily in his chair.

"I ain't on to all the catches and fine points about bank notes," he evaded, "but United States gold certificates and Treasury notes—or some of 'em anyhow—must be legal tender. You better go over and get either gold or gold certificates."

Doctor Blake hurriedly departed, returning at the end of ten minutes with a canvas bag in one hand and a linen one in the other.

"They haven't got any gold certificates," he said looking at me suspiciously. "Someone drew out all they had this morning. But—" he added in triumph, placing the canvas bag in front of me, "here's five thousand in gold bullion. I guess that'll fix it."

"Perhaps," I said. "Is that your tender on Mrs. Pulaski's option?"

"You bet your life!" he grinned, "and just to hedge against any more of your technicalities here's this for good measure. I took all the cash they had in the drawer."

Just at that moment the noon whistle on Sampson's lumber mill blew.

"You ran it pretty close, Doctor," I said. "Although I haven't counted it, if there is five thousand dollars here in legal tender of the United States I shall have to direct my client, Mrs. Pulaski, to execute the deed. Now that the time for executing the option has expired, we can proceed more leisurely."

I poured out the hoard of gold.

"Here are five thousand dollars in gold coin of the United States," I said, having counted it, "but these gold pieces are not legal tender 'if below the standard weight and limit of tolerance provided by law for the single piece,' and—'when reduced in weight below such standard and tolerance—are only legal tender at valuation in proportion to their actual weight'—that value being figured according to law at 25.8 grains to the dollar."

"Do you mean you're goin' to weigh it?" sneered Mason.

"Surely," I said. "I am going to ask Mr. McLaurin, the jeweler, to bring his scales over here."

Twenty minutes later, the weighing completed, Mr. McLaurin after some elaborate calculations declared the total weight of the gold pieces to be nearly twenty-five hundred grams less than "standard weight and limit of tolerance" and hence, owing to abrasion, a little over a hundred dollars short of five thousand dollars.

"That's all right!" said Blake. "Here's more than enough to make it up—all the cash in the till."

He emptied the contents of the linen sack in a huge mound of coin which I separated into stacks of twenty-three silver dollars, thirty-eight in halves, thirty-four in quarters, twenty-one dollars in dimes, twelve dollars and a half in nickels, and forty-nine coppers—in all one hundred and ten dollars and ninety-nine cents.

Then I took down Mason's copy of the "Code of Laws of the United States" and turned to Title 1, "Money and Finance"; Chapter 9, "Legal Tender"; Sections 451 to 461.

"This miscellaneous collection of chicken feed," I declared, "represents only thirty-three dollars and twenty-four cents in legal tender. The twenty-three silver dollars are good as such under Section 458; but, under Section 459—entitled 'Subsidiary Silver Coins—smaller denominations than one dollar can be used only to the amount of ten dollars; and as to the rest, according to Section 490, 'the minor coins of the United States shall be a legal tender at their nominal value for any amount not exceeding twenty-five cents in any one payment. Thus, you see, you are short on your whole amount by at least seventy-seven dollars and seventy-four cents."

Doctor Blake turned furiously on the unfortunate Squire.

"You're a hell of a lawyer not to know what's legal tender," he snarled. "Your ignorance is going to cost me half a million dollars!"

"Let's hope it will mean that much to Mrs. Pulaski!" I smiled.

My perhaps surprising knowledge of this esoteric subject was due to the fact that John H. Mackay, the father of my friend, Clarence H. Mackay, had several years before acquired "Harbor Hill," a baronial estate at Roslyn, Long Island, under somewhat similar circumstances. The original owners, having given an option of purchase expiring at noon on a certain day to a Mr. X, had meanwhile received a vastly higher offer from Mr. Mackay. On the closing day Mr. X, the holder of the option, attempted to take it up by presenting a check drawn on State banking funds and certified by the Treasurer of the State of New York. This was refused as not a good legal tender. There was no time to make another and Mr. Mackay secured the property. How many of my readers know what is legal tender today in the United States?

As it turned out, my adventures with Doctor Blake were not yet over. I have, in an earlier part of these reminiscences, told of the action which as a young lawyer I successfully brought against the Rev. Drum in behalf of Ma Best's father, old Cap Barrows, for false arrest. Cap, now over ninety, was still alive, although quite balmy. He hung about the Phoenix House, rambling on to all who cared to listen about his financial career during which, he asserted, he had been hand in glove with J. Pierpont Morgan, John W. Gates, John D. Rockefeller, and other magnates. Doc had never been quite right in the upper story but, like many others who were, saw no reason why he should not, in the fashion then prevalent, become a multi-millionaire through the "development" of properties and the flotation of "securities." He had spent a year or so in Sing Sing, to which he had gone protesting that the bonds which he had unloaded upon the horny-handed yokels of Somerset County were perfectly good—or would be in time if the holders would only have patience; and that the legal mistakes made in regard to them by the courts would eventually be rectified. If he had had any knowledge that what he had done was wrong, it was certainly only what Doctor Hunziger had so aptly termed an "insane knowledge."

Cap had always been grateful to me for my defense of his character and one day, during my visit to Pottsville, took me into the Phoenix House attic and showed me a dusty, cobweb-covered, dress suit case, concealed behind a pile of lumber and filled nearly to bursting with the ostensible obligations of various corporations. Dumping them out on a square of sunlight under the dirt-encrusted window, he said:

"These are my jewels! There's millions represented here!" He lifted one tenderly and held it to the light, fresh as it came from the engraver's press—a $1,000 first mortgage bond of The Chicago Water Front & Terminal Co. "Look at that! Good as gold—if the courts only knew the law."

On the back of one of these valueless obligations was depicted an old-fashioned locomotive, from whose bell-shaped funnel the smoke poured in picturesque black clouds, dragging behind it a chain of funny little passenger coaches and driving furiously through fields rich with corn and wheat amid a border of dollar signs.

"The Great Lakes & Canadian Southern," he crooned lovingly. "The child of my heart! The district attorney kept all the rest—as evidence, as he claimed, but some day you'll see he'll bring an action against The Lake Shore or the New York Central based on these bonds. Yes, sir. They're all right."

He pawed them over, picking out favorites here and there and excitedly extolling the merits of the imaginary properties they represented. There were the repudiated bonds of Southern States and municipalities; of railroads upon whose tracks no wheel had ever turned; of factories never built except in Cap's addled brain; of companies which had defaulted and given stock for their worthless obligations; certificates of oil, mining and land companies; deeds to tracts now covered with skyscrapers in Pittsburgh, St. Louis and New York—each and every one of them not worth the paper they were printed on except to some crook who dealt in high finance. But they were exquisitely engraved, quite lovely to look at, and Cap gloated upon them with scintillating eyes.

"Ain't they beauties?" he sighed. "Some day—yes, sir!—some day they'll be worth real money. I paid it for 'em. But they're yours—all yours!"

He gathered them up with care and returned them to the suit case, then fastened the clasp and patted it with his hand.

"They are yours, sir!" he exclaimed dramatically. "They're no good to me now and I want you to take them as your fee in that case you won for me against Drum. I never paid you, you know."

I confess I wasn't quite sure in my own mind whether Cap was merely desirous of showing his good will or in fact a bit anxious lest, if the bonds were discovered, he might land again in the hoosegow. At any rate, thinking that they were better out of his hands, I took them down to my room and locked them in the closet.

It transpired that Somerset County had proved a happy hunting ground for Doctor Blake, for he and a well organized band of salesmen, assisted by a "dowser" who claimed that he could detect the presence of oil by means of a willow wand, had been distributing worthless oil stock by hundreds of thousands of shares, which were paying—for the time being and so long as the harvest was still in progress—twenty per cent dividends out of the new money taken in. The gang had offices in Albany, Binghamton, Buffalo, Utica and New York City.

One day, shortly after I had rescued Mrs. Pulaski from Blake's clutches, a Miss Wheeler called at the Phoenix House and asked to see me. She had been born in Pottsville seventy years before and, after working most of her life as a trained nurse, had invested her savings amounting to $20,000 in government bonds. Before leaving New York City she had fallen into the clutches of Doctor Blake, who had pointed out to her the advantage of owning oil stock which paid twenty per cent over United States securities paying only two and a half, offering to sell her three hundred and thirty thousand shares of the capital stock of the Great Geyser Texas Petroleum & Llano Estacado Land Company for twenty thousand dollars and personally to guarantee her four thousand dollars per year in dividends for five years. Thus, he said, she could not lose, but on the other hand when the stock went up, as it was bound to do, would reap a fortune. Miss Wheeler had fallen for the scheme, but instead of handing over her bonds in exchange for the stock she fortunately had taken them to her bank and used them as collateral for a loan at five per cent. In this way, she figured, she would net $3,500 per year and still have her securities.

While visiting in Pottsville she had heard of the Pulaski affair and Doctor Blake's part in it; and realizing that she was in the hands of crooks she had come to me for advice. Now it happened that the printed prospectus of the Great Geyser Petroleum listed among its assets the land belonging to Mrs. Pulaski on which it had only an option. This would probably not, in itself, have been enough upon which to base criminal proceedings against Blake but it showed the unscrupulous character of those behind the scheme and enabled me to point out to Miss Wheeler that she had thrown away her money. It was a peculiarly outrageous case, for she who had given her entire life to the service of others, had been unusually gullible. A mere glance at the spiritual expression of her delicate features would have convinced anyone of her unworldliness. It was this fact that enabled me in the end to rescue her, since she was able to play the part I assigned to her without arousing the slightest suspicion on Blake's part. Indeed, I felt there was a poetic justice in utilizing what had been her undoing as a lure for her deceiver.

"E. J. Blake & Co., Investment Securities," occupied a gilt-edged office just opposite J. P. Morgan & Co., but its appearance was deceitful. It was merely a den of thieves. I carefully instructed Miss Wheeler what to do and after a little hesitation she agreed. This was to call on Doctor Blake and tell him that she was so much pleased with the returns from her investment that she wished to hand over to him all the securities she possessed, in order that he might sell them and put the proceeds into more stock of the Great Geyser. She was to explain to him about her $20,000 note at the bank and how she would have to pay it off in order to release her collateral. I figured, correctly as it turned out, that he would be anxious to get his hands on the securities themselves by advancing her the necessary funds to liquidate her obligation. I had her sign a written order on the bank instructing it to deliver to Blake, if and when he should pay the note, all her securities, of whatever kind and amount, deposited as collateral.

There was where Cap Barrows' crisp new bonds came into play, and I made up a bundle of about $100,000 in securities out of his hoard. There were ten of the beautiful bonds of the Great Lakes & Canadian Southern Railroad Co. with their miniature locomotives and fields of wheat, and ten equally lovely bits of engraving belonging to the defunct Bluff Creek and Iowa Central, ten more superb lithographs issued by the Mohawk & Housatonic in 1867 and paid off in 1882, and a variety of gorgeous chromos of Indians and buffaloes, of factories and steamships spouting clouds of soft coal smoke; and on the top of all was a pile of the First Mortgage Gold Six Per Cent obligations of the Chicago

Water Front & Terminal Co.—all of them crisp and fresh, with that faintly acrid smell which though not agreeable to the nostrils nevertheless delights the banker's soul.

Then I took Miss Wheeler over to see Tom McKeever, the loan clerk of the Omega Trust Co. who happened to be a member of my Saturday Evening poker club. I told him that my client wished to sell the $20,000 government bonds now serving as collateral and offered personally to endorse her note in their stead. To this he readily agreed. I then said that she had a lot of other securities with her, most of them of little or no value, which he might as well have for what they might be worth as security in addition to my endorsement and he accordingly placed them with the note.

An hour later Miss Wheeler called on Doctor Blake. At first he imagined that she was dissatisfied with her investment in Great Geyser, but when he discovered the pretended object of her visit he beamed with pleasure.

"I just thought," she said timidly, "that if I could only have my note paid off at the Trust Company I'd get you to sell the collateral and invest the proceeds in your gusher."

"What you ask is rather unusual," returned Blake, "but I think I can manage it for you."

Accordingly he called up the Omega Trust and spoke to McKeever.

"I understand you hold Miss Edna Wheeler's note for $20,000. May I ask if it is secured?"

"Who is this?" inquired McKeever.

"One of her friends," replied Blake amiably.

"We don't discuss our clients' affairs over the telephone. You had better come in here if you have any inquiries to make."

"But I want to pay the note," explained Blake. "In that case I suppose you'd turn over whatever collateral is on deposit?"

"If we were so directed."

"May I ask what collateral there is?"

"I don't know."

"Well, I have an order from Miss Wheeler directing you on my payment of the note to deliver to me whatever securities are now deposited as collateral."

"In that case you'll get 'em," said McKeever gruffly. "I'll have 'em ready for you."

Ten minutes later Doctor Blake handed his certified check for $20,000 to McKeever and received from him the bundle of beautifully engraved securities I had selected from those given me by Cap Barrows. Then he hurried back to his office, spread them out on his desk, and with gloating eyes was counting them as I came in.

"Miss Wheeler has changed her mind," I said. "She does not want you to sell her securities."

"Oh, doesn't she?" he retorted. "Well, you're too late. I've paid her note and I'm going to carry out the rest of our agreement."

"And put her money into your bogus oil company?" I taunted him.

"I stand on my rights!" he asserted. "Anyhow I can legally sell enough of these securities to pay myself back my twenty thousand dollars."

"And then steal the rest?"

"I've got her written order. She can't go back on it now. I've got these bonds and I'm going to dispose of them."

"You will do so at your own risk," I said taking twenty one-thousand dollar bills from my pocket. "On behalf of Miss Wheeler I make you a legal tender of the twenty thousand dollars you have just paid to cancel her note and I demand the return of her securities. Incidentally, I beg to inform you that they're not worth the paper they're printed on."

"Indeed!" he sneered. "Well, my good friend, you can keep the money, and I'll keep the bonds."

I put the bills back in my pocket.

"You absolutely decline to give up the securities?"

"Absolutely and finally!" he mocked me.

"Well, have it your own way," I sighed. "If you dig through that junk you'll find Miss Wheeler's certificate of stock in your gusher for 330,000 shares properly endorsed for transfer. Maybe you can use it on someone else. Anyhow, she's about $4,000 to the good. It isn't every sucker who can collect twenty per cent and then get his money back in full."

Then I hastily withdrew.

XII

I JOIN THE ARMY

MY worry about the due administration of the laws was temporarily superseded by the cataclysm in Europe. At first it seemed a long way off, an unfortunate flare-up which would probably be over in a few weeks. Anyhow, it wasn't our funeral. Then one August morning Dick Davis, who was just back from Mexico, called me on the telephone and said: "Well Eph I'm off for the front—sailing tonight on the Lusitania."

At last I realized that there was a real war.

Dick wrote me from London that the State Department had refused to accredit him to Kitchener's army and had given the only American place to Fred Palmer, but that he was going to try to get along on his regular passport. The next I heard of him was when I read his classic description of the entrance of the German army into Brussels. His account of that never-ending gray tide pouring through the city sent shivers down my back. "All through the night, like a tumult of a river when it races between the cliffs of a canyon, in my sleep I could hear the steady roar of the passing army. And when early in the morning I went to the window the chain of steel was still unbroken. . . . For three days and three nights the column of gray, with hundreds of thousands of bayonets and hundreds of thousands of lances, with gray transport wagons, gray ammunition carts, gray ambulances, gray cannon, like a river of steel, cut Brussels in two. . . ."

He ended with the prophetic words:

"It is, perhaps, the most efficient organization of modern times; and its purpose only is death. Those who cast it loose upon Europe are military-mad. And they are only a small part of the German people. But to preserve their class they have in their own image created this terrible engine of destruction. For the present it is their servant. But this monster to which they gave life may turn and rend them." Arno Dosch-Fleurot called it the finest piece of reporting of the war, a picture of "imperialism itself coming down the road."

A few days later having no proper papers he was arrested by the Germans near Enghein and nearly shot as a spy. He talked himself free—to return to Brussels on foot, and after many hazards reached that city in safety. He knew now first hand the risks he ran without credentials, but he wasn't the man to turn back and after another futile attempt in London to receive an appointment as a correspondent with the British he left England for Paris where he was persecuted and harrassed by the French, until finding his efforts useless he returned in September to the United States to write his book *With the Allies* urging America to prepare.

Dick was fifty-one years old, but in August 1915 he enlisted in the business men's camp at Plattsburg where in spite of the warning pains around his heart, he participated in gruelling marches with men just out of college, which undoubtedly hastened his end.

On April 11, 1916 at his home in Mt. Kisco, New York, having just finished an article on preparedness, he left his desk to make a telephone call and dropped dead. He had given his life for his country.

But the United States were not in the war, and it seemed unlikely that we should be. President Wilson's chief interest was in domestic affairs and even Colonel House could not get him to give much attention to the European crisis. He was earnestly sincere in his insistence upon American neutrality; so also at first was Theodore Roosevelt.* The country in general took the position that the war was none of our business, and this continued to be so for a far longer period than is today realized. Even the torpedoing of the Lusitania on May 7, 1915, with a loss of 1,198

---

* Roosevelt wrote in the *Outlook* of September 23, 1914: "We should remain entirely neutral and nothing but urgent need would warrant breaking our neutrality and taking sides one way or the other."

lives, including 63 infants and children, did not instantly arouse the nation. Personally I was anxious that we should declare war at once, but this was by no means the universal attitude. I can perfectly well recall that many people asked: "Well, why did they sail on her? They had due warning," or "The Germans had a right to sink her. She was carrying contraband."

During that summer I was invited to lunch by a distinguished New York lawyer, William D. Guthrie, at his country place on Long Island. There were, if I remember correctly, eighteen gentlemen present, all members of the bar. The Lusitania incident was discussed from every angle and at the conclusion of the meal a vote was taken as to whether the United States should declare war. The vote was in the negative 16–2, the only votes in the affirmative being those of Frederic R. Coudert, Jr. and myself.

Wilson was re-elected President in November 1916 on the slogan "He kept us out of the war," but he could not write notes fast enough to keep ahead of events, and Germany having removed all restrictions from her submarines, he asked Congress on April 6, 1917, to recognize that a state of war did exist between the United States and Germany. Leaving Otto to run the office as best he could I went to Washington, offered my services to the government in whatever capacity I could be most useful and, receiving a commission in the Military Intelligence Division of the General Staff, became for the time being "Major" Ephraim Tutt.

I was first assigned to duty in the Counter Espionage Service, the offices of which were located in a rookery on "F" Street, and spent a few days in supervising the labors of a lot of young gentlemen engaged in looking up such pressingly vital matters as the birthrate in Patagonia or the annual increment of Peruvian guano. With Huns and Doughboys bayonetting one another at Chateau Thierry it seemed ironically trivial.

The only ray of sunshine on that dunghill of scheming and wire-pulling was the unexpected presence of Captain Franklin P. Adams (the "F.P.A." then of *The New York World,* now of "Information Please"), who was acting as personnel officer. We speedily discovered that we had many ideas in common.

"I'm going to get out of this hell-hole," I declared. "Even if I have to desert."

"Yeah?" he inquired cynically. "Try it!"

I did try it and managed—Heaven knows how!—to wangle a transfer to the War College where, in company with pot-bellied army relics and other nondescripts, I received instruction in the preparation of field orders, etc. We were divided into small staffs under a brigadier, on which each man was supposed to perform his predestined paper-work in transferring divisions out of the line into rest billets and moving up the relief into the trenches. *"Quarante hommes ou huit chevaux!"* God help any one who might have tried to act upon anything I ever concocted!

Came the armistice and the long wait to get one's release. F.P.A.'s colonel sent for him one day and instructed him to draw up a list of men for discharge.

"Do you mean that I have authority to decide what officers are to be relieved?"

"Exactly!"

"What I say is final?"

"Absolutely."

"Okay, sir," said Adams, saluting.

That afternoon he handed his colonel the list. The name of "Franklin P. Adams, Captain, M.I.D." led all the rest. The Colonel looked a bit startled, but Frank went.

I had enlisted at the eleventh hour and had no excuse for accelerating my release. I hung about for awhile in Washington, and then was transferred to New York. The great Red Scare was on and owing to seniority in rank I had nominal command of Counter Espionage, to the great disgruntlement of the young men who were enthusiastically compiling lists of Enemies of the Republic, including such names as Lillian P. Wald, Oswald Garrison Villard, Amos Pinchot and, I think, even Jane Addams. The whole thing struck me as a farce. When they finally tried to seize and lock up Carl Sandburg on his arrival from Europe because he had a few Russian photographs of prisoners in his bag, I decided that suspicion had better be tempered with common sense and ordered his release. My attitude occasioned such umbrage among the lower ranks of spur-wearers that I began to see a gleam of hope.

Among the most active of the witch hunters was Ralph Easely, head of the Civic Federation of Employers and Employed. He saw red whenever the word "socialist" was so much as mentioned. According to his ideas, apparently every professor who had the slightest intellectual leaning towards socialistic theory ought to be interned. Based upon this idiosyncrasy I conceived and hatched a brilliant plan. I called on Mr. Easely, ostensibly to go over a list of "suspects," at his office in the Metropolitan Tower. Having finished my nominal business I remarked casually:

"I don't see any point in making such a fuss over socialists. Every thinking man is something of a socialist."

His eyes glared.

"What!" he shouted.

Two days later I was invited to lunch at the Racquet & Tennis Club by a very polite and genteel lieutenant-colonel in a beautiful new khaki uniform. It was an expensive lunch clearly designed to ameliorate a supposedly heartrending blow.

"You'll no doubt be glad to hear, Major, that you're going to get your discharge day after tomorrow."

I concealed my exhilaration.

"Really, sir? Isn't my work satisfactory?"

"O, perfect—of course! Your name has been reached, that's all! Congratulations."

I heard later that Easely had kept the Washington wires hot, until assured that my dangerous person would be at once removed. I wonder they did not court-martial me!

I was out of uniform, but I returned to civilian life in a confused and cockeyed world. The United States, now the world's richest and most powerful nation—could have preempted the place formerly occupied by Great Britain, but we were uncertain as to what we wanted except that we did not want responsibility. International trade had been paralyzed; the old moralities had been shattered; the country was skeptical about the peace. There were strikes, and a Red Scare, and a sick man in the White House.

Then came the campaign of 1920. The Republican bosses, who did not want Hoover or Wood or Lowden in the White House, picked Warren Harding of Ohio as their candidate. They had selected Irvine L. Lenroot as his running mate, but the delegates revolted against Senatorial control and chose instead Calvin Coolidge, who had become a national figure owing to his handling of the Boston police strike. When Cox, the Democratic candidate, endorsed Wilson's League of Nations he handed Harding the presidency on a gold plate. The Ohio gang took over and the orgy began. Harding had promised the country normalcy—and it got, as someone has said, "sub-normalcy."

For some reason that I never understood—probably because of my friendship for T.R., Pinchot and Mark Sullivan—I was invited to attend a Republican jollification party at Atlantic City. On the train I found myself sitting in the parlor car beside Mrs. Douglas Robinson, the former President's sister, Corinne Roosevelt, who was enthusiastic over the result of the election and the return of the G.O.P. to power. That evening a great banquet was given at one of the hotels and nationally known orators vied with one another's effulgent prophesies over the good time to come. America would be a land flowing with milk, honey, and champagne—for all good Republicans. Nothing was left to the imagination. The Prohibition Amendment to the Constitution had already been adopted * yet a colored motion picture was thrown on a screen above the speaker's dais showing a table heavily laden with bottles of every sort of liquor at sight of which the revellers, already exhilarated, went completely wild. I became so utterly disgusted that I left the room, changed my clothes, and took a late train back to New York. I was afterwards informed

* Declared in effect Jan. 16, 1920.

that Mrs. Robinson had done the same thing. It was a foretaste
of the "Incredible Era," the speak-easy and the gangster. Warren
Harding, worn out by worry and apprehension, died August 2,
1923, seventeen months after his inauguration and Calvin Coolidge became automatically president of the United States for the
remainder of his term.

Cal was just the man for the moment—conservative, cautious,
thrifty, unemotional. The very contrast of his appearance with
that of his handsome predecessor was an asset. He might be a
colorless and negative sit-tight, but with his hatchet face and his
expression, as William Allen White described it, of "looking down
his nose to locate that evil smell which seemed forever to affront
him" he resembled a Puritan tithing man and the country felt
that a godly and righteous hand was at the helm. But while
the Harding Administration had left plenty of those evil smells
behind it, Cal, who did not give too much evidence of being
affronted, played safe and the people were content.*

Already, before his election as Harding's successor in 1924,
the Congressional Committee of Investigation of which Senator
Walsh was chairman had established the most scandalous corruption on the part of the dead president's group of personal
political appointees. It had shown that Albert B. Fall, his Secretary of the Interior, had secretly leased without competitive bidding the fabulously rich Naval oil reserve No. 3 at Teapot Dome
to Harry F. Sinclair's Mammoth Oil Company and the Elk Hill
Naval reserve No. 1 at Elk Hills to Edward F. Doheny's Pan-
American Company.

Theodore Roosevelt, Jr. was Assistant Secretary of the Navy
and his younger brother Archie, vice-president of a subsidiary
of Sinclair's oil company. I had kept up my intimacy with the
Roosevelt family after T.R.'s death in 1919. Ethel had married
Dr. Richard Derby, an old friend of mine, and was living near
Sagamore Hill at Oyster Bay. An added bond between us was the

* To those interested in this period I recommend the colorful survey *Only
Yesterday* by my brilliant young friend, Fred Allen. Harper & Bros., 1931.

fact that she and her husband had bought the top of a hill in Cavendish not far from Leeds, my birthplace, and spent as much time there as they could.

One night during the hearings of the Walsh Committee which was investigating Fall, my doorbell on West Twenty-Third Street rang and Archie Roosevelt came in with Gracie, his pretty young wife. They were both in a state of considerable excitement. Archie had resigned his position with Sinclair and Ted was urging him to go on the stand as a volunteer witness, but Archie thought it better to wait till he was called by the Senate Investigating Committee. Would I go along and act as his counsel?

"Sinclair's confidential secretary, A. D. Wahlberg, has been getting very uneasy, especially since Sinclair himself has skipped off to Europe. Now he admits that 'somebody might have lent Mr. Fall money' and that Sinclair paid the manager of Fall's ranch sixty-eight thousand dollars," Archie said.

"Fine!" I answered. "What's the matter with that? Go ahead and spill it."

"Don't you think I need counsel?" he asked.

"Counsel! What for?"

"Someone acting for Sinclair might try to mix me up or put me in a false position, and then all chance of clearing up this dirty mess would be lost."

"Archie," I said, "if you can't go back to Washington and tell your story by yourself, take Gracie along. She's counsel enough for anybody."

They left somewhat reassured. Next morning Archie appeared before the Committee, told his story and made the front page of all the papers.

The following day Mr. Wahlberg took the stand. He was very nervous and perspired freely. He declared that Archie had got it all wrong—absolutely all wrong. He hadn't so much as mentioned sixty-eight thousand dollars. Mr. Roosevelt had entirely misunderstood him.

Chairman Walsh wanted to know what he *had* said.

"I might have said 'six or eight *cows*,'" explained Mr. Wahlberg. "Mr. Roosevelt probably thought I said 'sixty-eight *thous*.' They sound very much alike."

Next day the following quatrain appeared in a Washington newspaper:

> "He thought he saw a little check
> Of many, many 'thous',—
> He looked again, and saw it was
> A half a dozen 'cows'.
> 'Poor thing,' he said, 'poor silly thing,
> You'll cause a lot of rows'."

Archie did not need counsel to pull him out of that one.

But the oil scandals were only part of Cal's heritage from the Harding Administration. Charles R. Forbes, in charge of the Veterans' Bureau, had cost the government over two million dollars in less than two years of graft and had landed in Leavenworth; Colonel T. W. Miller, the Alien Property Custodian, had allowed a claim of the American Metal Company after a man named Merton had paid John T. King, Republican National Committeeman from Connecticut $441,000 in bonds, of which $200,000 were turned over to Jesse Smith, Attorney General Harry M. Dougherty's Man Friday; while Mal S. Dougherty, his brother, had sold at least $40,000 of them and deposited $49,000 to Harry Dougherty's account. Miller received a sentence of eighteen months in prison. Gaston B. Means charged that as agent for the Ohio gang he had collected seven million dollars from bootleggers which he had turned over to Jesse Smith, who shortly committed suicide. Hardly less shocking had been Nan Britton's book *The President's Daughter,* dedicated to "unwedded mothers and to their innocent children whose fathers are not usually known to the world," with its convincing picture of shabby sexuality.

I have never been able to understand the complaisance with which the country as a whole accepted the proof of these scandals. That the Republican Party or its leaders should have done so I might possibly have anticipated after my trip to the jollification and victory celebration at Atlantic City, but why the American people did not rise in their wrath and "throw the rascals out" is beyond me. Why was the harshest criticism directed not against the offenders themselves but against those who insisted on bringing the facts to light? I suppose the reason was that the businessmen of the country who had voted for "normalcy" preferred not to disturb it. They wanted to be left alone and to have in office a president who would not "rock the boat." Coolidge was honest and circumspect, and there was no sense in weakening confidence in his party, so why dwell on the past? It was much better to make light of it.

The good ship *Status Quo* was on an even keel again. Public confidence in her sailing capacity returned, and with Coolidge's re-election financial depression turned to elation and an apparently inexhaustible flood of money began to pour into Wall Street. The "billionaire era" had arrived—the era of big, bigger and even "bigger business" that was not to end until 1929. There was a tremendous expansion of industry; mergers arose controlling entire industries; billions of dollars worth of new securities were floated; there were "five million share days" on the Stock Exchange. "Coolidge Economy" had developed the "Coolidge Boom," the most extravagant, wasteful and reckless period in United States history.

XIII

INNS (AND OUTS) OF COURT

THE boom was reflected in the law offices. The wheels of industry were whirring, the air by day was black with the smoke from factory chimneys and by night illuminated by the flare of blast furnaces. Our firm was overwhelmed with corporate business, and since Otto's specialty was that of a legal adviser and expert pleader it fell to my lot to act as a negotiator. This took me all over the United States. I reorganized mining companies in Montana, oil companies in Texas, lumber companies in Oregon, railroads in the east, and cotton mills in the south. I had never travelled extensively before and for the first time I was astounded at the magnitude of the country's resources. I enjoyed the beauty and grandeur of the natural scenery, my talks with men who were doing big things in a big way, the chance to be in the open air. It was good fun.

But once back in the office things were very different. The staff was run ragged and Otto had been obliged to engage half a dozen extra law clerks who worked from nine in the morning until midnight. Wiegand & Tutt had become almost as much of a law factory as Hotchkiss, Levy & Hogan. Gone were the quiet evenings in my library, gone my frequent vacations to the Mohawk Valley. No longer did I have time to attend the theatre or opera, to see my friends, or to take my customary evening strolls with the "C.J." There was always some conference of directors, or general managers, or minority stockholders which demanded my presence. I could not even sit in at the sessions of the Bible Class which had temporarily moved to the Players' Club. It is true that we made money, made it in fact hand over fist, but it did me no good. In fact I became so thin that Mandy despaired of my health.

And then I got a lucky break. Otto and I had been working for several years on a reorganization which involved the rights of English stockholders. A referee had been appointed, thousands of pages of testimony had been taken, and after long negotiations a famous banking house had agreed to underwrite the new issues of securities. We only needed the consent of a board of directors in London and this hung on the attitude of their solicitors, who although over a million pounds were involved seemed, to put it mildly, casual about the whole thing.

The name of the firm was Fortesque, Saddlecloth & Co., but it should have been Hesitation, Procrastination & Delay. While a rather delicate question of law was involved,* it was not a vital obstacle to an agreement; but they were forever "taking the opinion of counsel" and weeks would go by before they condescended to answer a letter. Had the parties been in New York we could have settled the whole thing by compromise in a couple of hours. The bankers, becoming impatient, were threatening to withdraw if the papers were not signed by the first of April. It was now the middle of March, but in spite of our frantic cables nothing happened.

I had handled the matter from the beginning, and was thoroughly familiar with all the details; Otto had a case to argue before the United States Supreme Court; so, although I could ill spare the time, it was decided that the quickest way to get action was for me to go to London. The *Mauritania* was sailing at one o'clock on a Monday morning, she would normally dock the following Friday. I had never been abroad and, whatever I may have since become, I was then—or fancied myself to be—an energetic, up-and-coming American lawyer, rather scornful of our stuffy transatlantic brethren of the bar and their dilatory ways. I could get in touch with our solicitors that afternoon, finish the whole business within a few days, and take the *Mauritania* on her return trip. At most three weeks would do the trick. So I adjourned all my cases under an iron-clad agreement to be back by April 8th.

Very agreeably, I found on board Tom Saltonstall, of the

* The proper construction of Skellings *vs.* Mainwaring, 18 L. J. Ch. 251, and whether in point.

Harvard class of '91, a fellow fishing enthusiast, who spent much of his time in England. The voyage was not unpleasant for that time of year, but I was chaffing to reach London, hurry through my business and get home again. Saltonstall said little, but I thought I perceived a cynical twinkle in his eye when I outlined my plans.

I spent my last evening on the *Mauritania* putting my papers in shape and going over the points of the Northwyn matter in order to be in readiness for the conference next day. Reaching London at half after three in the afternoon I was given rooms at the Berkeley Hotel overlooking, on one side, the broad sweep of Green Park and, upon the other, Devonshire House with the gardens behind it. The trim chambermaid who opened my bags lit the fire and brought tea as a matter of course. Five days before —it seemed at least six months!—at this same hour I had been dictating at my desk in New York. Lounging before the soft-coal blaze, smoking my stogy and sipping a cup of fragrant Ceylon in the misty sunshine I told myself that this was a very comfortable way to practice law.

But that reminded me. I must get in touch at once with our solicitors. Accordingly I began searching the telephone directory for Fortesque, Saddlecloth & Co.—Fortescu, Forteskew, Fortesque—there it was!—Fortesque, The Lord Wilfred of Farrony, no it wasn't—Fortesque & Sons, House-breakers—I laughed— Fortesque, Viscount of Saltair, no—yes—Fortesque, Saddlecloth & Co., Solicitors, 13 Paperweight Chambers, Sealingwax Lane, Dane Street—London Wall 4831.

Grudgingly I raised the rusty receiver to my ear. It was ice cold and gritty in my hand. Nothing happened. I pressed the hook up and down without response. I was about to replace it and go to the office to make a fuss when a beautifully modulated female voice asked politely:

"Are you there, sir?"

"Yes," I replied, "I'm here. I've been here some time. I want London Wall 4831."

"Very sorry, sir. We're very much rushed at this hour. London Wall 4831. I'll put you through as soon as possible, sir."

It was impossible to be crabbed in the face of such courtesy, so having wrapped my handkerchief round the instrument to relieve the chill I sat patiently down upon the bed. I waited what seemed for hours. "I'm getting your number for you, sir!" Five—six— ten—twelve minutes more. Then the wire cracked and hummed and a thin voice miles away wheezed:

"Whom do you want?"

"Fortesque, Saddlecloth & Co."

There was a perceptible interval of time in which the person on the other end cogitated upon the reply.

"To whom do you wish to speak?"

"Mr. Saddlecloth. It's important."

A long interval.

"Who is this speaking?"

"Mr. Ephraim Tutt of New York—I've just landed from the *Mauretania* at Liverpool. I must see Mr. Saddlecloth—" The wire suddenly went dead, and the local operator broke in pleasantly with:

"Are you through, sir?"

"Through!" I expostulated. "I should say not!"

"But they answered!"

She cut off and there was more buzzing and snapping. Then came the wheezy voice acridly protesting:

"But—I say—you can't speak to Mr. Saddlecloth!"

"Why not?" I snapped. There was a click and a wall of silence descended.

"Are you through *now*, sir?" inquired the operator.

"No! No! Of course I'm not through!" I shouted. "I've only just started talking. Why can't you give me a chance to say something? I—"

There was a silver laugh from below.

"I'm sorry. I asked if you were 'through,' meaning did you get your number? I'll fetch him back at once, sir."

Sheepishly I resumed my previous patient attitude. After a long time London Wall 4831 deigned to answer again. This time I elicited the information that the reason I couldn't speak to Mr. Saddlecloth was because Mr. Saddlecloth had gone 'ome. What time had he gone 'ome? Half after four—as usual. I glanced at the clock in dismay. It was twenty minutes to five. Imperiously I demanded the whereabouts of Mr. Saddlecloth's residence. The gentleman on the other end did not know. I rudely doubted this. The gentleman protested that he was only the "junior clark"—and it was not his business to know where the firm dwelt, but he thought it was somewhere out Finsbury Park way—by tube. He'd ask Mr. Higgins, his senior.

There was the customary hiatus. Then the junior returned. Yes, Mr. Saddlecloth lived in Finsbury Park—by tube. Neither he nor Mr. Higgins knew the number of the house—or the street. Mr. Saddlecloth did not like being disturbed. No, he didn't have a telephone in his 'ouse. He never answered the telephone anyway—not even in the horffice. I interrupted him to ask for Mr. Fortesque, then. The clark said Mr. Fortesque had been dead for seventeen years. Was there anybody else there who knew anything about the Northwyn matter? No—nobody but Mr. Saddlecloth. Had Mr. Saddlecloth got a cable from America about it some ten days ago? The clark did not know—Mr. Saddlecloth usually attended to everything himself. I had a momentary but passionate desire to inquire what, if that were so, the two clarks found to do, but I refrained.

Gently, patiently, in words of one syllable, I explained the imperative necessity of my getting into communication with Mr. Saddlecloth at once. The junior listened with attention, then reluctantly summoned his senior. To him I repeated my exposition. The senior, in an even wheezier voice than the junior, replied that it would never do to disturb Mr. Saddlecloth at 'is 'ome; that no solicitor liked to be disturbed at 'is 'ome; that a solicitor disturbed at 'is 'ome was worse than useless to anybody, for the reason that he would promptly send the disturber away and direct him to make an appointment with 'is clark to see him at the horffice in the regular way.

There was conviction in the clark's voice. For the first time I found myself confronting the impenetrable wall of English legal tradition. He was clearly horrified at the mere thought of disturbing Mr. Saddlecloth in 'is 'ome, and something of this he managed to communicate to me. I yielded. Well, if it really "wasn't done, you know"—tomorrow might do after all. No use getting myself in wrong at the very start. So I asked the senior kindly to make an appointment for me with Mr. Saddlecloth for the following morning. After some five minutes the clark returned with the news that his employer was all booked up for the next day, but that he would speak to him about the matter upon his arrival, and with that perforce I had to be satisfied.

There is a peculiar peace, if not satisfaction, about the inevitable. Finding that I could do nothing further with respect to my business I smoked another stogy, bathed, sent a cable to Otto announcing my arrival in London, called up Claridge's where my friend Saltonstall was staying, and invited him to dinner and the theatre.

Later on, over a roast pheasant and a bottle of sparkling Moselle, I related my experience.

"You mustn't expect anything else over here," Saltonstall declared. "You can't budge 'em! The rules of the game are all settled—inviolate. To chase a solicitor or a barrister to his domicile would be an unpardonable breach of etiquette. For a thousand years they've been working out their scheme of existence, and now they move according to precepts as definite as mathematical formulae. And don't imagine they're anybody's fools, either. Besides having principle, character, tradition and tenacity, they're the canniest lot in creation, they know exactly what they're after, and their only idea is to get it, if it takes a hundred years!"

I had left no request to be called at the hotel office and when I awoke it was eleven o'clock. Shocked at my own laziness I pulled on my clothes, ordered breakfast in my room, called up London Wall 4831, and asked to be connected with Mr. Saddlecloth. The clark, whose voice I recognized, replied politely but firmly that his employer never answered the telephone himself, but volunteered to take him a message. Accordingly, putting my reasons as strongly as possible, I asked for an immediate appointment. Mr. Saddlecloth sent back word that he was sorry, but that he was full up—that he had, in fact, not a single open hour until the following Tuesday afternoon, when he would be glad to see me at three o'clock.

Next Tuesday at three o'clock? Jumping Jehosaphat! I'd show this purblind old dormouse that he couldn't keep an American business man hanging round in any such fashion as that! Stuffing down an egg or two, some toast and marmalade, I hailed a taxi and directed the driver to take me to Paperweight Chambers. It was half after twelve before I was deposited at the end of a murky passage between ponderous stone buildings, gray-black with decades of London soot.

"Sealingwax Lane, sir."

Beside each doorway were brass plates bearing the names of the solicitors hibernating within, and the steps were worn hollow with the scraping of generations of feet. Beyond, I came presently to a dingy court even darker than the rest of the neighborhood and perceived from an adjacent sign that I had reached Paperweight Chambers. It was clear that no soap or water had ever desecrated the windows which were covered with an opaque yellow scum. Here, according to the *graffito* on the wall, Fortesque, Saddlecloth & Co. passed their legal lives. Here too lingered, probably, the ghost of Fortesque. The massive door, with its brass knob, was open, disclosing an ominous stone flight leading upward into the gloom. I smiled in spite of my annoyance.

> When I was a lad I served a term
> As office boy to an attorney's firm:
> I cleaned the windows, I swept the floor,
> And I polished up the handle of the big front door.

"A lot he did!" I thought. "Well, here goes!"

The offices of Fortesque, Saddlecloth & Co. were at the top of three long, dreary flights, where three joint and several doors gave upon a landing. One marked "Clerk" offered a knocker. There was no bell, so I knocked. After a space during which I decided that the firm, including its employees, had all been translated to a better life, I was encouraged by the sound of a key being turned in a lock, and the door was partially opened to admit the passage of a human head evidently chosen from one of Hogarth's drawings. It was in fact a skull rather than a head, but it was still covered with tightly drawn, yellow skin upon which at irregular intervals appeared tufts of dusty brown hair. Where the eyes should have been were enormous horn-rimmed spectacles.

"What do you want?" queried Mr. Higgins, the senior clark in a hostile tone.

"I want to see Mr. Saddlecloth," I announced briskly. "And, what's more, I want to see him at once!"

A curious—almost a malicious—smile wrinkled the parchment wrapping of the skull in front of me.

"Er—*very* sorry, sir, but Mr. Saddlecloth left for Scotland at twelve o'clock. These be the Easter holidays. He won't be back until Tuesday noon."

"Suffering Moses!" I exploded, calling down the vengeance of all the gods upon the heads of Fortesque, Saddlecloth & Co., upon the Lord Chief Justice, the Lord Chancellor and the Master of the Rolls, upon the Lords Spiritual and Temporal and upon King John and Magna Charta, until a look of almost human sympathy had supplanted the fiendish grin on the face of Higgins.

"It can't be 'elped, sir. You've nothink to blame y'self for, sir. I object to it myself, sometimes, but Lor' bless you, sir, one *'as* to get used to it, *'asn't* one?"

"Didn't Mr. Saddlecloth leave any message for me?" I choked.

"No, sir. Not a word, sir!"

When I got back to my hotel I found Saltonstall lounging in the café.

"I just learned casually that the Easter holidays began at twelve o'clock, and that consequently you couldn't do any business," he remarked. "You better come down with me to my place on the Wye for a couple of days' fishing," he said.

There was nothing else to do, so I went. I caught four salmon weighing over thirty pounds each and for the time being forgot all about Fortesque, Saddlecloth & Co.

Once back in London, however, I became again, for the moment at least, eager to put through the matter in hand. But, even though I had a definite appointment with my solicitor, I had seen enough of the way things worked in England to realize that I would have to exert pressure if I expected to sail by Saturday. This time when I rapped upon the door of Fortesque, Saddlecloth & Co. the yellow-faced clerk greeted me with affection, and informed me that Mr. Saddlecloth was expecting me. Then, producing a bundle of huge keys, he crossed the landing, inserted the largest into the keyhole of the door opposite, opened it, disappeared inside, and presently popped up again.

"This way, sir."

I was ushered over the threshold into a sort of padded cell, where apparently, as a matter of form, I was first allowed to kick my heels for a few minutes, and then led into an inner sanctuary in which I could see nothing but a dim aura surrounding a highly polished bald head. At last I was in the presence of Mr. Saddlecloth.

"Ah!" said that gentleman in an aerated voice, whose attempted note of cheerfulness seemed strangely out of place in a mortuary chapel. "Mr. Ephraim Tutt, I presume?"

"Yes," I smiled. "Here is Dr. Livingston—at last!"

Mr. Saddlecloth's monocle flopped.

"Eh? What's that?" he stammered. "I say—aren't you the American who's been asking for an appointment?"

"Yes, yes!" I hastily assured him as the retreating Higgins locked us solidly in together. "I tried to get hold of you half a dozen times last week, but—"

"Easter holidays!" hastily interjected Mr. Saddlecloth, whose pallid visage gave off a glow like the ghost's in *Hamlet*. "Quite impossible, you understand."

He shook hands and then quickly took cover behind a grimy ambuscade of papers tied with green tape. There was dust—thick gray mats of it—on everything.

"I came over on that Northwyn matter."

"Came over?"

"Yes. We want to clean it up—get rid of it, you know."

Mr. Saddlecloth appeared dazed.

"You don't mean to say that you *crossed the Atlantic Ocean* just for that!"

"Just for that!"

"Certainly—er—enterprising," he remarked. "But you know I don't see why you did it, exactly," he added as if slightly piqued.

"We wanted some action."

"But we're taking the opinion of counsel. Things are following the regular course. You'd have had our decision in due time."

"Can't you stir up the barrister and pry an opinion out of him?"

Mr. Saddlecloth was patently shocked.

"My dear sir," he returned icily, "when one consults counsel, particularly a 'K.C.,' one usually doesn't try to 'stir him up' or 'pry things out of him,' as you so picturesquely phrase it. In fact, we prefer him to take his time in order that he will give the matter proper attention."

I resented his attitude.

"As you like," I said. "I'm sailing for America on Saturday."

"Sailing—on—*Saturday*.'—This *coming* Saturday!"

His watery gray eyes mirrored the conviction that I was courting incarceration in a madhouse.

"Yes," I said. "I want this thing settled before I go back."

"Um!—well, I will write to our counsel," he temporized in a soothing tone, "but I can hardly hope to get his opinion—"

"What's his name?" I interrupted suddenly, taking advantage of my supposed insanity.

"The Honorable Rothwell Sommersly, K.C., M.P.," answered Mr. Saddlecloth. "He is a very busy man."

"So am I," I countered. "Can't you call him up on the telephone? Or can't I drop in and see him this afternoon?"

Mr. Saddlecloth's features became contorted.

"My dear sir," he moaned, "one doesn't 'drop in,' as you call it, on distinguished counsel without an appointment. Nor does counsel give his opinions *viva voce* over the telephone. I will have my clark call up his clark and request an appointment for you at the earliest possible opportunity. I trust that will serve your purposes?"

Mr. Saddlecloth did something mysterious· resulting in the reappearance of Mr. Higgins, who thereafter went away on a long vacation, at the end of which he returned with the information that the Honorable Rothwell Sommersly, K.C., M.P., would be pleased to see Mr. Saddlecloth and myself the next afternoon at 3:25 precisely at his chambers in Pump Court.

"I trust that this will suit your purposes," repeated Mr. Saddlecloth severely and with what I took for a touch of cynicism. "I shall meet you in Pump Court tomorrow afternoon at three twenty-two precisely. I trust you will now excuse me as I have an appointment with another client who has, in fact, been waiting for several minutes already.—Good afternoon, sir."

I mastered my annoyance as well as I could. After all, it was only Tuesday afternoon. I could see Sommersly, K.C., next day and the ship didn't sail until midnight Saturday—plenty of time. Having nothing better to do I decided to take a look at the Temple and the Inns of Court and managed to find Chancery Lane without too much difficulty. Here I became lost. Then at the end of a dark and narrow alley, which turned unexpectedly off Fleet Street in the midst of its most noisy and crowded stretch, I suddenly found myself in another world—a world of ancient square brick buildings with dingy windows, of quiet courts in whose fountains sparrows chirped and bathed, of green gardens sloping down to the Thames. Overhead a sign read "Middle Temple Lane." Under an arch my eye caught sunlit court opening upon sunlit court. Behind some of the windows I could see heads vaguely outlined. Here and there hurried a wigged barrister, his gown clutched in one hand and held high above his knees. From behind me rose the smothered roar of Fleet Street's traffic. Here all was peaceful—mellow.

The door of one of the buildings was ajar and through it I caught a glimpse of a great dining hall with an open timbered ceiling of ancient oak, stained glass windows, and a long table upon a raised dais, with other tables set for dinner along walls lined with carved choir stalls. Ducking along a cloister I unexpectedly, with no intention of going there, found myself in Pump Court and confronted by a tin sign reading "Rothwell Sommersly, K.C." The window was open and near it was sitting a cadaverous person, in an alpaca jacket, smoking a large, meerschaum pipe and reading—was it possible?—a copy of Punch. Fascinated, I crept nearer, unobserved by the man inside. Yes, it *was* Punch! So that was how these barristers spent their days! From time to time the man in the alpaca jacket pursed his lips, took a long pull on his pipe, and smiled contentedly.

The following afternoon, having met Mr. Saddlecloth as appointed, I entered the chambers of the Honorable Rothwell Sommersly, K.C., M.P., in Pump Court "at three-twenty-five precisely." I could not understand why the hour had been set at three-twenty-five rather than three-thirty, or why if three-twenty-five it was not three-twenty-eight—but while I did not venture to ask, I discovered this in due time. No copy of *Punch* was visible upon our entrance—neither was any odor of tobacco noticeable. But I definitely established the identity of the man in the alpaca jacket;—it had been the Honorable Rothwell.

Mr. Saddlecloth, who, in the light of day, appeared pinker and less bald than on the previous afternoon, approached the barrister with an air of deprecating timidity. While he had treated me with brusqueness, almost hostility, he clearly regarded the person of the Honorable Rothwell as little less than sacred, as one whose legal shoes he was hardly worthy to unloose—and for his part the Honorable Rothwell treated him like the veriest dirt under those shoes. With me, however, he was urbane.

The Northwyn matter? Oh, yes—he rang a bell and directed his clerk to look up the papers—he had intended to write to Fortesque, Saddlecloth & Co. about it but it had slipped his mind. So Mr. Tutt had come from America to look into it, had he? Extr'd'n'ry! He hoped Mr. Saddlecloth had enjoyed the holidays? Yes, the barrister thanked him, the fishing at Scourie had been rather excepsh'n'ly good. Ah, there you were!—and he slowly undid the green tape that surrounded the Northwyn problem.

The fact was, he explained, that while he was clear in his *own* mind that *Skellings v. Mainwaring* was not in point, Sir William Tremayne—of whom Fortesque, Saddlecloth & Co. had at his, the Honorable Rothwell's suggestion also asked an opinion—had not got round to it. If he should happen to run into Sir William on the golf course at Sunningdale or possibly at his club he would speak to him if he thought of it. But Sir William was not a man to be hurried. The question was—did *Skellings v. Mainwaring* apply? *He* thought not, but Sir William, who was a specialist in such matters, might think differently. Anyhow he'd try to find some way to jog Sir William's memory.

I explained gently to the Honorable Rothwell that he'd have to find it pretty soon since by the following Sunday I expected to be under full steam headed for America. The barrister shook his head. You couldn't do things that way! Ever since Sir William Tremayne had "gone special" he was a hard man to get and you had to take your turn. Moreover, there was this to consider. If Sir William thought *Skellings v. Mainwaring* did *not* apply, it would settle the whole matter. "Don't you agree, Saddlecloth?" Mr. Saddlecloth, rubbing his hands, agreed.

I was flabbergasted. It simply boiled down to the Honorable

Rothwell Sommersly's not being willing to disturb the serenity of Sir William Thing-a-my-jig because the latter was an important old man; and I said so. I didn't put it that way exactly, but that was the substance of my remarks, and I did not try to disguise the fact that I was very much annoyed. The Honorable Rothwell was polite and most apologetic, but nothing would budge him. Then he suddenly looked at his watch and declared that he had a client waiting for a 3:55 appointment. He would see us again tomorrow—if we liked—at 4:10. Baffled, but not knowing what else in the world to do, I agreed to meet Mr. Saddlecloth at Pump Court at the barrister's chambers the next afternoon. As I did so, the vision of the Honorable Rothwell in his alpaca jacket, with his pipe and copy of *Punch*, was present in my mind. What was the meaning of it?

I went back to the hotel.

"You can't do anything about it," Saltonstall assured me. "It has always been done that way and it always will be. Half of it is swank, anyhow. Take this feller Saddlecloth, for instance. The clerk told you he was in Scotland, but the chances are he was in his office all the time."

The vision of the Honorable Rothwell and his pipe rose before my eyes.

"But what's the meaning of these extraordinary appointments they give you?—at three-nineteen day after tomorrow, and all that?" I asked.

"All part of the same game. Every barrister in London is assumed to be so overcrowded with work that he has difficulty in sandwiching in his clients. Hence you can never get an appointment on the same day, rarely inside of three, and hardly ever for more than half an hour at a time because they are supposed to charge only two guineas for each conference. They can't beat you on the price, so they beat you on the time. However, it has certain advantages. Nothing, at least in the law, is ever done in a hurry. It's all thought out carefully, and so a lot of litigation is saved. They get just as much done in the end. And those fellers make no end of money. Take Sir William Tremayne, for example. He must make twenty thousand pounds a year."

"Who—did you say?" I stammered.

"Tremayne—Sir William. He's our leading K.C. He's coming down to fish with me the end of this week."

"But he's retained in my case," I said. "I must meet him right off—tomorrow!—tonight—this afternoon. If I don't I'll never be able to sail on Saturday."

"Well, you can't meet him!" grinned Saltonstall, "because he's in Scotland. I mean he *really* is," he added grimly.

When I returned to Pump Court next day I found that Mr. Saddlecloth had preceded me and was engaged in writing out in longhand a memorandum to be used in conferring with counsel on the other side. There was a distinctly more friendly atmosphere, and when I opened my stogy case the Honorable Rothwell, while remarking that he didn't usually smoke in chambers (!), helped himself to one and became almost human.

"I've been talking it over with Saddlecloth," he remarked genially. "And while we both—you'll pardon me, I hope?— think your comin' over here, don't you know, quite unnecessary, still, we feel that now you're here we might as well take advantage of it and, while we're about it, get all your ideas. Eh— Saddlecloth?"

"Quite so!" agreed the solicitor. "Exactly."

"Which being the case," continued the Honorable Rothwell, "I've arranged for a series of double conferences with you here every afternoon during this week and the next—except Friday, Saturday and Sunday, of course."

"Of course!" echoed Saddlecloth.

"But I'm sailing on Saturday!" I exclaimed.

The Honorable Rothwell arched his fingers again.

"Er—you'll pardon me, I hope?" he began. "Now you're here, really it would be much better in every way if you didn't go back until the case is settled. You see, your comin' over here so unexpectedly this way rather bowled us over at first, but now you *are* here there are a lot of ways in which your knowledge can be of vital assistance to us and perhaps even be of some value to our leader, Sir William Tremayne."

"It seems to me," I answered, "that I ought to be able to tell you all I know at one session—this afternoon."

"Never!" exclaimed barrister and solicitor in the same breath.

"Well, we can try. 'Fire when ready, Gridley!' "

"Eh? 'Gridley'—who's he?" inquired the Honorable Rothwell.

"Just some American slang," I explained. "Go ahead. Shoot!"

When Sommersly began shooting, however, I discovered to my surprise that the barrister's knowledge of the Northwyn case was minute and thorough. For the first time I realized that I had not fully appreciated the legal difficulty of the case under the English decisions and perceived the wisdom of getting the best possible advice. I would gladly have gone on discussing the case all the afternoon—and evening for that matter—but at a few minutes to five the Honorable Rothwell closed the book lying in front of him.

"Well," he remarked amiably, "what do you say to a cup of tea?"

"Oh, let's go on!" I urged, as Saddlecloth assembled his numerous pages of notes, stenographers being clearly unknown animals.

"You'll pardon me?" hesitated the Honorable Rothwell. "You *will, won't you?* Well, we never work, you know, after tea, and we always have tea at five o'clock. One has to have rules, doesn't one? Eh—Saddlecloth—will you join us?"

"Oh, no, thank you very much!" replied the solicitor as if honored above all his profession by the invitation. "I must get back to the office. I've had a client waiting—"

I suppressed a snort of derision. After all, Saddlecloth had shown himself both a nimble penman and an expert upon the technicalities of the Northwyn tangle.

"Then you'll meet us here Monday next, same hour?" said Sommersly.

"Certainly," agreed the barrister.

"*But!*" I roared, "I told you I was sailing Saturday."

The Honorable Rothwell laid his hand paternally upon my shoulder.

"My dear feller!" he said coaxingly. "You'll pardon me, won't you? But really, you know, I can't let you go back next Saturday! Not possibly! Sir William will want to see you."

"You mean, I take it," I remarked ironically, "that he'll want to see me when he finds out I'm here—which will be when you happen to remember to tell him so!"

The Honorable Rothwell compressed his lips.

"You forget this isn't America, my dear sir!"

"Do you fancy I don't know it?" I retorted. "We'd have settled this thing in two hours in New York. Let's be sensible. Why not cut a little of this everlasting red tape and simply notify Sir William Tremayne that it is imperative that you see him at once or you'll have to get along without him?"

"Wh-a-a-t!" screamed Sommersly and Saddlecloth in unison.

"I mean it," I insisted. "He can't be the only pebble on the legal beach."

"Nothing of that sort could possibly be done," said Sommersly stiffly.

"But look here!" I demanded hotly. "Do you expect to diddle around until it occurs to him that he's been paid for an opinion and ought to deliver one? At that rate I might have to stay over here until next Christmas. Haven't you any definite idea when you can count on hearing from him?"

"Sir William is on a vacation in Scotland," said the Honorable Rothwell reprovingly. "Following that he goes into a heavy trial in Manchester Monday week and he'll have to prepare. It would be fatal to disturb him. Directly his Manchester case is over we'll try to get in touch with him."

"How long will the trial take?"

"Not over three weeks at the outside."

"So I may have to hang around here for five weeks before I can even so much as see him?"

They both nodded.

"You don't know Eph Tutt," I muttered to myself.

"All right!" I said aloud. "Put me down for all those double-double-toil-and-trouble conferences this week and next—except Fridays, Saturdays, Sundays, of course!' Now you must excuse me, for I have an engagement at 4:29. Good afternoon, gentlemen."

"Of course you can join us!" replied Saltonstall when on my return to the hotel I suggested spending the week end with him on the Wye. "There is enough room for a half a dozen rods on my water and there'll only be three of us—Sir William, yourself, and myself."

That was how I beat them to it—or thought I had. But if I'd only known it I was already licked. I suppose I must have been ripe for it, and it was Sir William who accomplished my unconditional surrender. After meeting him I was never quite the same. Can I be blamed for having visualized the most distinguished barrister in the British Isles as bent with the weight of learning, bald from thought—or at any rate white-haired with pondering upon the profundities of the law—shrivelled, ascetic, or judicially and equitably obese? Quite to the contrary this pundit of chancery turned out to be a husky, broad-shouldered athlete of something over six feet two, with a tanned clean-shaven face and, in spite of his seventy-three years, with eyes as humorously blue as if he had never opened a volume of the reports.

Moreover, he seemed to know as much about America and Americans, lawyers in particular, as I did. He had journeyed across the United States nine times, shot elk in Wyoming, mountain sheep in British Columbia, duck in Texas, and caught sailfish and tarpon in Florida. Incidentally, he was a non-resident member of the Cosmos Club of Washington, the Century of New

York, and belonged as well to the Garrick and Beefsteak of London. He had taken a "double first" at Oxford and had privately printed a poetical translation of the plays of Euripides.

He was a combination of Joseph H. Choate, John Milburn and old Judge Tompkins, raised to the nth power. I had gone down to the Wye with the firm intention of demanding his immediate attention to *Skellings vs. Mainwaring,* securing his opinion, and then of embarking on the *Mauretania* as I had planned. But I didn't. In the first place I discovered that this fishing trip was no mere cover for idleness on Sir William's part, since he had brought along a couple of brief-cases full of his Manchester papers and put in a good four hours work on them each day. I made a single attempt—but a feeble one—to accomplish my purpose, over our port the first evening.

"I'm over here to close up the Northwyn matter, Sir William," I remarked casually. "We're waiting on your opinion in regard to the applicability of *Skellings vs. Mainwaring.* Have you any idea how long it will be before you get around to it?"

"The Northwyn matter? Oh, yes. Rather an interesting point. I hope to take it up very shortly."

"I am planning to return to America this coming Saturday. It wouldn't be possible to give us some sort of opinion at once would it? A provisional one?"

Sir William looked at me amusedly.

"I know what you fellows are! Do you realize what my retainer in that brief amounts to?"

"No," I answered, glad to have at least caught his attention.

"Twenty-five hundred guineas. Well, I hope to earn it. That takes time. —Have you been to Oxford and Cambridge? Why don't you stay over and see a bit of England?"

He had me. There was no way out of it and, quite frankly, by this time I wasn't so sure that I wanted one. So I cabled Otto that I was unavoidably detained and not to expect me for another six weeks.

XIV

"THIS ENGLAND"

I HAD already seen the Inns of Court and the outside of London; now I hoped to see something of English life. Cyril Maude, the actor, who had crossed with us on the *Mauritania*, had offered to put me up at the Garrick Club, but I had declined his invitation because of the expected brevity of my visit. Now I called him up and gladly availed myself of it.

The Garrick was composed largely of men with literary and artistic tastes who gathered around the fire for port after lunch. It reminded me of The Century at home, and here I met Forbes Robertson, Gerald DuMaurier, Frederick Lonsdale, Harry Higgins, and many others who became my friends. Some of them like Sir James Barrie, John Sargent, Henry James and Granville Barker I had already met at Mrs. Cadwalader Jones' in New York. Robertson came there almost daily and I can see him now in recollection standing gracefully with his long legs apart in front of the glowing grate telling anecdote after anecdote with a dry smile on his distinguished features. In return I gave them "Doc Robinson" and they seemed to like it.

John Sargent asked me to tea and introduced me to Max Beerbohm, Sir Sidney Colvin, William Rothenstein, Sir John Lavery and Hazel, his beautiful wife. A few days afterwards Sir Sidney also invited me, and I met Hilaire Belloc, Arnold Bennett, E. V. Lucas, a middle-aged lady Dame Eva Anstruther, and handsome Lord Montagu of Beaulieu, a famous expert on motor transport. I was a bit out of my depth on both these occasions, but I put the Old Gray Mare at work again and made a sufficient impression to have Montagu, who had not addressed two words to me theretofore, say unexpectedly as we were leaving the house:

"How about running down for the week end at Beaulieu?"

"I'd be delighted!" I answered. "Where is it and how do I get there?"

"Twelve miles from Southhampton on the London & South-western—Brockhurst Station. Hope to see you."

I never discovered just why Montagu picked me to ask to Beaulieu Abbey, but it gave me a glimpse of rural England that I would not willingly have missed. On leaving the train I found the only vehicle in waiting to be a shabby fly, the driver of which inquired if I was the gentleman for Palace House. I said yes and climbed in. A golden silence hardly broken by a bird's note hushed the vaulted alleys of the New Forest down which my eyes seemed to follow endlessly between the brown oak trunks until sight was blurred by a tangle of shadow and foliage.

At last we topped a short rise from which I could look down upon the silver thread of a river that wound through low-lying fields, and half a mile beyond we entered a trim village with red slate roofs patched with bright green moss and shining windows filled with flower boxes. A postman touched his cap and some old gaffers smoking their pipes outside the "Beaulieu Arms" nodded as we passed. Then we rattled over a bridge and under the sudden gray-stone arch of a gate-house through which I could see an ancient castle with the Union Jack floating from its tower. The driveway swung round a weather-stained wing with gothic windows to the entrance of Palace House from which a lawn sloped down to the river through a gallery of green statuary of peacocks, pyramids and hour glasses carved by the gardener's scissors from box and yew, and a half dozen rooks, cawing a protest against this invasion of their privacy, rose out of the elms, hung for a moment festooned in mid air, and flapped languidly away. I wondered if it were real—or just a canvas and scantling setting for a movie. I fully expected a mail-clad warden to come out and blow a horn.

The warden duly appeared in the shape of a one-armed butler (he had lost the other at Ypres) who explained that Lord Montagu had not yet come in from fishing but that tea was being served in the library. For a moment I felt that I was in a museum. In the dim light of the hall I collided with a rusty suit of inebriated armor leaning forward by the door. All around against every wall, along the staircase, even upon the railings of the galleries, hung hundreds of ancestral Montagus—some in the cassock and cotta of the priest, others in judicial robes, some in doublet and hose, some in breast plate and greaves, some in the tight bodice and ruff of Elizabeth's time or the greater amplitude of Victoria. In the shadow I caught the droop of tattered flags and behind a glass the flash of a jewelled hilt; a boar's fangs grinned at me from above a doorway; and then I heard my name being announced by the butler beyond the threshold.

I was in a room lined with high book shelves topped with cases of stuffed birds, the air heavy with wood smoke from a great bed of ashes behind a leather fire seat. Several people arose to greet me as I came in—including the Dame Anstruther I had met at the Colvins, and—God save the mark!—none other than Sir William Tremayne himself. There were also a Sir Thomas and Lady Troubridge, Sir Owen Seaman, editor of *Punch* and Archibald Marshall the novelist—guests over the week end.

"John isn't in yet," said Dame Anstruther. "He's trying the pool below Buckler's Hard. Lemon or milk?"

There was a permeating sense of comfort about the room in which every period was represented in the much-worn furniture from that of the Spanish Armada to the Albert Memorial. Historic portraits hung side by side with water-color sketches done by former ladies of the Abbey, and relics of the Crusades, worsted mottoes, picture cards and calendars hung indiscriminately from the projections of the book cases; while the desks and tables were heaped with maps, diaries, record books bound in leather, newspapers, piles of letters, riding crops, tennis racquets, stray gloves, works on sanitary engineering, novels and games. Just at my shoulder a parchment scroll, evidently used as a lamp shade, covered with old English lettering and grotesque figures in color swung from an upright by a silken cord.

"That's an old manuscript telling how King John happened

to build the Abbey in 1204," said Sir Thomas Troubridge. "The abbots had come to seek his favor at a parliament which he was holding in Lincoln, but he was in an angry mood and he ordered his servants to trample the abbots under the feet of their horses, which they refused to do. That night King John had a dream. He seemed to be standing before a judge who ordered the abbots to beat him upon his back with scourges and rods. So when he awoke he sent for the abbots and begged their pardon and built them this monastery."

"Is that the King John whom the barons forced to sign Magna Carta?" I asked.

"The same," said Sir William. "It brings history pretty close, doesn't it?"

Montagu came in with a basket of trout and presently we separated to go to our rooms. Mine was the one occupied by George V when he had last visited them, but the only bathroom was at the other end of a corridor seemingly a hundred yards long.

We dined that evening in a great stone hall, beneath arches sacred to the memory of King John, at a huge oak refectory table, weighted with historic plate and antique tankards of silver. There were other guests for dinner from Lyndhurst and Brockenhurst—young married people for the most part, with a stray golfer or two from the neghboring country club, and a clear-eyed, redcheeked, vigorous old clergyman of seventy-eight, Rev. F. R. Powles, who in addition to having been the Vicar of Beaulieu Abbey for nearly half a century had the distinction of being the seventh son of a seventh son and who, they told me, could still hear the monks chanting their orisons in the ruined chapel. After the women arose the men drew up about Montagu, the port went round, and the last anecdote about Lloyd George and Clemenceau was told. I gathered that my host was a widower and that Dame Eva Anstruther, who occupied one of the many cottages on the property, was accustomed to act as chatelaine during his week-end parties. The vicar was obliged to leave early in order to make a parochial visit and after he had gone Montagu told a story of his powers of second sight.

"It was during the War, when my wife was alive," he said, "and while I was away she spent most of her time with Eva Anstruther. I was on the *Persia* when she was torpedoed in the Eastern Mediterranean on December 30, 1915. I found myself in the water and climbed onto an upturned boat with twenty or thirty Lascars on the keel. We picked up four or five other people, managed to right the boat and get in. A high sea was running and there was a stiff breeze that drove us away from all the other craft. Every once in a while a big wave would sweep off one or more of the Lascars until finally there were only eleven of us left on board. We hung on as best we could for thirty hours, but the destroyers that came out from Alexandria had overlooked us and I was reported missing. I was all in and didn't think I'd last out the night. I looked at my wrist watch and it was just eight o'clock. 'They'll think I'm lost,' I said to myself, 'and my wife will have gone down to be with Eva Anstruther.' Then I saw lights and the Alfred Holt liner *Ming Chow* picked us up. Now it was a fact that my wife had seen by the papers that I was missing and had gone down after supper to sit with Eva Anstruther at her cottage just as I had envisioned. Presently the vicar turned up there, having been first to the Abbey to find my wife.

" 'Have you any news of John?' he asked her.

" 'John is dead,' she replied. 'He's not on the list of saved.'

" 'John is alive,' he assured her positively. 'A moment ago he joined me at the door of Palace House from which I have come, accompanied me here, and has only just left me.' It was exactly eight o'clock."

Gradually I began to find out what a distinguished man John Scott Montagu was. Besides being the owner of probably the most magnificent Abbey ruin in England with its ten thousand surrounding acres, he had been Director General of Motor Transport in India during the war and in the Railroad Strike in 1919 had volunteered as a locomotive engineer and driven an engine between Waterloo and Bournemouth.

Next morning when I awoke I could see through the leaded casement the boughs of trees just bursting into leaf and hear the song of many birds. The lawn, softly green in the sunlight, was dotted all the way to the river-bank with crocuses, snow drops, early tulips and hyacinths. Here and there ran small, trim robins with an occasional chaffinch or magpie. and on a nearby twig a bullfinch sat and eyed me, its lovely red throat almost within reach of my hand. A film of cloud made a white background for the dull reds and greens of the village, and under the ivy-clad bridge the stream eddied into a wide blue pool before spreading out in lighter color to the frieze of willows that marked the beginning of the river where in earlier days Nelson had built the *Agamemnon* and other ships. I had never seen anything more quietly beautiful.

Think of owning a place like that! Of always having it to dream about and to come back to. To fight for!

"This blessed plot, this earth, this realm, this England."

There was something in this ownership of land—in this belonging to the soil. It put its stamp on a man, gave him responsibilities, character, individuality. Having come to which momentous conclusion I put on a dressing gown, traversed a corridor once paced by monks thumbing their breviaries, and plunged into a tin tub much resembling in size and shape a mammoth sarcophagus in which, had I not been careful I might easily have been drowned.

After a hearty English breakfast we strolled across the greensward to the old historic Abbey church and heard the vicar read the service, and after lunch Montagu motored me over to Christ Church to have tea with General Stuart Wortley and his wife at Highcliffe Castle, which the Kaiser had rented when he visited England in 1907, and which stands directly on a bluff overlooking the Solent and the Isle of Wight.

I felt that I had qualified for Kipling's American:

> "Enslaved, illogical, elate,
>   He greets the embarrassed Gods, nor fears
> To shake the iron hand of Fate
>   Or match with Destiny for beers."

For a moment I flirted with the idea of becoming a London barrister and buying a bit of English land wheron to spend my declining years—perhaps an acre or two of Beaulieu by the river. What was I practicing for amid the turmoil of New York? Where had it got me? I thought of the story of the Italian laborer who said: "I digga da ditch to getta da mon to eatta da food to getta da strength to digga da ditch."

Before supper I wandered down the long stone alley known as The Drum Way, towards the old Guest House where in the time of the monks ecclesiastical visitors were housed. Through the Chapter House gate the afternoon sun streamed across the grassy cloisters and threw our shadows far in advance of us. The vicar called my attention to a curious marble box lying on a shelf just inside of the old Wine Press.

"That is a double heart-coffin," he explained. "It used to be the custom in monastic times to bury the heart of any particularly distinguished or beloved person in a place different to that where the body was. They say that box once contained the heart of Richard, Earl of Cornwall and King of the Romans—the other heart was that of Muriel—his countess."

Over in the cloisters two robins were calling to one another in liquid tones and the sun was creeping up the moss-stained gable-end wall. It was exquisite, but I knew now why I should never leave America. My heart was there.

Our little party broke up next morning. I left Beaulieu with regret, feeling that now I really understood the English until, as I put on my coat in the front hall, the one-armed butler politely handed me a folded sheet of paper on a silver tray. It was a bill for five shillings for the station fly.

"Of course you don't know London until you've met Rosa Lewis," said Saltonstall on my return. "Let's move over to the Hotel Cavendish for a while."

It was an old-fashioned, three storied affair on Jermyn Street, with a plain stone facade and unostentatious foyer in which we were confronted by a handsome, middle-aged, sloppily dressed woman holding a glass of champagne. Beside her stood a dirty-white little dog.

"Hello, Rosa!" said Saltonstall. "Here we are again! —Hello, Kippy!"

"W'y if it ain't old Salty!" she cried. "W'erever did you come from? 'Ow's Wacky and Tim? An' 'oo's 'is nibs with you?"

"This is my friend the Prince of Pottsville," replied Tommy.

"Prince my pants!" she retorted. " 'Oo is 'e?"

"A famous American jurist named Ephraim Tutt—a friend of Mr. Choate's."

"You're just in time for a snifter. Old Lord Cederly is 'ere for his usual," said Mrs. Lewis, leading the way into a small sitting-room office where a rickety gentleman stood unsteadily before the fireplace. "That's Lord Cederly—'Im with the monocle. 'Arry, you know Salty—an ole, ole friend of mine. And this 'ere is Judge Tutt—a cousin of Lady Astor's."

"Howjado?" muttered his lordship fingering his monocle.

"Stefany!" yelled Rosa to the butler, "this calls for another bottle."

While Rosa questioned my friend as to various Cabots, Lowells, McKeevers, Hitchcocks and Whitneys, I glanced over the signed photographs which crowded the walls. They included, so far as I could see, all the crowned heads of Europe; Bishop Potter and Lillie Langtry, Theodore Roosevelt and Mrs. Patrick Campbell, J. P. Morgan, Sr. and Mary Anderson hung side by side; while Tommy Hitchcock, Dev Milburn and other young men in uniform, hunting and polo costume jostled King Edward VII, Lord Kitchener, Aldous Huxley and Marion Davies.

"I suppose you'd like to look at some rooms," remarked Rosa

finally. "You stay right 'ere, 'Arry, and finish that bottle. Come along, boys!"

I now discovered that the Cavendish despite the modesty of its exterior consisted of nine adjoining houses opening into one another on varying levels and built around an inner court filled with potted trees. Its exterior in fact was its only modest feature.

"I've got two rooms somew'ere," she said stumping up the stairs. "Let's try this one!" Without knocking she threw open a door. There was a startled scream as a young woman in her panties scuttled from sight. "Lady Waxham!" sniffed Rosa. "She won't mind.—It's all right, sweetie!" she called over her shoulder.

After a couple of similar adventures in which we uncovered a be-ribboned general having brandy and soda on a sofa with a lady presumably his wife, and a gentleman engaged in shaving who was entirely naked except for shorts, we found two rooms looking out onto the court and Rosa ordered up our baggage and another bottle of champagne.

"You've got to tyke dinner with me tonight," she said. "Only you two, and Percy 'Argrove—a wounded haviator 'oo's livin' 'ere—and Lord Fothenoy, unless I pick up a girl or two—that Waxham bitch might come. I'll have to ask Eddie Fothenoy because we'll be usin' his rooms. I'd tyke Ribblesdale's if it wasn't for the stairs and I've got flat feet. Well, don't go on any exploring expeditions. Eight o'clock!"

"And just who is that remarkably engaging and extremely vulgar person?" I asked Saltonstall. Tommy threw himself into a chintz-covered, wing armchair under a Hogarth print.

"A scullery maid who became the greatest *chef* in London. The friend of kings and emperors," he said. "Rosa's an institution—a female Robin Hood. She literally knows the entire aristocracy—all the stage and literary celebrities. Lady Randolph Churchill introduced her to the Prince of Wales before he became Edward VII and after that no one could entertain him unless Rosa cooked the dinner. The Marlborough House set turned night into day here. There are no fixed prices and Rosa runs the Cavendish to suit herself. It's liberty hall while you're here and whatever is yours is hers. No doubt that fellow in shorts will be wearing my pajamas tonight and God only knows what the Waxham bitch will be doing. After the Armistice all the generals had their farewell banquets here. During the season she's given thirty great parties in six weeks and handled them all herself. When the Kaiser came on his famous visit he insisted that Rosa should cook for him and she did. When he asked her how he could show his appreciation she said: 'Your Majesty, let me 'ave the *Hohenzollern* for a day!' and she sailed around the Solent on the royal yacht all by herself. She's made and thrown away several fortunes—and she'll cook and serve our dinner tonight. Maybe we'll pay for it and maybe someone will who wasn't invited."

At eight o'clock Saltonstall and I went to Lord Fothenoy's suite and found a table set in front of the fire. The only others present were a frail looking young man on crutches and Fothenoy himself, a colorless person who rented the rooms the year round. We began with cocktails and by the time Rosa arrived with the soup were on very friendly terms. Having opened a bottle of champagne she pulled up a chair and entertained us with anecdotes of royal escapades and reminiscences of the private lives of some of her guests in a composite of Cockney vulgarity, aristocratic profanity, and Elizabethan frankness regarding the so-called facts of life garnished with four letter words.

That she must have been a beauty was evident, for although her figure had gone to pieces, her complexion was still rose-leaf and her features really lovely. Between each course she departed to prepare the next, then reappeared with a fresh bottle. As the evening wore on and these increased in number she forsook reminiscence for philosophy.

"Never tyke more than you can give is wot I says!" she declared. "I remember a young lord, a nice lookin' feller 'e was, takin' me out to dinner once and then suggestin' goin' somewheres afterwards. I knew wot 'e was after. Well, I pulled up me evenin' dress above me knees and said: 'Look 'ere Bertie! This is as much as you'll ever see of me, or as much as you'll ever know of me, so if you're expectin' anythin' more, you can save your money and your disappointment afterwards and say so now!"

Rosa glared around the circle.

"Goddamn right I was! Couldn't have been fairer than that could I?"

"We all agreed that she couldn't possibly have been fairer—or franker, although I suspect that she had somewhat Bowdlerized the original dialogue. I was beginning to feel extremely benign and a bit blown up. Rosa's face was hidden behind a haze. Suddenly she said to me:

"You go tyke a walk 'round the garden, Eph, ole top! Percy, you and Eddie go with 'im. A bit of fresh hair, you know."

So supported by a wounded airman on crutches and a peer of the realm I circled the court until my wheeziness had passed.

There was a glamor about the Cavendish. It was part of Rosa's fantastic spell that the moment one crossed the threshold she was able to impart—perhaps by the aid of alcohol—a conviction of reality to a social environment that had no actual existence. One had a feeling of intimacy with the great and naughty; a delicious sense of at least vicarious sin. It was a sort of club, a place of joyous relaxation, where gallant men and alluring women could abandon convention—so long as they had the proper social status and did not object to the cost. Inside it they were above the law, just as Rosa was above the law. She saved many a reputation that perhaps had better have been lost.

But one might go there time and again and be wholly unaware that it was anything but a first class hotel with an exquisite cuisine and furnished with marvellous antique furniture. I am sure that Bishop Potter, Chauncey Depew, Mr. Choate and all the other good Americans who stayed at the Cavendish had no suspicion of what it stood for. A prelate might be dining quietly with his family in one of her nine houses, a royal banquet being given in another, and a debauch going on in a third—and none of the guests be any the wiser. You could stay there and believe yourself to be either in a country parsonage or a bawdy house, depending upon which of the domiciles you occupied. It was the best hotel in England, the most charmingly wicked, and the enchantress that made it possible was a gray-haired woman with cold, blue appraising eyes, an isolent, ribald, witty tongue, flat feet and housemaid's knee.

Rosa was undoubtedly warm hearted, impulsive, and at times generous, but she traded on her intimate knowledge of her guests' private affairs and her bills were never questioned. She would go to any party in London she chose whether invited or not because no one dared to keep her out. She would have a shindig with unlimited champagne in her "Elinor Glyn Room" for some one she took a fancy to and, if she didn't see anyone at the moment rich enough to pay the bill, would send her maid Edith upstairs to drag down some elderly peer who was already too fuddle-headed to know what was going on and charge it to him.

She had been a part of the era of England's imperial greatness. I never saw Rosa without a glass of champagne in her hand. She took no other liquor and must have drunk twenty thousand quarts in the course of her existence. She admired dash, courage, gaiety, rank and wealth. With the First World War the Cavendish became headquarters for smart officers leaving for the front and an oasis for those on leave who poured into London from the trenches. Here for a few days it was Rosa's task, no matter what they wanted, to make them happy before they must return. It made no difference whether they paid or left I.O.U.'s which were never honored. To give them a good time was Rosa's bit, and on their departure she gave to each a basket containing a bird, a bottle, pastry and a couple of five pound notes. She said that the war cost her £150,000. Probably the truth was that under the circumstances she could have made that much additional profit had she been less open-handed. But the War did not ruin her, for at its conclusion she bought two country places.

But it was only the officers. They could always have a magnum of champagne for the asking, their boots polished like mirrors, their uniforms cleaned and smartly. pressed; while outside the hollow-faced exhausted men of the lower classes in the ranks slogged by in their heavy haversacks and entrenching tools, dirty uniforms and muddy boots, at a shilling a day. No birds, bottles or five pound notes for them!

"Oh, England is a pleasant place for them that's rich and high,
But England is a cruel place for such poor folk as I."

Why should a staid American lawyer, take the trouble to thus record his impressions of Rosa Lewis? Because the Cavendish typified what we call the Edwardian era,—the era of privilege. After the War nothing was the same. She could still cast her spell, but the people were all different and the things she cared about no longer counted. Her day was over. "But it was a sweet time!" she told me. During the present war a German bomb demolished the Cavendish. There will never be another, for there will never be another Rosa.

Perhaps because Rosa may have regarded us as representatives of her quieter American trade—successors so to speak of Mr. Choate and Bishop Potter—Tommy and I escaped from the Cavendish for a minimum ransom, our bills containing, even more surprisingly, not a single item for champagne.

By this time I was feeling quite at home in London, for the English whom I met did not seem to me to be noticeably different from ourselves. A barrister or solicitor would ask me to lunch just as readily as a business acquaintance in New York would have done, although he might be slower about inviting me to his house. He would begin with five o'clock tea, so that his wife could give me the once-over and, if I passed muster, might come across with an invitation to family dinner about a week later. There was none of our "Why not drop in this evening and take pot luck with us?" at the first meeting. As I remember them those family dinners weren't so good anyhow—boiled mutton.

Even the formal affairs had their drawbacks. As a boy I slept in a freezing Vermont attic, but I have never been so cold in my life as at a London dinner party in March. English mansions had no central heating, and during the winter the cold accumulated to a point which made an ice-house seem warm by comparison. After dinner the guests in evening dress sat in a shivering circle around the drawing room blaze, congealed behind and roasted in front like trappers about a camp fire. Once on such an occasion I was called to the telephone and, descending to the basement, where for some mysterious reason it was located, stood holding the instrument in my hand for some twenty minutes to find at the end of the conversation that my right arm was temporarily paralyzed.

Of course the English and Americans had different colloquialisms and manner of speech. Neither a Britisher nor a Continental abbreviates his questions in the way customary with us—one has to explain everything. I was once crossing Hyde Park Corner trying to find my way to Harrod's Furniture Store. On a circular elevation in the center directing traffic stood a gigantic bobby, looking at least ten feet in height—a human lighthouse. Dodging the motors I reached safety beside him and, pointing at a building opposite, inquired: "Harrod's?"

He looked down upon me with puzzled disdain.

"And wot of hit?" he inquired loftily.

I spent a good deal of time in the courts—especially the criminal courts—and was impressed by the celerity and apparent accuracy with which justice was administered. The judge usurped, or at least exercised, a far greater importance than with us in America, freely expressing his opinion of the evidence and indicating without reserve what he thought the jury should do. This I attributed to the historic tradition which so long obtained in England that judges were but agents of the crown to enforce the King's Peace, a tradition which had more or less continued in spite of the great democratic movements of the Eighteenth Century. The verdicts I heard returned would have been reversed on appeal in most American jurisdictions on account of the unwarranted interference of the judge, since we have statutes expressly limiting his powers.

On the other hand I was struck by the utter lack of prejudice against a person on account of his race or creed, a principle to which many Americans do only lip service. For example, many of the most prominent, if not the leading, families in London society were Jews—to mention but a few, the de Rothschilds, Montefiores, Speyers and Castles. Many of King Edward VII's intimates were Jews—and it is hinted that he may even have had a strain of Jewish blood himself.

During my stay I became friendly with a gentleman of social prominence who hospitably suggested that he and his wife would like to give a dinner for me. It was a very fashionable affair and with but a single exception all the guests had titles. I took in a Lady Baring. I had never been in such distinguished company. The exception was an oldish, picturesque looking man with curly yellow ringlets and an extremely hooked nose who sat nearly opposite me. Being but a commoner and a Yankee at that, although the dinner was given for me, I sat so to speak below the salt, but when the ladies left the table the host escorted me to a place beside him at the head of the table. After some desultory conversation I indicated the gentleman with the curls, remarking lightly! "That old fellow ought to have rings in his ears! He looks like a Jew."

"He is," said my friend. "Now," he continued after an almost imperceptible pause, "I'm going to give you a glass of the best port in England—the Gee port. How it got its name is a curious story. It comes from the cellars of a Mr. Gee, who chose the wine for King Edward VII and was also his personal friend. Gee was originally butler for two elderly maiden ladies, heiresses in their own right, who became so dependent upon him that when he announced that he was going to retire they were in despair.

"Finally the younger one suggested to her sister that perhaps Gee might be induced to stay if she married him. So she proposed and he, rather diffidently I assume, accepted, and the menage continued as theretofore. Then the older sister died leaving everything she owned to the younger, and eventually Mrs. Gee herself died leaving everything to Gee. The relatives tried unsuccessfully to upset the will, Gee being represented in the litigation by a young barrister named Preston whom he had met quite accidentally.

"Gee, the ex-butler, was now one of the richest men in England. He wasn't too old to enjoy good living, so he bought a string of race horses, and in this way met King Edward, who took a fancy to him. Before long he became quite a figure in society, and one of the inner court circle.

"He greatly admired Preston, of whose services in the will contest he held an exaggerated opinion, so, when he came to make his own will, and had disposed of a large part of his fortune to charity, he told Preston that he would leave the rest to him on condition that he should assume the name of Gee (thereafter calling himself Preston-Gee), should marry and have male issue before he reached the age of forty years. Preston, expressing proper appreciation, said that he would do his best.

" 'But,' said Preston, 'to whom is it to go if I don't fulfill the conditions?' Gee couldn't think of a living soul.

" 'Haven't you any relatives?' asked Preston.

" 'They are all dead,' answered Gee.

" 'How about friends?'

" 'You're the only real friend I've got, Mr. Preston,' replied Gee.

" 'Well,' said Preston, 'why not leave it to someone who has been kind to you?'

"Gee pondered a long time. Finally he said:

" 'Except for my dear wife and her sister I can't think of anyone who has ever been kind to me—unless it was a young chap who once gave me a salmon! I forget his name but he was staying with us in Scotland and one day when he came in from fishing he said: 'Hello, Gee! How would you like to have a salmon?' And

I said: 'Very much, thank you, sir,' and he turned to the gilly and told him to give me one. Yes, he was kind to me. Let's put him in.'

"'What was his name,' asked Preston.

"'I don't remember,' said Gee, 'but I think I can find it if I look over my diaries.'

"He did find it and the young man's name was inserted in the will without his knowledge as the contingent remainder-man who should take if Preston did not fulfill the conditions. Well, not long after Gee was gathered in and Preston, who had in the property what you and I would call 'a life interest subject to be divested', started in to enjoy himself. He, too, bought a string of race horses, but although he married an attractive girl he never had a male child and was killed in the hunting field at the age of thirty-nine years and six months!"

"And the young man with the salmon inherited the entire property?" I asked.

"Right you are! And he has it yet. But Gee had owned so much wine—particularly port—that a few years ago the salmon lad sold part of it and I was lucky enough to capture a bottle or two."

"Quite a yarn!" I murmured. Somehow the port seemed to have acquired an extra throaty flavor while he had been telling it. And yet, I thought afterwards, the story of the Gee port was not much more fantastic than my own experience with those three other old maids, the Ewen sisters, and the bogus Baron Botto von Koenitz.

Encountering Lord Montagu at the Garrick Club not long after, I told him in response to his inquiry as to how I had been spending my time, about the grand dinner that had been given for me, including a complete roster of the titled guests, the Gee port, and the man with the curls.

"The Gee story is quite correct," he nodded. "It was a famous case." He paused with a whimsical expression. "And you actually told your host that the curly-haired man looked like a Jew?"

"I did," I replied. "And he was!"

Montagu collapsed into an armchair.

"My dear fellow," he said, "every person at the dinner, except yourself, was a Jew!"

A couple of my Harvard contemporaries had become dons at Cambridge and I spent a week there, lodging with a Mrs. Winter at "The Miller's House" by the ancient bridge over the Cam three miles distant at Grantchester. The Miller's House was several hundred years old having been built on the alleged site of that occupied by the miller in Chaucer's Canterbury Tales. It was surrounded by a garden and orchard which, adjoining those of Rupert Brooke next door, sloped gently to the river. It was pleasant to stroll across the meadows, watching the Cantabs punting on the lazy stream, with the delicate spires of Trinity in the distance, until I reached the green lawns of the "Backs" where I would lie in the shade smoking a stogy and dream of the history that had been made in those ancient quadrangles behind me. Nowhere else had I so realized the overwhelming influence of tradition which makes Englishmen so insistent upon their rights, —especially when one of my dons told me that, according to immemorial custom, even today a student could claim the privilege of playing marbles on the steps of the Senate or of setting up a target in Petty Curie, the town's busiest street, and using it as a place in which to practice archery.

I went back to London with haunting memories of ivy-covered walls, of dinners in hall with scholars of international reputation, of breakfasts in the chambers of dons in flowered dressing gowns, who quoted Grecian odes while weighing the comparative merits of various vintages of port, and of long afternoons upon the river where I sometimes had to part the overhanging branches to let my wherry through, and of dinners in Mrs. Winter's garden in the late English sunlight.

Among the guests at Lord Montagu's had been a Mrs. Calthrop, an attractive young American woman married to an

Englishman and living at nearby Lyndhurst. We had inter-
changed but a few words and I was naturally surprised a fortnight later to receive a telegram from her stating that she would
like to retain my services and asking me to meet her at the Ritz
next day, but not to reply since she would be there in any event.
My curiosity thus aroused I managed to find Montagu at the
Royal Automobile Club and asked him to tell me something
about her.

"Nora Calthrop is one of the finest women in the world," he
said. "Her father is old Frank Wendell of Pittsburgh and one of
the richest men in America. Woodley Calthrop, her husband, a
younger son of Lord Hammersly, married her for her money and
he's been openly unfaithful to her ever since. There are two
children—Peter, four years old, and Bess, two. Calthrop hasn't a
cent. He lives on the allowance her father gives her."

"Why doesn't she divorce him?" I asked.

"She can't under our law, which requires proof of cruelty in
addition to that of adultery and he's been careful not to be cruel
in the technical sense."

"Why doesn't she take the children and leave him?"

"Because if she did she'd land in jail. Calthrop's got clever
counsel. He's been shrewd enough to deposit £50 to the credit
of each child with the Lord Chancellor, which makes them wards
in Chancery. She can't take them out of England without making
herself liable to imprisonment for contempt."

"Hasn't she got lawyers of her own?"

"She has excellent solicitors—Skiffington, Wells & Co. They
tell her she's helpless under English law unless she accedes to
Calthrop's terms."

"What do you mean—'terms'?"

"He's willing to sell her the boy and girl for £100,000 apiece."

"What an infernal skunk!"

"He's a bad 'un!" agreed Montagu.

I spent the afternoon in Sir Rothwell Sommersly's chambers
checking on the English divorce law and when I went to the Ritz

to meet my client next day I had a clear idea of the plight she was in.

Mrs. Calthrop must have been a beauty once, but already her dark-brown hair had lost its lustre and there were hollows around her eyes. She told me her story in a few words, adding that while her father would like nothing better than to have her return home to America and bring the grandchildren with her, he refused to be blackmailed by her rascally husband. She was absolutely at the end of her rope, she said, and begged me to do something for her. I don't know why, but she seemed to have faith that I could.

I asked her if she was willing to defy the law and to undergo some hardship and even risk for the sake of her freedom, and to this she replied that she would do anything to get her children safely out of England. I already had a plan—suggested curiously enough by my visit to Highcliffe Castle a few Sundays before— simply to have Nora Calthrop kidnap her children, put them on a steamer, and take them across the Atlantic. It would cost money and some delicate manoeuvering but, although I realized that her every movement was watched, I felt that with a free hand I could handle the matter successfully.

I now thanked Heaven for the delay occasioned by Sir William Tremayne's press of business. First, I told her, she ought to consult her solicitors and offer to let them undertake the affair. Only if they refused would I act independently. Skiffington, Wells & Co. not only did refuse when the proposition was put up to them but expressed the utmost legal horror. That left me free. Now it so happened that old Frank Wendell was president of the Pittsburgh Iron & Steel Company for which Wiegand & Tutt had recently won a case, and I cabled him direct outlining the situation and its difficulties and asking for his approval and an expense account of £10,000. His reply was short and to the point.

"Am cabling funds to your order Brown Bros. Also to my London associates in Standard Oil Co. for whatever assistance may be needed. Go as far as you like."

The Standard Oil Company officials proved most cooperative and informed me that an empty tanker happened to be sailing for New York the next week. It would be simple to anchor her in the Solent a mile or two off Christ Church. All Mrs. Calthrop need do would be to get aboard her.

The children presented the only real difficulty—Calthrop might refuse to let them leave Lyndhurst. Nora thought she could get around that by telling him that they needed to see a dentist in London. Calthrop, if he came down over Sunday, always returned to the city on Monday morning. If so the rest ought to be easy. The tanker would arrive on Sunday. On Monday afternoon or on whatever day her husband left Lyndhurst she, her maid and the two children would take the afternoon train for London, having bought through tickets to avoid suspicion. At Basingstoke, however, they should all get out. I would be waiting for them there in a closed car and motor them back to the coast to a hamlet near Christ Church where a launch would be waiting. By midnight they would be outside the three-mile limit and the Lord Chancellor could go hang.

It seemed hard to believe that I wasn't talking balderdash, that in the twentieth century, when fifteen million men had just died for freedom, an Englishman who was brazenly unfaithful to his wife and did nothing to support her or her children could nevertheless hold them all prisoners under a legal fiction, and could arbitrarily refuse to allow a woman, whom he had deceived and with whom he no longer wished to live, to take the children and return to her family. Was it conceivable that in that quiet countryside, if she took a single step to exert her natural maternal rights over her offspring, some bewigged functionary, sitting in smoky chambers before a green baise-covered desk in London, would issue a writ of attachment, and hand it to a clerk, who would deliver it to a sheriff commanding him to "take into his custody the body of said Nora, the wife of said Woodley Calthrop, and produce her before him, the said Lord Chancellor, for chastisement," or that if the said Nora wanted to keep her body for her own uses and refused to go with the sheriff or whatever, the telegraph instruments would begin to click, and sleepy constables would be routed out of bed, and posses assembled, and the yeomanry summoned if need be, and the coast guard notified, and the Admiralty send wireless messages for destroyers—all because said Nora, out of love for her children, wished to bring them up beyond the reach of a drunken, dissolute father? Could that be England?

I took Montagu into my confidence, wished myself on him for another visit at Beaulieu, and from there prowled up and down the coast until I had found the place I wanted. Then I chartered a sea-worthy motor boat for a week on liberal terms. Sunday I motored to Highcliffe and watched the empty tanker as, her Plymsol line high out of water, she swung slowly in and stopped two miles off shore. That night I prayed for clear weather and got it. Monday was an absolutely still day. I didn't dare telephone Nora at Lyndhurst, but I knew that she would have let me know if anything had occurred to spike our plan.

So I motored to Basingstoke and waited for her train to come by; and no sooner had the engine stopped than they all tumbled out, Nora white faced and jittery. Next instant I had slammed the door of the limousine and we were off, roaring southward in the dusk whence she had come, now slowing up to rumble through a half-lighted town, then hurtling on through miles of countryside. The weather had changed and by the time we reached Southampton it was raining and we were running along narrow country by-roads through a thick mist which turned back the headlights like a stone wall. Once near Munster we stopped suddenly, confronted by the huge white face of an astounded cart horse surrounded by a frosty halo, and shortly after that we slowed down as the road became soft and rutty, and now and again a bush scratched the sides.

I felt as if we had been traveling all night and began to wonder if we would ever find the place where I had ordered the boat to be. And then I smelled the sea, I saw the distant lights of Christ

Church and with a bump and a lurch we stopped. A sailor in dripping oilskins stood by the roadside holding a lantern and I knew that the launch was only a few yards away hidden in the reeds. We followed him through the slime of the marsh to where it lay and next instant its bottom ground over the silt, slid free and slipped into the current. The tide was running out and the launch swayed and swung half round sideways. Distant lights—white lights—were running by in streaks. She began to bob up and down. There was a stench of gasoline.

Suddenly with a roar the engine started and she straightened out and spanking the waves shot ahead. We ran into a high sea and bucked it for twenty minutes, the launch doing all sorts of queer things, lifting itself high into the air and gyrating downward again with a strange, scooping motion, then rising again on a staggering roller that I thought would overturn us— up—up—into a blinding yellow beam. Hoarse shouts from above were borne on the wind. The engine stopped and we shot around the tanker's stern into still water to the companion-way. Rough but kindly hands grasped Nora and Peter and Bess and lifted them to safety. I stood clinging to the ropework looking after her. Once on deck she turned and threw me a kiss.

"Goodbye! Thanks! God bless you!" she called down.

"God bless you!" I answered.

When the launch reached the cove the tanker was far out to sea with only her stern lights visible. I gave the engineer and the sailor an extra £5 apiece and sloughed through the mud back to the car, only realizing as I sank against its cushions what a strain I had been under.

And the Lord Chancellor never uttered a peep! Nora Calthrop reached America safely, secured a divorce from her English husband and a few years afterwards married again. She is one of my best friends and clients. While I have never practiced law in England I feel that I have done the next best thing to it. Important changes in the English divorce laws were made by the

Matrimonial Causes Act of 1937. No similar situation to that I have described could arise today.

And then, just as I was wondering whether I hadn't better take a motor trip with Saltonstall through the Lake Country and perhaps visit the Scottish Highlands, Sir William Tremayne unexpectedly announced that in his opinion *Skillings* vs. *Mainwaring* did not apply and, before I knew it, Fortesque, Saddlecloth & Co. had settled the case, and I had no excuse for staying in England any longer.

XV

PERSONAL HISTORY

MY TRIP to England had a permanent influence upon my point of view. I was fifty-four years old. I had worked hard and won a considerable success. I had lived frugally and could, in fact, have retired on the modest income from my investments. I was tired of advising corporations and of defending cases the only result of which would be that someone got a lot of money that usually might just as well have belonged to someone else. I longed for complete independence, for cases involving more human interest, for time to read and to think and, above all, to get into the woods. If I could not be a Sir William Tremayne, I could at least be a smaller edition of him. I had my little house, I had Mandy and I had another C.J. If I could get off for three solid months of fishing every summer what more could I ask?

Otto was now an outstanding figure at the bar; his works on corporation and constitutional law were standard authorities; so when Governor Whitman designated him to fill an unexpired term on the Supreme Court bench it was natural that he should have accepted it and, a few months later after receiving a joint nomination by both major political parties, have been elected. I was alone again. Of course I could have tied up with some other firm and gone right on: In fact I did receive several flattering offers; but I wanted to live the rest of my life in my own way.

Through Otto I had become a friend of Associate Justice Oliver Wendell Holmes. Whenever I went to Washington I made a point of calling upon him and paying my respects, for I always came away refreshed and stimulated. On the whole he was the greatest gentleman I have ever been privileged to know—a distinguished legal cavalier. No one would have suspected from his modest and almost child-like simplicity that he was the most illustrious figure ever to have sat as a Justice of the Supreme Court of the United States. At home he was both gay and familiar, but behind it one always felt the reserve that came from his New England tradition and patrician position. A voluble and picturesque talker with an obvious liking for paradox and startling analogy, he combined with it an extraordinary gift for compression that may have made him seem profounder than he was. What fascinated me was his impatience with question-begging words and the way he cut to the root of things. Although there was more than a hint of scepticism in his philosophy, you felt while listening to him that you were taking part in a romantic adventure and that life was a thrilling experience to be lived valiantly and dangerously.

One afternoon after having tea with him I found a telephone message at my hotel asking me to go over to the White House. I had not seen Cal for over a year. Naturally I had not wanted to force myself upon him now that he occupied so exalted a position, and I wondered how he knew of my whereabouts. I got there about six o'clock and an aide took me at once to the Lincoln Study where he was at work. He got up with a faint smile and shook hands rather limply. He naturally looked older and plumper but in general his contours were the same. His carroty hair, which had first turned chestnut, was beginning to look a dusty gray. But he had the same strong nose and firm chin, intelligent, eager eyes and rather mean mouth. We sat down and I waited for him to speak, but he didn't. We just sat. Finally he said:

"Eph, how'd you like to be a judge of the United States Circuit Court of Appeals?"

The suggestion startled me.

"You do me a great honor, Mr. President," I replied after a moment. "But I'm afraid I'd make a very poor judge. I haven't the temperament. Anyhow, I much prefer to remain in private practice." He showed no surprise.

"Holmes mentioned you," he said. "I thought I'd give you a chance at it. There's a pretty good salary attached."

"I've got enough money for my wants," I said.

There was another long silence, and to break it I asked:

"Do you get any fishing these days?"

"All I want," he said. "I never did care for it half as much as you did." He looked at me with what seemed like complete solemnity. "I guess the main reason I used to go with you back home was so I could trade you those worms for pins."

"How does it feel to be President of the United States?"

He weighed the question for nearly a quarter of a minute.

"Well," he said finally, "you got to be mighty careful."

He was a long way from Windsor County, Vermont, but I sensed that he was even further than that from me. Cal Coolidge had expressed his entire philosophy in those six words—"You got to be mighty careful!"

I went back to New York fully satisfied with my decision. I had spoken truly when I had said that I did not have the judicial temperament. I never could have brought myself "to play the game according to the rules"—as Holmes once said it was a judge's business to do. I did not like rules which did not make for specific justice, and I wanted to be free to speak my mind about them as I am doing in this book.

Later when Cal learned that I was coming to Washington again to attend the Gridiron Club dinner he invited me to spend a week end at the White House. I arrived about five o'clock and was at once shown upstairs where Grace was having tea. She gave me a hearty welcome and explained that the president was taking a nap in preparation for the evening's festivities. She had not changed in the slightest. She was the same attractive, cordial, interested woman she had been when I knew her in Northampton. It is no wonder that she is said to have inspired more real affection among the people of Washington than any other Lady of the White House in history. Her popularity almost made up for Cal's lack of it.

It is only to be expected that an effort should have been made for political reasons to gloss over his peculiarities and picture him as a sort of Yankee Will Rogers with a dry wit that showed itself in pithy sayings. Well, I knew Cal for over half a century.

I never heard him say anything that I regarded as witty, and many of the remarks that were heralded as examples of Coolidge humor he meant seriously. He had a perverse streak that led him to do and say eccentric things which he did not intend to be funny at all. I think the truth of the matter to be that he was a thin lipped, cautious New Englander, and since the Americans as a whole did not understand him they had to invent another and somewhat more appealing figure. I sat near him that night at the Gridiron Club dinner and for two hours he neither cracked a smile nor uttered a word. He did not enjoy the jokes at his expense and on the way back to the White House he remarked that "all that tom-foolery" was a waste of money.

One morning the Negro valet waked me at half-past six and told me that the President was going to take his usual walk before breakfast and hoped that I would go with him. I was not enthusiastic over the idea but I saw no way out of it, got up, and dressed. Cal was already in the hall when I came down. So was Jim Haley the secret service man assigned as his bodyguard.

"Come along, Eph," he said, "I'll tell that long-legged Haley man to stay behind."

We walked for forty-five minutes but there was no further conversation until we were coming up the drive to the portico.

"I'm having some Congressmen to breakfast," he said. "They won't stay long."

The Congressmen—two senators and three members of the House of Representatives—were waiting for him and Cal shook hands perfunctorily and then led the way to the dining room. I expected that these statesmen had been called together to discuss some important matter connected with public policy, but it soon transpired that this was not the case. The President made no conversational effort and the others, embarrassed, muttered or whispered among themselves. No one knew why they had been asked and apparently Cal did not either—except to eat breakfast. At the end of about thirty minutes he got up, gave each a handshake and a mumbled "Glad you could come" and they departed.

These breakfasts were so notoriously dismal that those who were invited would resort to every imaginable excuse to avoid coming. In one instance eight senators declined in a row. I found out afterwards that a meal at which a public official had been a guest could be charged to "public entertaining." Cal was certainly economical. During his incumbency the White House bought the supplies for its kitchen and pantry from the Piggly-Wiggly and Sanitary Grocery Chain.

I never could tell whether economy or eccentricity was the controlling element in some of his acts. For example he never allowed anyone to sit in the same automobile with him when he went to church. The following Sunday morning there were two open cars standing under the portico. Grace had a headache and was not going, so I naturally expected to sit with Cal. Not at all! He climbed into the first by himself and pointing to the other said "You take that one, Eph." The result was that he rode alone while I followed in the car behind. I wish some psychologist would explain why he did this. Did Cal wish to savor his importance by riding in solitary state? It seems hardly likely. Did he consider that the White House chauffeurs had too easy a time? Possibly. Or did he regard the garage and its contents as something which he was entitled to use and wished to make the most of the privilege while it lasted? Probably a mixture of all three or some other mysterious factor of which he was unaware himself. Did he perhaps in small ways like to exercise power, as when, pointing to the Stuart portrait of John Adams which he could see from the state dining room as it hung on the wall of the Red Room, he said according to Ike Hoover: "I'm tired of seeing that old bald head. Have some hair put on it." *

Ike told me that out in South Dakota near the presidential lodge among the Black Hills the local inhabitants released fifteen hundred trout in the stream nearby, keeping them within bounds with nets. Cal fished with worms, but he wore white gloves and

---

* In point of fact the picture was touched up with turpentine so that it did look as if it had some hair.

the hook was baited and the fish grudgingly removed by the secret service men. Once a stranger caught some trout just in front of the Coolidge Camp. Cal sent one of the men to take them away from him, saying: "They are my fish." Grace made such fun of his wearing the white gloves that he eventually replaced them with a darker shade. Whether he fished because the trout were there and he thought he might as well have them, or because it seemed like good publicity, I don't know.

Cal may have been too careful. He had been president six years and there was the threat of a third term issue being raised if he ran in 1928, but he was canny enough to know, as William Allen White had said, that he represented "something definite in the American heart." I am aware of the strong evidence that has been adduced to prove that, when he issued his statement in August 1927 "I do not choose to run for president in Nineteen Twenty-eight," he had made up his mind not to do so. But with my knowledge of his character I am personally of the opinion that he chose his words carefully to see what the reaction would be and never really intended his declaration to be taken as it was. It was in the nature of a "trial balloon." I believe that he was bitterly disappointed at the result, for he was the logical Republican candidate; and that in the end he was humiliated and angry at not being re-nominated and would not have been disturbed had Hoover lost the election.

But to come back to my law practice again. I had plenty to keep me as busy as I wanted to be. My old Cambridge friend, Miss Abegail Pidgeon, had died, leaving a will naming me as executor and trustee of her residuary estate amounting to half a million dollars, the income of which she directed me to distribute at my discretion "among such victims of injustice as shall be in need of legal assistance or otherwise." Thus I had at my disposal between fifteen and twenty thousand dollars a year to give away. Of course I could have turned all, or part of it, over to the New York Legal Aid Society and, such of the balance as I did not personally distribute, to the Association for Improving the Condition of the Poor, but I know that that would not have met her wishes. She wanted the money distributed directly and without red tape by someone in whom she had confidence and who had personal knowledge of the needs of the recipients. I would not have had the fun of giving this money away had I become a judge or had my clients continued to be bankers, industrialists or the heads of corporations. I must go out into the highways and byways—along the water front, to the East Side, to the foreign sections, back to the criminal courts, for the kind of persons Miss Pidgeon had in mind.

Not that I intended to give up general practice. I had an excellent working staff, headed by Minerva Wiggin, my efficient chief clerk, now a gray-haired woman, with Bonnie Doon, Ezra Scraggs, my alcoholic scrivener, and Willie Toothaker, already grown to manhood and admitted to the bar. If, as I planned to do from now on, I practiced law for the fun of it, they would be all the help I needed. We would shut up shop at 5:30 p.m. and close entirely on Saturdays.

So on January 1, 1924, I moved into a small sunny suite on the top floor of a Broadway building from the windows of which I could look across the Hudson to the Palisades and down the harbor to where Liberty stood holding her flaming torch. I hung "Wasgatt's Cow" over the fireplace and stuck my rods, creel and fishing things in the corner where they'd be handy in the event of a hurry call.

"Minerva," I announced, "I don't want any window dressing to this office—no 'dog,' as the expression is, except, of course, the Chief Justice—and he can sleep under my desk. If I want anything I propose to yell for it. If anyone asks to see me, shoot him in. In this office all peddlers, musicians, book agents, vagabonds and dogs are going to be welcome. Moreover, I propose to have five o'clock tea every afternoon for the entire office force, and I want you to serve it.—Understand?"

Her gray eyes regarded me whimsically; Minerva is really a very nice looking woman.

"If we can induce Mr. Scraggs to drink tea, I'm all for it. I'm all for it, anyway, I guess. You're old enough to know what you want." She glanced at my widely distributed piscatorial paraphernalia. "Even if this place does look more like a sporting goods store than a law office!"

"All the better!" I retorted. "It'll help our clients to forget their troubles."

She shook her head.

"I'm afraid you won't have any clients. Can you imagine a railroad president handing you any business with that stuffed codfish up there grinning down at him?"

I winced.

"Please! Don't call it a cod, Minerva! It's a trout—a *salvelinus fontinalis*—the biggest ever caught in the Mohawk Valley!"

She went over and examined it.

"That ivory plate says it's a cow.—It reads 'Wasgatt's Cow. May 13, 1895.'"

So I explained to her how I had credited the trout against my fee in a chattel mortgage case.

"No wonder you didn't make any money!" she said.

"I had a lot of fun—and now I'm going to have it again!" I said. "I shall take all the time off I want."

But it did not work out that way. Most of Wiegand & Tutt's old clients followed me to Broadway, and since I had no one to carry on in my absence, I found my vacations seriously curtailed. It was not the trial end—I could almost always persuade a judge to grant me an adjournment—but the consultations and preparation of cases that interfered with my liberty. In fact I was sometimes tempted to give up the law entirely. What I needed was a responsible partner to brief my cases and carry on when I went on my fishing trips. Where would I ever find another O-T-T-O, always "the same coming and going" as he used to say—who would sacrifice his own well-earned leisure, and put up with my idiosyncrasies and vagaries?

One day along in the spring of 1925, when I had just received a telegram from my guide Donald McKay in New Brunswick that the ice had gone out of the Miramichi and that the salmon were taking the fly, Minerva announced that a Mr. Tutt was calling to see me. She seemed highly amused.

"Tutt?" I exclaimed. "I thought I was the one and only Tutt—anyhow in this neck of the woods! Show him in by all means!"

The new Tutt was a stocky, bespectacled, carefully dressed man between forty-five and fifty, with a pronounced abdominal convexity, round red cheeks, and a pointed nose. Standing in the doorway, with his hands under his coat tails and his abdomen thrust out in front of him while he teetered slowly back and forth on his heels, he made me think of an oversized woodpecker. He spoke like one, too, in sharp quick raps.

"My name's Tutt, Mr. Tutt," he said. "Samuel. Any opening in your office?"

He looked in fact exactly as a man named Tutt should look.

"I don't know," I answered. "Why do you come to me?"

"Because with you I should be associated with a good name," he answered seriously, although I could have sworn that he winked.

"That might go double," I said. "Where do you come from?"

"Bangor, Maine," he answered. "Belong to the Abijah Tutt branch. You're one of the Elijahs. Same family, though. Twin brothers back in 1635. We're sixteenth cousins.—Not near enough to kiss."

"God forbid!" I said.

"Metaphorically only! My other assets: AB and LL.B. University of Maine, five years' practice in Bangor, ten years in New York as managing clerk for Nickerson, Spratt & Greely—five years by myself.—Don't get on with my wife.—Like work. Keeps me away from her." He spoke innocently but, although I couldn't be sure, I thought he winked again. At that moment Chief Justice II emerged from under the table, sniffed Tutt critically around the pant-cuffs, then placing his paws on one of the carefully creased trouser-legs wagged his tail. "Woof!" he said, meaning "Judgment for the plaintiff."

"You have been approved by the Committee on Admissions," I said. "It so happens that I've just been called away on important business. I shall be gone about three weeks. You can take over in my absence and, if the office is still here on my return and no one has sued me for malpractice, we can talk turkey."

That was the origin of the firm of Tutt & Tutt. Pure chance! And I might have combed the New York bar for years without finding a man so nearly ideal for my purpose. He was thoroughly read in the law, an expert pleader and draughtsman, revelled in technicalities and, in preparing a case for trial, left no point uncovered. When Tutt hands me a brief I don't have to interview the witnesses in advance of trial or look up any law. Everything is down in black and white, right in front of me. Tutt even puts in stage directions, such as "Rub chin here," or "At this point get off that old gag about bananas," or "Here show indignation."

The members of the firm of Tutt & Tutt are today the necessary component parts of a harmonious legal whole. We are—or at least were for a long time—the only Tutts in the city and it seemed appropriate—if we had not already been hanged separately—that we should now hang together. Tutt's industry, activity and ingenuity have made him indispensable to me, and he has a dry New England humor that warms the cockles of my heart. It is immaterial to him what a case is about—whether it deals with the "next eventual estate" or the proper damages for a dog bite; he tackles them all with equal enthusiasm, and, largely due to Tutt, the firm has prospered in spite of my increasing absences. He also affords, after Otto's intense gravity, an element of comic relief.

By the time I had returned, after having transacted the important business on the Miramichi on which I had been called away at the time of Tutt's arrival, he had already started on the road to fame. One of our clients, a Mr. Newbegin, having ordered a kidney stew at the restaurant of a certain well-known hotel, discovered that it contained a well-cooked mouse and was greatly wroth. In vain the owner of the hostelry offered to furnish him with the most elaborate meal that could be prepared, champagne included, free of charge, but Mr. Newbegin, carefully preserving the remains of the mouse in an envelope, sought the legal advice of my new partner, who promptly sued the proprietor of the hotel for damages, and proving his case by the articulated bones—a neat job—won a verdict of $3,500. The Court of Appeals later sustained the verdict in the following words, quoted verbatim from Tutt's brief:

"The only legal question in the case, or so it appears to us, is whether there is such a sale of food to a guest on the part of the proprietor as will sustain a warranty. If we are not in error, however, the law is settled and has been since the reign of Henry the Sixth. In the Ninth Year Book of that Monarch's reign there is a case in which it was held that 'If I go to a tavern to eat, and the taverner gives and sells me meat and it corrupted, whereby I am made very sick, action lies against him without any express warranty for there is a warranty in law; and in the time of Henry the Seventh the learned Justice Keilway said, 'No man can justify selling corrupt victual, but an action lies against the seller, whether the victual was warranted to be good or not.' Now, certainly, whether mouse meat be or be not deleterious to health a guest at a hotel who orders a portion of kidney stew has the right to expect, and the hotel keeper impliedly warrants, that such dish will contain no ingredients beyond those ordinarily placed therein."

"Thirty-five hundred dollars!" chirped Tutt. "I'd eat mouse any day in the week for $3,500."

Probably in no other New York law office was there a scene similar to that enacted daily in that of Tutt & Tutt. Promptly at five o'clock, irrespective of what business might be on hand, Willie Toothaker dragged out the old gate-leg table, brought in the tea things, lit the kettle, and then hurried out for scones and muffins. Gradually the force would assemble around Miss Wiggin;—myself, as head of the office, then Tutt, followed by old Scraggs, Miss Sondheim the chief stenographer, and usually last Bonnie Doon. Here we would have as many cups as we liked and munching our scones engage in office chit chat and go over the events of the day. On these occasions all bars were down and anyone was free to say anything that came into his or her head. It is a pleasant and friendly custom which I still keep up.

Minerva Wiggin had a lot of fun pulling my new partner's leg. I remember one afternoon as she handed him his cup of tea he remarked casually: "Oscar Wilde says in his 'The Decay of Lying' that there is no essential incongruity between crime and culture."

"I go him one better," she answered. "I say that there is a distinct relationship between crime and progress."

"How do you make that out?" he asked, taking a bite out of a muffin.

"It's very simple," she said. "Crime is the violation of the will of the majority as expressed in the statutes. The law is arbitrary and depends upon public opinion. Acts which are crimes in one century or country may be virtues in another. Moreover, there is no difference, except one of degree, between infractions of etiquette and of law, each of which expresses the feelings and ideas of society at a given moment. Violations of good taste, manners, morals, wrongs, illegalities, crimes are fundamentally the same thing, the insistence on one's will in defiance of society as a whole. The man who keeps his hat on in a drawing room is essentially a criminal because he prefers his own way of doing things to that adopted by his fellows."

"That's all right, but how about progress?" he demanded.

"The man who refuses to bow to habit, tradition, or law, who thinks for himself, who evolves new theories, who has the courage of his convictions and stakes his life and liberty upon them—that man is either a statesman, a prophet or a criminal. In the end he is either hailed as a hero and a liberator or is sent into prison, burned at the stake, or crucified."

"I see," said Tutt. "Your proposition is that progress depends on development and development depends on new ideas. If the new idea is contrary to those of society it very likely is criminal. If its inventor gets away with it—persuades society that he is right—he becomes a leader in the march of progress. If he fails he goes to jail. Very interesting. Why not say that crime *is* progress?"

"If successful it is. In New York it is a crime to kill one's grandmother; among certain savages it is regarded as a virtuous act. If I convince society that to kill one's grandmother is a good thing it ceases to be a crime. Society has progressed."

"Has it?" inquired Tutt. "I don't agree with you. I like my grandmother. Looking at it that way, you'd think criminals were rather to be admired!"

"Well, some of them are, and certainly a great number of them were," she said. "All the Christian martyrs were technically criminals. Every rebel begins as a traitor and hence a criminal; if he succeeds he may become the 'Father of His Country.'"

"Are you by any chance referring to George Washington?" he snorted. "I never heard such sophistry. It sounds all right but you can drive a horse and cart right through it. The fact that some saints and patriots were criminals, doesn't make all criminals saints and patriots by a long shot. Your proposition is only a half truth."

"It is nothing of the sort," retorted Minerva. "I say that the man who wears a red necktie in violation of the taste of his community or eats peas with his knife is just as much a criminal as a man who spits on a subway platform when there's a law against it. Nevertheless he may become a Ward McAllister or an Emily Post."

"The moral of which," I interpolated, "is that the law ought to be very careful about locking people up—it might catch a patriot or a prophet."

"At any rate it ought to be careful about punishing those who have violated laws upon which there can be a difference of opinion," commented Minerva.

"That's where Tutt & Tutt come in," said Tutt. "We make a difference even if there was none before."

"We perform a dual service to society," I declared. "We prevent the law from making mistakes and so keep it from falling into disrepute, and we show up its weak points and thus enable it to be improved."

"You've got a crumb on your chin," said Minerva. "You're a criminal, but you're a dear!"

I cannot say that since leaving Pottsville I had never looked after a pretty woman, but to use the phrase of Anthony Trollope "no skirt had rustled for me." The only women I ever thought about were my mother and Esther, although the one had been dead nearly forty years and I had not seen the other for thirty. Esther was now the president of Ramona, a woman's college in California, and her husband was still alive, going stronger than ever. She was by this time nearly fifty, but her letters showed that she had retained her youthful spirit and outlook, and although I might have met her without danger to my emotional stability I preferred to think of her as I remembered her and as she was in the photograph above my desk. Our devotion had not lessened with the years but had in fact increased with our mutual knowledge of each other's character. I loved her more than ever, but it was like being in love with a charming ghost with whom I could regularly converse. That part of my life was in another and sacred dimension to which only Esther and I had access. So I never joined the baldheaded row or played the elderly uncle to young girls. Although I liked to watch beautiful women and listen to clever ones I rarely thought about them afterwards and I had few women friends.

Uncle Isaac Furman, however, although now a very old man liked to have them around him. He frequently gave little dinners at his house, afterwards taking his guests to the opera and when he was short of men I sometimes filled in. His box, at the end of the auditorium next to Mrs. Cornelius Vanderbilt's, was exceptionally large, easy of exit and fitted with upholstered armchairs. It was opera-going *de luxe*. One night he called me up at the last minute and asked me to take the place of a man who had unexpectedly been obliged to drop out. There were eight in the party, two married couples, Miss Beekman, Uncle Isaac, myself, and a plump bejewelled woman, with an elaborate coiffure of palpably dyed blond hair. Mrs. Spofford's obvious effort to make herself agreeable to me I attributed to the number of cocktails she imbibed before dinner, but during the intermission, the rest of the party having left the box, she turned abruptly and demanded: "Don't you recognize me, Ephraim?"

I was naturally embarrassed. I have an excellent memory for faces, if not for names, but I had no recollection of having ever before laid eyes on the lady.

"I must apologize for my wretched memory!" I said. "I'm afraid I'm getting old—"

"Nonsense!" she interrupted. "You're exactly fifty-five—in the prime of life. Do you mean to say that you have entirely forgotten Priscilla Boardman?"

I stared blankly at her. Could this be the dark, slender, boyish girl I had taught in my Harvard vacations? Everything that had been soft about her face had disappeared, leaving an enamelled masque of stereotyped beauty. It wasn't possible!

She gave a short impatient laugh.

"I can't say you're very complimentary. Of course you'll say it's the name and the hair—not the thirty-three years! But I know all about you, Ephraim. I've read of your cases and followed your career. Uncle Isaac is my trustee, you see."

The orchestra was returning to their places, and the audience drifting back to their seats.

"It's so nice to meet you again, Ephraim," she said hurriedly as the draft from the box door swayed the curtains. "I'd love a chat about the old days. I hear you have a charming house. I'm leaving tomorrow morning. Couldn't you whisk me over there just for a minute after the opera? You can say that you're dropping me at my hotel."

It was both an order and an appeal.

"I should be honored," I answered as the others took their seats.

The windows of London Terrace were dark, but I unlocked the door, turned on the lights and escorted my former love up the stairs to the library where she sank somewhat out of breath into one of my low armchairs. Then I pulled up a table, opened a bottle of Burgundy, and filled a couple of glasses.

"Here's to old times!" I said.

"I'd rather drink to the future!" she replied. "Think of my being here after all these years! I suppose the last time you heard of me was when I was married to Winthrop Winslow. Well, that only lasted four years. It was just as much a *mariage de convenance* as anything in Europe. We had nothing in common but our friends and the fact that we were used to doing the same things and living in a certain sort of way. I might just as well have married any other Porcellian man as Win. We were divorced way back in 1901."

She paused to light a cigarette.

"I want to tell you about my life, Ephraim, because after all you are one of my very oldest friends. I went abroad for awhile, and then I tried it again—this time with a man from Portland, Oregon. He was immensely rich and in all sorts of things. But I hadn't learned my lesson even then.—Basically it was the same sort of marriage as my first. Jack was all right, but I was simply bored to death. You can't believe how dull it was out there. I kept coming back east for longer and longer, until eventually I spent about twice as much time here as there. Even so we stayed married for twenty-three years. Then we decided there was nothing to it. Now I'm alone. Well, that's my sad story, Ephraim!"

"Poor Priscilla!" I said.

"Oh, there's plenty of kick in me yet," she retorted with her old sideways smile. "I get around—go places and have a good time, but sometimes I long for a home of my own. I've nothing to come back to!"

I asked her about her family. Her father and mother were both dead, she explained, and her brother, Eliot, Jr., was now a State Street bond broker. She never went back to Boston; it was too stuffy and provincial. London, Paris, New York were the only places fit to live in. And then she put up her lorgnette and began to scrutinize my library. It wasn't exactly condescending, it was rather proprietary, savoring of an incidental preliminary appraisal connected with a transaction she had tentatively decided upon.

"Very comfortable!" she said. "Quaint, but with possibilities. One could do a lot with it."

"I'm afraid it's a pretty shabby old affair—like its owner," I said.

"And you live here all by yourself?"

"Except for my dog and my cook."

She twisted the empty glass in her hand.

"Aren't you ever lonely?"

"Often," I admitted.

She put down the glass and looked at me.

"Everyone needs companionship—real companionship. It's terrible to look forward to a lonely old age."

"I have my books and my memories."

"I hope some of them are of—of Nahant!" she said. "Those summers by the sea were really wonderful, weren't they? We were so young and—everything!"

"To me—an inexperienced country boy—it was like fairy-land," I said. "I dreamed a lot of air castles in those days—but most of them crashed."

She looked at me again.

"As one gets older one realizes one's mistakes," she said.

There was a rather long pause as if she were waiting for something. The only sound was the soft hiss of the burning sea-coal on the hearth. Priscilla broke the silence.

"Have you ever thought of getting married?" she asked.

I let her wait. Then I got up and with a glance at the photograph over my desk gave the fire a poke.

"The woman I want to marry has a husband already," I told her. "I shall never marry any other."

I must admit that she took it very well.

"I understand," she answered. "Well, it's getting late and I must be moving along. It's been so nice to renew our acquaintance, Ephraim. You must come to see me sometime."

But she did not say where or when. I called a taxi and put her in it. She would not let me accompany her to her hotel.

"I'm used to looking out for myself," she said. "Goodbye!"

And then it came over me that Priscilla had undoubtedly been contaminated by the demoralizing atmosphere in which she lived—of casinos, beauty parlors, night clubs and suggestive reviews—and was now, too late, seeing the flatness and unreality of it. She had had an attack of fever and it had burned out, leaving her a discontented convalescent.

I had come back from England to a lawless America. The Prohibition Amendment had eaten into the moral fabric of the nation. If it was proper to beat the law by dealing with a bootlegger why wasn't it all right to bribe a Federal Income Tax agent? Speak-easy life was demoralizing morals even more than the Cavendish had done in London, for the speak-easy and blind tiger were to be found in every town and village in the land. Rosa Lewis at least had served her patrons with the best of vintage champagnes, but here the bootlegged gin was not only "cut" but often made from wood alcohol which caused permanent blindness.

There had been a revolution in the moral code of the country. The whole idea of modesty had gone by the board. Elderly women showed their calves and the flappers almost everything. There was a recognized conspiracy on the part of the young to have their fling and learn by experience, and fathers and mothers who agonized over the palpable lies their children told as to their whereabouts of the night before, were presently contaminated themselves. Lurid movies, sex and "confession" magazines aroused not only the adolescent but the mature, who began to wonder if they hadn't missed something they might just as well have had.

But the nation-wide revolt against convention that expressed itself in this lawlessness and the reckless satisfaction of sensual appetite had another side. It was also a revolt against the smug hypocrisy of those who hoped to keep things as they were and hence proclaimed them good. But the younger generation wanted to know why. They challenged all the accepted doctrines. This was particularly true of the youth who came back from the war. They not only perceived quite clearly that they could never earn a million dollars but they no longer much wanted to. This surprising fact also had its influence on the fathers who had managed to amass fortunes. *Cui bono?* The rich began to realize that man could not live by caviar and champagne alone. There was a recognition of and an outreaching towards new values. The youths whose ambition in 1900 had been to own a brownstone front, a Victoria with two men on the box, and to entertain the Vanderbilts, now derided the whole thing as "baloney." Why work yourself to death in order to give stuffy dinner parties of twenty, even if you did eat off gold plates? You had only one life to live, make the most of it. They were willing to work, to earn their bread, to prove their worth—but not to be bored; and the girls who had been brought up to eat off gold plates did bore them. Everything that savored of artificiality ceased to have attraction save for "sissies" and "pansies." They wanted a girl who knew something about life, who had wits and guts, could steer a canoe down a rapid and leave her French maid at home. So they married stenographers, business women, artists and writers, just girls who could cook and make beds as well as lie in them.

It wasn't confined to the boys, either. Plenty of rich debutantes after a fling at Newport and Bar Harbor married cowboys, chauffeurs, electricians and small town lads they happened to meet nobody knew where. None of them any longer expected to live on Fifth Avenue, were quite happy in a converted barn or on a ranch. "Society"—as an institution—ceased to exist. This was all very confusing to some of my worthy contemporaries who, sensible and able as they undoubtedly were, were still under the English spell of class and who regarded the Social Register as the next thing to Burke's Peerage.

Just as 1912 had been a red letter year for me, so for many reasons 1927 was another. I had visited England for the first time, declined the offer of a Federal judgeship, formed the firm of Tutt & Tutt and escaped the wiles of Priscilla Boardman. That was almost enough. Yet other things had happened more important to America at large and equally memorable.

Lindbergh had flown the Atlantic; Sacco and Vanzetti had been put to death after seven long years; business had become the American religion; the income of the Capone gang, then nearing its apogee, had reached the gigantic total of $100,000,-000; and Cal Coolidge had chosen not to run again thus leaving Herbert Hoover, the newly elected president of the United States, holding the bag—a bag stuffed with vastly greater troubles than Theodore Roosevelt in 1908 had bequeathed to Taft.

XVI

MURDER AND ITS DEFENSE

DESPITE its happy-go-lucky methods my new firm acquired before long a rather amazing practice together with a reputation for being able to pull legal rabbits out of hats. It was not entirely undeserved, since my partner had an uncanny gift for unearthing moribund or forgotten statutes or testing familiar ones by novel theories. Thus in addition to our regular business there flowed through our office a never-ending stream of peculiar matters; either turned over to us by other lawyers, who were doubtful as to their ability to handle them, or brought by unexpected clients who had heard of the supposed miracles we had wrought, but each having an exciting problem and leaving behind it some residuum of gold however small.

Samuel Tutt was an enthusiast in the defense of murder cases, and his ingenuity constantly amazed me. Statutes which up to that time had seemed as plain as the nose on one's face became under his analytical eye morasses of ambiguity. One day in 1931 while waiting to argue a motion in Part One, I was for a time an involuntary spectator at the trial of Eric Martin, a youth, hardly more than a boy, charged with a murder committed during a burglary, that is to say "felony murder." The prosecution claimed that he, with two others, had plotted to rob the pawnshop of one Leo Goldstein on Doyers Street; and that, while his accomplices went in and held up the owner, he had waited outside in a truck to assist in the getaway. Martin insisted that he had had no idea that any crime was contemplated and had driven the others to the place purely as an act of friendship. His story, however, was denied by one of the co-defendants, who although an ex-convict, had been permitted by the district attorney to turn State's evidence.

Eric, an overgrown boy with blue eyes, freckles and tow-colored hair, did not look in the least like a criminal, and I felt positive that the supposed accomplice had implicated him merely to save his own skin. It was not my case and I might not have thought of it again had it not been for a rather dramatic incident. Mrs. Martin, a respectable-looking middle-aged woman, having testified to the excellence of the defendant's reputation for peace and quiet, was asked rather pointedly by Robert Townsend, the assistant district attorney trying the case, whether she were not the boy's mother. No one was prepared for the result of his question—least of all the defendant. Turning pale and clutching the arms of her chair Mrs. Martin looked pathetically at the judge.

"Must I answer that question?" she implored him.

"I'm afraid you must," answered His Honor.

"No, I'm not," she faltered. "He was an adopted child—but I never told him."

At this point the trial was suspended so that I could argue my motion, after which I returned to the office, where I described to my partner the scene I had just witnessed, including the apparently extreme youth of the defendant.

"You say this boy is indicted for a homicide committed by an accomplice during a robbery?" asked Tutt.

"Exactly—felony murder," I said.

"If he's under sixteen, the General Sessions can have no jurisdiction. Under the statute he can be guilty only of juvenile delinquency, triable in the Children's Court.—How old is he?"

"I don't know, but it makes no difference because the juvenile delinquency law does not apply to an act which, if committed by an adult, would be punishable by death or life imprisonment, and murder is punishable by death."

Tutt thrust out his tummy, teetered and pursed his lips.

"Give me a stogy!" he said. "This question is worth some consideration. Are you going to be around here this afternoon?"

"I am," I said, "and if you can beat that one I'll give you a dozen bottles of Old Doc Robinson's Malt Extract."

A little after four o'clock I heard a whoop from Tutt's cubicle and he came hopping into my office.

"I've got it. Listen! This boy is charged with complicity in a felony murder committed during a robbery. Since the crime of robbery is punishable by neither death nor life imprisonment, a boy under sixteen can't be guilty of robbery—but only of juvenile delinquency which is not a felony. Hence he can't be guilty of a killing while engaged in a felony."

"Rather neat!" I admitted. "It's worth one drink anyway!" I fished in the bookcase behind the reports of Messrs. Meeson & Welsby. "But I fear you're splitting hairs! Isn't it rather obvious that since all murders, whether committed in the course of a felony or otherwise, are punishable by death, the Legislature must have intended to except them all from the operation of the statute as to juvenile delinquency?"

"On the contrary it's much more obvious to me that, if the Legislature intended that a child under sixteen could be guilty of felony murder, they'd have said so!"

I set down my glass.

"I believe you've got something," I conceded.

"All you have to do is to prove that this boy is under sixteen years of age!" he asserted.

It was the first time I had ever mixed into another lawyer's case uninvited, but the time was short. Eric Martin might be convicted of the murder of Leo Goldstein by half past ten o'clock the next morning, and it was now nearly five. I grabbed my hat, rushed up to the Criminal Courts Building and secured Mrs. Martin's address from Eddie Carroll, the clerk. She told me that Eric when a baby had been left in her care by an actress named Mary Wollaston who had boarded with her during the latter half of 1915 but never returned. She described the mother as a petite blonde with brown eyes and golden hair; she had never heard of her since.

An actress! There was only one man I knew in New York City who might possibly help me to trace her. I found David Belasco in his suite over the proscenium arch of his theatre—a combination of shabby apartment, office, junk shop and property room.

"Wollaston? Wollaston!" he meditated. "There used to be a hoofer of that name on the variety stage. He did a turn in one of my shows." The picturesque old man, his sable-silvered locks brushed back in a rolling pompadour, turned to the immense row of scrap books behind him.

"There you are!" he said, at length. "Wollaston, La Belle & Quinn—Song and Dance Team. They worked for me for a fortnight in 1914. Wollaston and La Belle were dancers, Quinn was the stooge. They weren't bad either. Wollaston died a couple of years later. I don't know what has happened to La Belle, but Joe Quinn has become quite a famous comic. He's playing on Broadway now in Blue Devils."

Ten minutes later I was in Joe Quinn's dressing room, where he was slapping grease paint on his fat cheeks. Sure he'd worked with Wollaston and La Belle! He remembered Wollaston—*Eric* Wollaston, well. La Belle was his partner. But that was only her stage name. Her real moniker was Mary Mulvaney—a blonde about five feet three with brown eyes. She and Wollaston were supposed to be married, but she had walked out on the team while they were playing at the Trocadero, after some sort of a row with her partner. It was all I needed. When court opened the next morning I had in my hand the duly authenticated birth certificate of a white male child born to Mary Mulvaney on May 25, 1915 at the Women's and Children's Hospital in New York City.

Calling aside the young attorney assigned to the defense I explained what I had done. He was very grateful and at his request I was assigned by the court as associate counsel. What happened thereafter renewed my faith in human nature.

First, of course, it was necessary to show that Eric Martin was in fact Eric Mulvaney. For this purpose I had subpoenaed Joe Quinn who, dressed and looking like a revived Mr. Micawber, took the stand and repeated what he had told me the evening before about the song and dance team of Wollaston, La Belle & Quinn, and how La Belle was known as Eric Wollaston's wife, her real name being Mary Mulvaney.

"Does the defendant, Eric Martin, in your opinion, Mr. Quinn, resemble Eric Wollaston?" I asked.

"He's his spittin' image!" declared Quinn with conviction.

"I don't know what you're driving at, Eph," interrupted old Bob Townsend, "but, if you wish, I'm perfectly willing to concede that this defendant is the son of Mary Mulvaney Wollaston."

I handed him the birth certificate.

"And do you further concede that this defendant is under sixteen years of age?"

"Sure! Why not?"

"Then," said I, "I move for the dismissal of the indictment. Section 2186 of the New York Penal Law provides that 'a child of less than sixteen years, who shall commit any act which, if committed by an adult would be a crime not punishable by death and life imprisonment, shall not be deemed guilty of any crime but of juvenile delinquency only.' Robbery is not punishable by either death or life imprisonment, therefore the defendant was legally incapable of committing it. If so, how could he be guilty of murder committed during the perpetration of the felony of robbery?"

Old Bob stared at me without attempting a reply. Then the Judge did a courageous thing. After a study of the statute he said:

"There is much virtue in your argument, Mr. Tutt. Certainly there is enough to raise a doubt as to the Legislature's intention in such a case as this. Just as the jury must give the prisoner every reasonable doubt upon the facts, so I as judge should give it to him upon the law. Your motion is granted. Indictment dismissed."

Quinn who had been waiting nervously on a front bench stepped to the rail.

"Your Honor," he said, "I'm sure this kid is a good kid. His mother was a swell little woman. I've plenty of dough. If you can fix it up to let him go I'll see that he gets a good education."

"I join in that!" wheezed Old Bob with a benevolent smile. "This prosecution was a mistake."

In the course of my career I have prosecuted or defended upwards of five hundred homicide cases. Murder, until recently at least, has always held the chief place in human interest from the Cain-Abel case, as reported in the earliest edition of Genesis, down through the Jael-Sisera and Judith-Holfernes homicides, to those of Lizzie Borden and Harry Thaw. It is in murder cases that a lawyer's reputation as an advocate is most easily won or lost, the only chance he has today for equal publicity with that of a movie star.

Abraham Lincoln, Rufus Choate, Daniel Webster and many of the greatest judges and advocates of the English bar gained fame by their defense of persons accused of murder. Myriads of books have been written about it and much of the output of contemporary English and American authors is devoted to it; but murder—at least as a fine art—has practically ceased to exist. Cases involving the ingenious use of poisons like that in the Patrick, Buchanan, Molineux and Carlisle Harris cases are negligible. There are occasional involved "murder mysteries," like the Elwell, Dot King and Hall-Mills cases, or disappearances like that of Dorothy Arnold, but the really interesting murder cases are few. While technically there are as many homicides as ever—and perhaps more—they are usually the result of gangster feuds or "felony murders" committed during the perpetration of other crimes. That people should no longer plot to kill each other by means of poison may be due to the general progress of civilization, but more probably it is the result of the increased efficiency of modern crime detection.

Every accused is entitled to his day in court. This includes the right to be represented by competent counsel, and if he cannot afford a lawyer the court will assign one to defend him. It is the recognized duty of such an attorney to represent his client to the best of his ability. The judge appointing him to this perhaps unpleasant duty will not allow him to say "I think this man is guilty, so I refuse to defend him," since the law will not suffer him to deprive a prisoner of his defense. Similarly where one accused of crime has the means to retain a lawyer the latter should not allow his own distaste to prejudice the rights of his prospective client. As a member of the bar it is his duty to render his services to such as seek them.

Under the Constitution and Statutes of the United States, and of every State, no man can be punished unless convicted by a jury of his peers after a fair and impartial trial conducted in accordance with due process of law. This is the chief palladium of those liberties embodied in Magna Carta.* If this were not so, none of us would be safe.

Indeed, the law is so technical that sometimes a man who makes no denial of the facts involved in the charge against him cannot know whether he be actually guilty or not. Fine distinctions are frequently involved. Often, moreover, the precise meaning of a statute is not known until it has been interpreted on appeal, and lawyers have been known to advise their clients to plead guilty only to find later that the law was unconstitutional or had been misconstrued in the lower courts. There are also numerous cases of record where innocent people have imagined or believed themselves guilty when in fact they were not. That is one reason why defendants are not permitted to plead guilty to first degree murder. It is important that in any case such persons have the advice of counsel. Even where a defendant acknowledges to his lawyer that he has committed the act charged against him and the law seems to be clear, he is entitled to have it proven beyond a reasonable doubt to the satisfaction of a jury, in which case it

* Magna Carta (1215) Cap. 39: "No free man shall be taken or imprisoned or disseised, or outlawed, or exiled, or anyways destroyed; nor will we go upon him, nor will we send upon him, unless by the lawful judgment of his peers, or by the law of the land."

is the duty of the attorney to see that this is done in a proper legal manner. Under such circumstances, of course, the lawyer will not countenance his client's committing perjury upon the witness stand, but will merely insist that adequate proof be introduced by the prosecution before the case is sent to the jury.

Neither is there any odium in the introduction of what is sometimes called a "technical" defense, since the technicality may go to the essence of the crime. Justice Holmes was fond of pointing out there is no such thing as "evading a law." The law draws a line and you are either on one side or the other. In some cases the line drawn by the law may be an actual physical one, as in a challenge to the jurisdiction of the court. Nothing is more vital to our liberties than that officials should not be allowed to exceed the scope of their legal powers. Yet, in one sense, such a plea is "technical," since it does not involve the general issue of the defendant's guilt. I once had an interesting case in which I successfully interposed such a defense not only once, but twice in succession.

Morris Neck, on that part of Long Island Sound known as the East River, is only a mile or two from Fordham Parkway and the Boston Post Road. On it is what is left of old Fort Morris, a defunct and dismantled relic of the War of 1812, originally planned to guard New York City from British approach. Submerged in a small forest of alders and willows it was, during the prohibition period, largely used as a hide-out for rum-runners.

Antonio di Marco, a simple-minded Italian laborer who knew the lay of the land, had been hired by a revenue agent to guide him alone through the woods to a gangsters' cache, while the cutter's crew was sent around to the other side of the Neck to cut off their escape. But the criminals were on the alert, the revenue agent was shot dead from ambush, and since Antonio was on the spot and there was no one to corroborate his story, he was indicted by a Federal Grand Jury for the murder.

At the first trial in the United States District Court I showed that the special act of the Legislature by which New York State in 1809 ceded jurisdiction over Morris Neck to the United States Government contained the clause: "that such jurisdiction shall continue in the United States so long only as the land shall be used and occupied for the purpose of cession," and claimed that the fort, having been virtually abandoned, the United States had lost its jurisdiction to prosecute offenses committed on its property. As both the law and the facts seemed clear the judge granted my motion to dismiss the indictment, the case was turned over to the State officers, and my client re-indicted by the Bronx County Grand Jury.

It seemed that this time Toni's goose was surely cooked, since the circumstantial evidence against him was very strong. Luckily, however, I was able at the trial to raise some slight doubt as to his guilt in the jury's minds. I then called the adjutant general of the State and proved by him that Fort Morris was still listed as Government property and appeared as such upon the ordnance maps. Arguing that the action of the Federal Court was not conclusive, I claimed that it was for the present jury to determine the question of whether or not the United States had in fact abandoned the property.

In my address to the jury I pointed out that abandonment was a question of intention, that the purpose of cession was for the erection of a fort, that the fort had been built and was still there, and that the land had been continuously "used and occupied"— in the words of the special act—"for that purpose." How, I asked, could a piece of property be any more "occupied" than by a solid mass of masonry covering a large part of its surface? A merely temporary neglect to keep the fort up-to-date meant nothing; there was no need to maintain it as a complete military establishment; but there might be need of it some day.

Happily for my client the jury accepted my view and found him not guilty on the ground that the United States had never intended to abandon Fort Morris and hence that the State Court had no jurisdiction. I was greatly aided by the fact that the Federal judge, before whom the original indictment had been moved for trial, regarded the question as one of law to be decided by himself, while the next judge sought refuge from responsibility by leaving it to the jury.

XVII

CASE AND COMMENT

A LAWYER'S life, particularly if he be an elderly bachelor of sedentary habits, is just one case after another. He goes to court, he interviews witnesses, but the rest of the time for the most part he sits in his office or his library—and thinks. That is not to say he doesn't get a lot of fun out of it. If he has not become too desiccated, if his heart is still warm and he retains his sense of humor, the trial of a case can be more exciting than any melodrama, for he is dealing with real and not simulated emotions.

What apparently could be less inspiring than the bulky envelopes in a lawyer's cabinet, the printed briefs on appeal, the dusty minutes of trials, the yellowing piles of documents, the packages of faded letters tied with green or red tape! Doubtless they would remain so to the casual eye of the stranger, but to the attorney who was responsible for the outcome of the issues they may smell of violets or of blood—or at least be good for a chuckle.

Glancing through my diaries and files I find at least a hundred matters which I feel sure would, if set forth in their entirety, interest either lawyer or layman.

For instance, here is the record of young Mr. Thornton Willoughby who borrowed $5,000 from a friend with which to buy a motor car and then sought to avoid payment on his note on the ground that at the time he signed it he had been in the eyes of the law an infant. His defense might seem at first to be legally sound since indubitably he had made the note on June 10, 1934 and his twenty-first birthday fell on June 11, the next day. This availed him naught, however, when Tutt & Tutt to the surprise of Mr. Willoughby's own lawyer proved beyond peradventure that he became of age at one second past midnight on June 10 and hence was fully able to bind himself. If the reader has any doubt as to this let him look in Blackstone's *Commentaries* at page 497 where it says: "Full age in male or female is twenty-one years, which age is completed on the day preceding the anniversary of one's birth." My penciled note cites Fitzburgh *vs.* Dennington, 2 Lord Raymond 1094, and Wells *vs.* Wells, 6 Indiana 447.

Here is old Mrs. Silsby who lived on Route 1 near Cherryfield, Maine in an ancient historic house with a pannelled drawing room of carved walnut on which was a frieze of mural paintings with a priceless marine set in the over-mantel. Mrs. Silsby was seventy-eight and miserably poor, but she refused to sell her family heirlooms. At last one day when she was practically starving an unscrupulous dealer appeared and persuaded her to sell him "the room without the furniture" for $500, whereas the paintings were in fact worth nearer $50,000. Tutt & Tutt refused to deliver them while tendering the rest of the interior, on the ground that, since they were not actually painted on the wainscoting itself but on plaques which although fastened were detachable, they were personal property and did not pass under the agreement. See 2 *Columbia Law Review* 407, and Towne *vs.* Fiske, 127 Mass 125.

Then there was the Barton case. A gentleman named William Kissam Barton came into our office one afternoon with blood in his eye. He had, he said, given his wife as a wedding gift a diamond necklace which he had purchased of a well-known firm of jewellers on Fifth Avenue for $12,000. She had worn it constantly, until a few weeks before, when he had noticed that she seemed nervous and distrait. After a few days her spirits had revived and the necklace had once more made its appearance. When later she had again exhibited signs of unhappiness he had pressed her for an explanation and she had confessed that the necklace she was wearing was not the one he had given her.

Extravagant by nature, she had become heavily in debt. Her husband was a man of violent temper and the thought of appealing to him was distasteful to her. Casting about for an expedient, she hit upon what seemed to be an ingenious and delightfully easy plan. She needed ready money—a lot of it. Why not go to the jewellers from whom her husband had bought the necklace, sell it back to them for cash and buy a new one on credit exactly like it, so that he would never know? With the necklace in her handbag she drove to the jewellers and asking for the manager made her extraordinary suggestion.

"This is not in our line of business," he said, as he might to a presumptuous child, "but, simply to accommodate you, we will make an exception in your case, buy back our necklace and make you another that cannot be told apart from it."

"How much cash shall I get?" asked the lady.

"Diamonds have gone down," he answered. "All we can allow you will be $6000."

"How much will the new necklace cost?"

"I shall have to discuss that with the head of the firm," said the manager, disappearing into an adjacent office. Apparently this time diamonds had gone up, for when he returned he announced:

"The price of the new necklace will be $12,000, but you need not pay for it until it is convenient for you to do so."

"Give me the $6000!" she replied quickly, handing him the necklace.

Shortly there was delivered at her house a necklace so like the first that even she, who knew the secret, could not tell one from the other!

Her husband was a thick-set English squire type of fellow and, as he recounted this exotic yarn, his neck swelled until it almost burst his collar.

"I want you to go after those bastards and show 'em up!" he shouted. "I don't care what it costs! Expose 'em for the swindlers that they are!"

I did not have a much higher opinion of what the jewellers had done than he had, but I doubted extremely if the manager had simply taken the wife's necklace with one hand and given it back to her with the other. The transaction was sufficiently profitable without necessitating actual fraud.

I accordingly called on the firm, explained the situation, demanded to see their books, and was given the privilege. The records substantiated their claim that they had made a new necklace, but unfortunately contained the phrase "old setting." This entry absolutely confirmed my client in his belief that his wife had been deliberately cheated and he proceeded to tell the story wherever he went, stigmatizing the famous firm as cheats, thieves, robbers, etc.

Meanwhile the story got into the papers—front-page stuff with pictures of the lady, the necklace, and the husband, with the result that the jewellers had no choice but to sue or forever lose caste.

"I'll never pay the rascals one cent!" declared my client. "I'll fight to the last ditch!"

Accordingly I engaged an expert and made a thorough study of diamonds. I found out how to detect imitations, how to tell a "doublet" or a "triplet" (a diamond with a genuine top but a false bottom or bottoms), the difference between "Jagersfontein" and "Bloemfontein," the history of the "Orloff," the "Koh-i-noor," the "Cullinan," the "Florentine," the "Braganza" and the "Great Mogul," the normal profits of the trade, etc., etc. But most important of all I learned that practically all diamonds have flaws of one sort or another. Microscopic examination revealed that the now famous necklace was no exception. Therefore, in addition to my claim that nothing was actually due upon the necklace, since the agreement had been to the effect that she was to pay only when it was "convenient," I put in a separate defense to the effect that the stones of the necklace contained latent defects of such a character as to render them unmerchantable.

Meantime I had my client's wife come down to the office and rehearse her testimony. In point of fact I had little expectation of successfully defending the suit, my only hope being that, rather than have the story re-hashed in open court, the jewellers would drop it in order to avoid publicity. Neither side could, however, afford to make any move towards settlement, since that would have been taken as a sign of weakness. Both dug in and waited as the case drew nearer and nearer the top of the calendar.

The lovely lady who had caused all the rumpus, in despair at the idea of having to be pilloried on the witness stand, besought me to spare no effort to have the case disposed of without getting into court. But I could think of no way out of it. I hadn't her ingenuity. But at last I had an inspiration.

I ordered a diagram made some five feet in length and two in width depicting the necklace in gigantic form, each stone fully six inches in diameter. But while, in the reproduction, the surface of each facet shone clear and bright and of the exact and proper color of the original stone, beneath in every case appeared a horrible gangrenous admixture of reds, greens, blacks, purples and yellows, which in animal or vegetable matter would have indicated an advanced stage of decomposition.

This "exhibit" I placed conspicuously upon an easel in the corner of my office. I then made an excuse for the attorney for the jewellers to come there, offered him a stogy and casually discussed the possibility of a settlement, by which my client should refund the $6000 cash received for the original necklace and the jewellers should abandon any claim for the second. This proposition he naturally declined with some heat. As he arose to go his eye for the first time rested on my diagram.

"What's that?" he inquired.

"That?" I replied. "Why, that is just an exhibit I am going to use at the trial—a diagram of the necklace."

"But what are those green and purple splotches?"

"Those are the flaws, slightly magnified to be sure, but each and every one exactly as it exists, as our experts will testify!"

"Of course you can't put it in evidence," he protested.

"No? Well, it's drawn to scale and fulfills all legal requirements. I'll manage to get it in somehow."

I had hardly put the horrid thing away after his departure before my telephone rang, and he was on the other end of it.

"There's no use having an eternal row over this thing," he said. "My clients are willing to discontinue, if you'll return the necklace."

"Not much!" I retorted. "We like it. What is that? If we'll pay you back the six thousand dollars? Sure, but only when convenient!"

While some attorneys may complain of the monotony of their practice, my own cases, whether civil or criminal, have never lacked interest and excitement. Indeed, some of them have been more bizarre and fantastic than Kipling's *Naulahka* or the *Arabian Nights*. That "truth is stranger than fiction" is only due to the fact that the fiction writer, in order to convey the conviction of reality, must keep his story within the bounds of human probability. As Aristotle says: "Better a probable impossibility than an impossible probability." Life has no such limitation. It certainly did not in the case of Colonel Glyn-Villiers, which occurred during the days of Wiegand & Tutt. Were it not for the typewritten affidavits now lying before me I could hardly bring myself to believe what I know to be literally true.

The record begins with a telegram dated May 5, 1919 from our legal correspondent in Seattle.

"Lady coming look out for her."

This laconic wire whether a warning or retainer—preceded by only a few hours the arrival of the lady herself. She was a tall, gawky, horse-faced woman of about thirty-five partially clad in an extremely diaphanous muslin dress with a sash of baby blue. Accompanying her was a handsome, dark, heavily-built, oldish man in a tropical silk suit and Panama hat.

"I'm Ada Jonsen," she introduced herself. "Senator Caleb Baxter sent me to you. This is Colonel Percy Glyn-Villiers of the British Army."

We shook hands all around. The Colonel offered cigarettes from a jewelled case. It was a hot day and the exotic atmosphere surrounding the pair made me think of a Somerset Maugham story laid on a club veranda in the South Seas.

"We're in a mess!" she informed me, and her companion nodded silently.

She was a voluble talker, but the Colonel, whether taciturn or merely out of caution, did not commit himself. In the interest of space I shall reproduce her narrative in the third person.

She was, she said, the daughter of a well-known London banker, Alfred Montague, one of several sisters, and the divorced wife of a Swedish shipbuilder, Captain Ole Jonsen, who happened to be at the moment on business in San Francisco where she had recently gone to re-marry him. Pending the ceremony she had unexpectedly received a telegram from her friend Colonel Glyn-Villiers in New York, requesting her appearance as a witness in his behalf before United States Commissioner Shields, who was holding him on a warrant of extradition issued by the Government of India for deportation to Calcutta on the charge of "cheating" under the English penal code. The reason for the visit to me was that Mrs. Montague-Jonsen did not wish to testify, since owing to the attendant publicity it might militate against her planned re-marriage to her former husband. On the other hand Colonel Glyn-Villiers was insistent that she should, and she in turn seemed for some reason afraid not to acquiesce in his demand. The complainant, Mahommed Ali Babu, a Hindu "dealer in grain and pearls," had accompanied the government agent charged with the execution of the extradition warrant from India and was now staying at the Waldorf-Astoria awaiting his revenge. The question for my decision was whether Ada had better stay on and testify as requested, or go back to Seattle and lie doggo until the fate of her friend the Colonel had been officially decided. Apparently my legal friend in California had passed the buck to me.

Although a good deal had met my eye already, it was nothing to what gradually rose to the cloudy surface of Colonel Glyn-Villiers' variegated past. Some of it Ada told me privately; a lot he unconcernedly admitted. It appeared that the Colonel came of a good family in the Midlands, had gone to Winchester, then to Sandhurst and been commissioned a lieutenant in the English army in the gay days of the end of the last century. He had been very handsome—traces of this still remained—a favorite with women, debonair, extravagant, a famous polo player and financially, at least, unreliable. Having been cashiered and discharged from the army for non-payment of debts he had begun the prodigal career which he had ever since pursued, moving from watering place to watering place, and from capitol to capitol, just ahead of his creditors, meanwhile endeavoring to marry an heiress and so solve all his difficulties. This he had nearly succeeded in doing in a number of instances. He knew everyone in Continental and English society and naturally those to whom he was indebted would have been only too glad to have him attain solvency. But something always went wrong and, as time went on, he had found it more and more difficult to elude the sheriff.

Having unsuccessfully worked through the matrimonial market upon the other side of the Atlantic he had sailed for America— and more specifically Newport—with letters of introduction in his pocket to various claimants to social leadership who were delighted to have such a handsome English officer on their lists as an extra man. Under these circumstances he pursued and easily won a young woman whom he supposed to be an heiress—she on her side believing him to be the scion of an aristocratic family who would in due course inherit a title. Since both were in fact penniless the marriage resulted in a speedy divorce, and Glyn-Villiers, taking care not to be deceived again, presently married the daughter of a millionaire manufacturer of plumbing fixtures —"After us the deluge"—took her back to England, paid off his more pressing obligations and for a while lived a life of humdrum domesticity.

Then came the outbreak of the first World War. Trained officers being sorely needed Glyn-Villiers, in spite of his unfortunate record, managed to wangle his way back into the army as a captain in the Black Watch, and with his customary perspicacity secured an appointment as treasurer of his mess. The A.D.C. on the staff was a Colonel Buckley Ivers-Ross whose wife was the only daughter of a multimillionaire industrialist named Quinn.

In addition to being blonde, winsome and petite she was something to look at. Colonel Buckley unwisely showed Glyn-Villiers
her photograph and, what was more to the point, expatiated upon
the vast extent of her father's wealth. Running true to form the
good Captain, before the ill-fated Gallipoli expedition had made
its fatal landing, was found £400 short in his accounts, court-
martialled, dishonorably discharged and sent home.

He did not, however, go back to his comfortable seat among
the plumbing fixtures, but immediately sought out Mrs. Ivers-
Ross and introducing himself as a bachelor friend of her husband,
came, saw and conquered. In fact they had such a good time
together that they decided to continue it. The question was where
to go. At length Mrs. Ivers-Ross recalled that a school friend
of hers, the former Ada Montague, had married a Captain Ole
Jonsen and was living in Oslo. So hither they repaired and,
landing without previous fanfare upon Captain Ole's doorstep,
were received with open arms by his wife. Everything went well
for several days, until Captain Ole suspected that Ada was taking
too great an interest in her military visitor and ejected all three
from the family mansion and the rectangle became a triangle.

Thereupon the Captain and the two ladies moved over to
the Hotel Royal-Splendid and held a covenant of war. None of
them had any funds, but that was nothing new to Glyn-Villiers
who promptly subjected the two to an exhaustive cross-examination as to their resources, from which he ascertained that when
Ada Montague had married Captain Jonsen she had put her
dot of £10,000 into his shipping business. Owing to the war
her share had enormously increased in value and under Captain
Glyn-Villiers' expert advice she now brought an action against
her husband for an accounting and received an award of
£50,000. Thus through his kindly interest in another man's wife
the captain now had his hands upon two hundred and fifty thousand dollars in cold cash. Visions of luxurious adventure opened
before their eyes. None of them wanted to remain in England
or Scandinavia when, in the Far East, temple bells were calling,

so having purchased the requisite paraphernalia they took the trans-Siberian for Vladivostock while mutual suits for divorce ripened behind them in the Divorce and Admiralty Division of the King's Bench—Jonsen *vs.* Jonsen, Ivers-Ross *vs.* Ivers-Ross, and Glyn-Villiers *vs.* Glyn-Villiers.

Then began a trip through the Orient such as Hollywood has never pictured as these three good companions ate, drank and gambled their way along the Asiatic coast from Tokio to Korea, Hong Kong, and the Straits Settlements, to Ceylon and India, throwing away money like drunken sailors. They bought all the jewelry they could carry and what they couldn't they shipped to America, but true to his principles, Glyn-Villiers never let them pay cash for anything when credit would suffice. Thus he lightly purchased for himself a black pearl scarf pin for £600 from one Kanar Kanee at Colombo, paying him therefor by a draft at ninety days on what he alleged was a London bank but what was in reality a boarding house. The real splurge began at Bombay where the "Captain" became a "Colonel," hired a bungalow near the polo field for his "sisters" and himself, and entertained the social world. Here on the veranda each afternoon would congregate the leading jewelers of the city, salaaming as they laid out their wares before the reclining ladies, who between gin rickies would languidly look them over with a "I'll take that necklace" or "I'll take those earrings"—on "London at ninety days." But before the ninety days were over the three were far away on the broad Pacific on their way to the United States.

On reaching America, it being summer, the two ladies and their escort first went to the White Mountains, then to Bar Harbor and finally to New London. Here they learned that decrees had been entered in their respective suits and that all of them were now divorced. This presented a delicate problem in ethics. Which lady should the Colonel marry? The solution was really very simple. While Ada's money—the £50,000—had already been spent; Mrs. Ivers-Ross was still her father's daughter and Quinn, the manufacturer, was very rich. So Glyn, as one might expect, married her, but, instead of taking her on a wedding trip and in order that Ada might not feel too disappointed, he invited Ada on an excursion to New Orleans.

Meanwhile when their drafts came back "no funds" Kanar Kanee and Mohammed ali Babu were very wroth. Down they went to the Criminal Term of the High Presidency Court in Bombay and commenced criminal proceedings against Glyn-Villiers on the charge of cheating. A warrant of extradition was secured, and the two Hindus together with a government agent sailed in pursuit. Hot on the trail, they overtook the Colonel and the former Mrs. Jonsen at the St. Charles Hotel where Kanar Kanee had his defrauder arrested and thrown into jail pending a hearing on the warrant of extradition. Bail was set at $15,000 and the Colonel didn't have it. Next day the New Orleans papers printed an item that Mrs. Montague-Jonsen was in town. This was picked up in Seattle where it was read by Capt. Jonsen, who being of a forgiving nature and probably thinking that Ada had had her fling, telegraphed suggesting that she return to him and asking whether she needed money. Ada promptly wired back that she need fifteen thousand dollars—although she did not say what for—and Ole sent it.

Meanwhile something else had happened. A lovely girl, whose heart was full of sympathy for those deprived of their liberty by the cruel processes of the law, visited the jail presumably with a Bible in one hand and a bunch of calla lilies in the other. Passing along the corridor without finding any enthusiastic candidate for spiritual regeneration she came finally to a cell door through the bars of which a dark, handsome face peered at her with yearning, liquid eyes—our friend Glyn-Villiers. Need I go on? Must I say that he was converted then and there? Anyhow he was, they became engaged to be married, and her father—there was always a rich father in the background of the Colonel's experiences—hastened to put up the fifteen thousand dollars necessary to release his prospective son-in-law, who in turn hurried to the St. Charles Hotel, only to find that Ada had fled to Seattle and the arms of her former husband. The rich father then retained a lawyer for the Colonel—such a clever one in fact that he found a defect in the extradition warrant, with the result that the defendant was set free.

Kanar Kanee having been defeated in his search for justice, the Colonel made his customary excuses and went north. On the train unknown to him went Mohammed Ali Babu. Once in New York he was again arrested, and this time there was no hole in the warrant. Things looked ominous for the gallant soldier. In India, where native testimony was not taken against that of a white, he could have laughed Mohammed Ali Babu out of court. But in the United States it was different. It would be his oath against the Hindu's, and somehow he had a hunch that the court would prefer the latter's. Under these circumstances he had wired Ada to rally to his defense and testify to what might be necessary to get him off—namely that he had not told Mohammed Ali Babu that the London draft was on a bank. Ada in great agitation had gone to Ole's lawyer who was arranging for their re-marriage. She told him just enough to lead him to think that perhaps she had better take a flying trip to New York and confer with counsel.

That was the story to date. Ada told it, and Percy pieced it out. He did not deny any of it. I reduced the yarn to writing, attached all the various exhibits and had her sign and swear to it. Among these papers was the bill for a pearl necklace Glyn-Villiers had bought for her from Mohammed Ali Babu and upon which the charge of cheating was predicated. Ada said the price was £5000, but the bill said £6000. I asked how was that. Ada said it was all right—that Percy lost it "tossin'."

" 'Tossin'?" I repeated, baffled.

"Yes, tossin'," echoed the Colonel.

"I don't know any such word!" I protested.

"Tossin'?" exclaimed Ada. "Didn't you ever hear of tossin' a coin? I must say Percy was rather clever about that. You see, after we'd bought anything of the Hindus—they're great gamblers, you know—Percy would offer to toss them for a thousand.

If he lost he had 'em just add it to the bill, but if he won he made 'em pay spot cash."

It was quite obvious that Ada still had a lingering regard for Percy. At this time, however, he had lost what must have been his earlier dash and was settling down to heavy flesh. There was nothing of the Smart Alec about him, none of the arrogance or brass of the ordinary cheap Englishman. On the contrary he was quiet, gentlemanly, reserved, and almost appallingly frank, the reason being probably, that long experience had taught him just how far he could afford to go in his admissions without criminally implicating himself. This was suggested by his habit of never actually dotting the i or crossing the t when describing some dubious episode with which he had been connected. He would ride straight at the gate and then, with a wave of his cigarette, would veer aside with a cheery "And there you are!"

Ada told me that on his own statement he had never spent less than $100,000 a year and did so by the simple formula made famous by Thackeray's Rawdon Crawley and other professional dead beats, namely by owing such immense sums that it would be to no one's interest to try to collect the comparatively infinitesimal percentage represented by a single debt, while at the same time holding out the golden hope that with good luck he could sometime pay it all.

After I had extracted all the information from him I could get I told Ada that she had better hurry back to Seattle at once, remarry her Ole, and let the law take its course. She admitted the wisdom of my advice and said that she would do so next day—that she wanted one more evening of the Colonel's society.

"I don't see how you can possibly have anything more to do with the man," I protested. "Look what he has already done to you. Your little trip to India cost you two hundred and fifty thousand dollars."

Ada looked dreamily out of the window.

"Ye-s," she said, then turning to me she added with feeling: "But it was worth it!"

Maybe it was. Maybe her evening with the Colonel repaid her for the two black eyes with which she appeared in my office next day.

"What on earth happened to you?" I asked.

"Just a little accident," she replied.

"There aren't going to be any more such accidents," I declared. "You're going to pack your things and get on the very next train for Seattle."

So I put her in charge of Willie Toothaker, who convoyed her back to her hotel, watched while she packed, bought her tickets and saw her off. I mailed her statement to my friend in Seattle with a letter explaining that the less she saw of Glyn-Villiers the better and that I hoped that he would be extradited to India where he could pursue his career among the Maharanees. Then I disappeared into the Canadian wilderness. On my return a month later I was greeted by a grinning Bonnie Doon.

"You went away too soon," he said. "There's been quite a time here. Glyn-Villiers was afraid to face Mohammed Ali Babu before the Commissioner without your client Mrs. Montague-Jonsen as a witness, and so, after his lawyer had secured a couple of adjournments, he faked illness and was allowed to go to St. Luke's Hospital under the same bail. Then one night he climbed out a window and disappeared—for the time being. But that's not the best of it," he continued, handing me a letter dated Seattle. "Who did you think our correspondent was representing when he sent you his original telegram?"

"Mrs. Montague-Jonsen, of course."

"That's where you made a trifling mistake," he laughed. "He's really Jonsen's lawyer, and the first thing he did after receiving that statement you drew up was to show it to him. It was the first time Jonsen had known the whole story. He flew into a terrible rage and swore that he'd be damned if he'd marry her again, and now his former wife, who had been buying her trousseau, is suing him for breach of promise!"

The case is matter of record. Colonel Glyn-Villiers was finally caught, brought back to New York, and on the testimony of Mohammed Ali Babu, ordered sent back to India. He immediately secured a writ of *habeas corpus* from the United States District Court, which denied him relief. From this judgment he appealed to the Circuit Court of Appeals—where he also lost. Then as a last resort he appealed to the United States Supreme Court and lost again. Two years elapsed between the New York hearing and his eventual extradition to India.

With the Colenel safely on his way to India I again dismissed the matter from my mind. Another year went by and then I received a clipping from a Bombay paper—perhaps sent by the Colonel. In substance it was:

High Presidency Court of Bombay—Criminal Term. The charge against Colonel Percy Glyn-Villiers for violating Sec. 111 of the India Penal Code against cheating, brought by Mohammed Ali Babu, was today dismissed on the ground that the only testimony in support of said charge was that of natives.

XVIII

THE LAW—"MODEL T"

No LAWYER can practice his profession in the courts without realizing speedily that there is no greater mockery than the oath taken by any witness "to tell the truth, the whole truth and nothing but the truth," since he is neither asked to tell the truth nor would he be permitted to tell it if he were. On the continent of Europe a witness is allowed, usually without interruption, to tell whatever he thinks he knows about a case—what he saw himself, what others told him, the reputation of the parties, their possible motives for misstating the facts, his own opinion as to the issue and his reasons for thinking as he does. He rattles on, unhampered, telling his story as he is accustomed to recount the happenings in his daily life, and by the time he finishes the jury have a very fair idea of what sort of a fellow he is and how much he really knows.

In this country he no sooner opens his mouth than he is choked off by a barrage of objections until, even if these be overruled, he does not know whether he is on his head or his heels. Indeed, a foreigner who dropped into an American courtroom might suppose that our theory of the best way to elicit important information is to gag and blindfold the witness, punch him in the nose, whirl him around and upside down, and after knocking all the breath out of his body limit him to answering "yes" or "no" to a series of questions put by someone who does not know half as much about the case as he does.

This is not so extravagant as it may sound. The Anglo-Saxon law of evidence may be compared to a soundly rooted and once symmetrical tree which in the course of years has become lopsided, full of dry rot and so entangled with vines and creepers that it not only obscures the light but it is impossible to tell which are branches and which are parasites.

For one thing no witness is allowed to testify to anything save facts which he himself has observed. He may not characterize either an act or a person's conduct, for that would be merely his opinion, and his opinion might "improperly influence" the jury. He is forbidden to state the simplest, most elementary, and natural conclusion from what he has seen.

Again, the ancient rule of hearsay still prevents the jury from receiving vital information. Thus if A has been standing in front of a house, hears a shot, and a few seconds later B rushes out crying "I just saw Smith shoot Jones and he's hiding right now in a closet in the second story rear room with the pistol in his pocket," A will not be permitted to testify to what B told him even if Smith was, in fact, immediately arrested with the reeking pistol in his pocket in the closet as B stated, and B has since died or is otherwise unavailable.

It long ago became apparent, even to the complacent judges of the common law, that if the hearsay rule were strictly applied the resulting failure of testimony would work many injustices. So the courts began to make exceptions—dozens of them. One was the so-called "dying declaration" rule, where a man who has been attacked and is on the point of death—*in extremis,* as it is called—identifies his assailant, in which case, if he dies, the law allows his accusation to be repeated in court on the theory that the solemnity of approaching death gives his statement the same validity as if made in court under oath.

I was reading in my library when a young woman leading a child by the hand and carrying another in her arms followed Mandy upstairs. Nora McCann was in great trouble. Her husband, who had recently been discharged from prison, had been indicted for the murder of a well-known racketeer. It was the prosecution's theory that the homicide was the result of a gangster quarrel in which McCann, having been double-crossed by his boss and forced to take the rap in his place, had later sought revenge by killing him. The circumstantial evidence against him was strong, for he had been in close proximity to the scene of the crime, and was known to have made threats against the deceased. Nora assured me that her husband, an innocent man, was being made a scapegoat for the real murderer. Why, she asked, should her Tom, after having not seen her or the children for three years, rush off the instant he got out of jail and commit a crime for which he might be sent to the chair or at least to prison for life?

Her argument appealed to me. Anyhow I decided that Mc-Cann must be a good fellow if he had such a nice wife and children, and I agreed to defend him. It was a hard-fought trial and everything went against me, but on the night before the case was to go to the jury, in answer to a mysterious telephone call, I went to an address on the East Side where on the top landing of a rear tenement I reached a half open door. Inside a man lay in bed, his face bandaged and stained with blood. He was obviously dying and hardly able to speak, but when I identified myself as McCann's counsel, he mustered enough strength to whisper that my client was innocent, that he himself had committed the murder, and that since he was going to die, he wanted to clear both his conscience and the accused. Praying that he would live long enough to sign a written confession I reduced his statement to affidavit form and administered the oath.

I now supposed of course that my client would go free, but the district attorney, who was determined on a conviction, refused to allow me either to testify or to put the document in evidence. We had a violent argument, during which he cited precedent after precedent to prove the testimony incompetent under the strict rules of evidence.

Then one of those curious human incidents occurred that give the laugh to logic. The judge, who throughout the discussion had sustained the district attorney, suddenly changed his attitude, and alleging that the rule was mediaeval in its barbarity, permitted me over the prosecutor's protests to testify to everything that had occurred and admitted the affidavit in evidence. Naturally my client was acquitted. I was greatly puzzled at the judges *volte face* until I learned that during the discussion His Honor had been confidentially apprized that the assistant district attorney, who ostensibly was supporting the judge's candidacy for re-election, was in fact seeking the place for himself.

Observe the artificiality of the law! Where A is on trial for his life, charged with the murder of B, the law will permit a witness to testify that B on his deathbed told him that A was his assailant, whereas if C, on the point of death, confesses under equally solemn circumstances that he, and not A, killed B, his confession cannot be introduced to save A from the electric chair! No wonder old Mr. Tuckerman called the law "wonderful fiddle-sticks."

But this is not all. The law long ago introduced another exception to the hearsay rule, known as "an admission against interest," based on the theory that no one would ever be such a fool as to admit that he owed another person money unless he actually did so. Therefore in a suit over mere money, involving the question of whether A, or his representative, is indebted to B, the law allows the production of A's books, or a reported statement by A, although he be dead, to prove it. Now which is the greater "admission against interest," an admission of a debt or a confession of a murder?

Frankly, in a case such as I have outlined, where the law as it stands literally on the books is pure nonsense, how far should the counsel for a man on trial for homicide feel himself bound by it? Shall he tamely submit to seeing his client condemned to death because judges and legislatures in the past have been too hidebound by precedent to do away with moribund rules, many of them fantastic, which they would not think of applying in their own daily lives? Must he wait until his client is convicted, sentenced, and in the death house to make his appeal on the law's absurdity to a group of old men who, if they can, will try to find some way to dodge the issue and, if not, may—and probably will—rule against him? Or shall he say, as I confess to having said myself many times, "To Hell with it!"

The rules governing the admission of evidence are technical beyond belief. I once committed the unpardonable legal offense of losing a client's will. It was that of a Miss Caroline Grover, who had executed it only ten days before, and having attended at its execution, I had placed it in our will box. After her death I had removed it for examination, and then it disappeared! We turned the office upside down, emptied out all the drawers in my desk, moved the furniture, lifted the rugs, probed into baskets of papers which had been undisturbed for years—all without avail. It was a tragic situation since the old lady, who had only distant relatives, had bequeathed her entire estate to a Miss Lucy Aymar, a charming girl, her loyal companion for many years. I had not only drawn the will, but had kept a copy of it, as well as a memorandum in Miss Caroline's own handwriting instructing me as to her desires and endorsed "Memo. of my will, June 10, 1931, Caroline Grover." But, unfortunately as it turned out, I had not acted as a witness, Miss Grover having invited three elderly lady friends to do so.

It may be asked why, under these circumstances, there could be any possible difficulty in establishing her testamentary intentions. The answer is simple, if technical. Section 1865 of the New York Code of Civil Procedure at that time provided that in an action to establish a lost will, judgment could not be had unless (a) the will was in existence at the time of the testator's death, and (b) its provisions were clearly and distinctly proved by at least two credible witnesses, a correct copy or draft being equivalent to one witness.

Anyone not befogged by the law would naturally suppose that, since I had a copy of the will which would count as one witness, I could myself act as the other. But here, alas! another statute intervened—the one relating to confidential communications between an attorney and client which provides that: "an attorney or counsellor-at-law shall not be allowed to disclose communication made by his client to him, or his advice given thereon, in the course of his professional employment." It then goes on to say that this provision applies "to any examination of a person as a witness unless the provisions thereof are expressly waived upon the trial or examination by the . . . client." The only exception is in the case of an attorney who has acted as a subscribing witness to a will, which I was not. Hence my lips were sealed.

I filed a petition to probate the lost will, and the two applications—mine for the appointment of Miss Aymar as executrix, and that of the relatives to have their kinswoman declared intestate and for the appointment of an administrator—came up before Surrogate Rufus R. Pettingill. I called a Miss Eliza Pratt, one of the witnesses, who had read the will the evening before its execution and identified it as the instrument she had signed next day. She swore positively that Miss Grover had left all her property to Miss Aymar. Judge Pettingill thereupon ruled that under the circumstances, he would count Miss Pratt as one witness, provided I produced a draft or copy corroborating her testimony.

I then played my next card—a low one. I called Miss Aymar and asked her if Miss Grover had told her anything as to the contents of her proposed will. Her testimony was of course properly excluded on the ground that she was an interested party. I then played another—not much better—by asking to be sworn personally as a witness.

"Did you," I asked myself, "prepare the last will and testament of Caroline Grover in accordance with her instructions?"

To this Judge Pettingill sustained an objection on the ground that my answer would clearly come within the prohibition of the statute regarding professional communications, since the drawing of a will had been expressly held to be such in Loden *vs.* Whelpley, 111 N. Y. 239. In desperation I summoned the clerk who had actually drawn the will from Miss Caroline's memorandum, engrossed it, and preserved a copy. But when I asked him to state what was in the memorandum the Judge ruled out the question on the ground that the will engrossed by the witness was not shown to be the same as that signed by the testatrix, because although I had mailed it to Miss Grover, she might or might not have received it.

"But," I argued, "the contents will prove them to have been the same!"

"That," retorted the casuist Pettingill, "would be putting the cart before the horse. You are trying to prove the contents of the will, and to do that you must prove that the paper signed by Miss Grover was the identical paper drawn up by the witness. Until that has been done he may not tell us what the paper contained, for the two documents have not been identified as one and the same. On the other hand, if you offer his testimony as a declaration of intention on the part of the testatrix it comes, like your own, within the prohibition as to confidential communications, for he stands *pari passu* with his employer."

Things looked pretty hopeless, but again offering myself as a witness I tried to introduce my copy of the will as being equivalent to another witness, in addition to Miss Pratt. Bang! Pettingill nearly kicked me out of the box! I was once more, he charged, violating the statute regarding professional communications. It did me no good to quote Prof. Wigmore to the effect that while "it can hardly be doubted that the execution and especially the contents of a will are impliedly desired by the client to be kept secret during his lifetime, it is plain that this confidence is intended to be temporary only, and that after the testator's death the attorney should be at liberty to disclose all that affects the execution and terms of the will. Otherwise what is intended for the client's protection may become the means of defeating his wishes." That, declared the Surrogate, was not the law of New York.

Beaten at every point, I secured an adjournment until the following morning. On the way back to the office Bonnie Doon, who had followed my legal run-around with interest, asked me casually whether if either the draft or the copy had been found among Miss Grover's private papers—and not produced by me as her attorney—it would not have been admitted. I said yes. That was all! Nothing more! I laid the memorandum with the other papers in the case on my desk and went home. About nine o'clock that evening Miss Aymar called me on the telephone.

"I think I've got good news for you," she said excitedly. "Mr. Doon came up here after dinner and suggested that we take another look at Miss Grover's desk. So we got Maggie, the waitress, to help us and went through all the drawers again. What do you suppose? Right in the top one Maggie found a paper in Miss Grover's handwriting marked 'Memo. of my will, June 10, 1931.' Shall I bring it down to court?"

Next morning I called Maggie as a witness to the stand. She identified the handwriting on the paper as that of her mistress, stated where she had found it, and I offered it in evidence without objection, no question of privilege being involved. Taken with the testimony of Miss Pratt it established the lost will. Miss Aymar was awarded the estate. That is the whole story—except that about a month afterwards the original instrument signed by Miss Caroline was found as a marker in a book on salmon fishing which I had been reading.

"*De minimis non curat lex*" is a familiar legal maxim. It may be translated as "The law does not concern itself with very small matters." No one knows exactly what it means. After all, just where Miss Grover's memorandum as to her will happened to be at the moment of her death seems a very small thing indeed. At least I hope it was!

My friend, John Henry Wigmore, has paid his respects to certain of these legal anachronisms in his celebrated work on Evidence, in which he declares that "Of these rulings all that can be said is that they belong rather to some system which decides controversies by mumbling magic formulas before a fetish." As Mr. Justice Holmes said: "It is revolting to have no better reason for a rule of law than that so it was laid down in the time of Henry IV. It is still more revolting if the grounds upon which it was laid down have vanished long since, and the rule simply persists from blind imitation of the past."

I am glad to state that due to the manifest absurdity of the situation in this case and others, the New York law has recently been changed, so that an attorney who now draws a will may testify to the testator's instructions and produce a copy of it although he be not a witness to its execution.

But even assuming that witnesses are permitted to answer the questions put to them, it by no means follows that their testimony will be either accurate or truthful. The most honest witness is fallible, the value of his testimony depending entirely upon his original capacity to observe, the extent to which his memory is accurate, and upon how far he is able to communicate his recollections to the jury. At the conclusion of a trial every participant in the proceeding, including the judge, has a different idea of what has been testified to and what probably happened. Each relies upon his own memory of what others think they have remembered. Moreover, the ability of the witnesses to dramatize their accounts of what they supposedly saw varies to such an amazing extent that trustworthy testimony is often obscured by what is more sensational. It is also safe to say that by the time a case is reached for trial a witness remembers far less of what he actually observed than of what he has previously stated in affidavits and examinations, the details of which have astonishingly proliferated since his first depositions, but to which he is now committed either through personal interest or fear of self-contradiction.

Occasionally even a sworn affidavit is inadequate to keep an unreliable witness in line. I once had a case to which my distinguished friend Mr. Joseph S. Auerback refers in his interesting work *The Bar of Other Days*. While I regret to be thus relegated to the past the incident illustrates my point too well to be omitted here. An accident had occurred owing to the carelessness of an automobile owner who having had it filled with gas at a station drove it directly out upon the highway in the path of an oncoming truck. Now the truck company was one of my clients and within an hour I had arrived at the filling station and taken the sworn deposition of the Negro attendant in which in greatest detail he placed the blame where it belonged. As I expected, however, the car owner sued the company. When the case was called we were obliged to wait until another should be concluded and during this period there was a good deal of talk about "refreshing" the memory. I had no anxiety as to the outcome for the only disinterested witness was the gas attendant and I had his affidavit in my pocket, but to my horror he proceeded on being sworn to give a version of what had occurred diametrically opposed to what it contained.

"Wellington," I said, "didn't you sign this affidavit and swear to its truth within an hour of the accident?"

"Yassuh, Mr. Tutt," he replied, "Ah sho' did."

"Well, read it," I told him, "and see if it doesn't contradict what you now say, in every particular."

Napoleon Washington Wellington studied his deposition carefully, then looked up.

"Ah reckons it does, Mr. Tutt."

"Wasn't I the first person you talked to after the accident?" I asked.

"Yassuh, Mr. Tutt—the very fust pussun."

"In that case," I demanded, "how do you account for the fact that you have changed your story?"

Napoleon glanced around the court room with a semi-professional air.

"Ah reckon mah memory's done been refreshed," he answered.

Excluding the large amount of perjured and exaggerated testimony due to unconscious partisanship the opportunity for mistake is still enormous. It is as absurd to say that no innocent man is ever convicted of crime as that no guilty man is ever acquitted. Tragic mistakes do occur in the administration of criminal justice. Many men have suffered the death penalty through having been erroneously identified as someone else by perfectly honest witnesses. Anyone inclined to doubt this should read the book of Professor Edwin M. Borchard, professor of law at Yale University, entitled *Convicting the Innocent*, in which he recounts sixty-five such cases taken at random from all over the United States. Of these, twenty-nine were due to identifications later proved to be false.*

"The emotional balance of the victim or eye-witness," he says, "is so disturbed by his extraordinary experience that his power of perception becomes distorted and his identification is frequently most untrustworthy. Into the identification enter other motives, not necessarily stimulated originally by the accused personally—the desire to requite a crime, to exact vengeance upon the person believed guilty, to find a scape-goat, to support, consciously or unconsciously, an identification already made by another."

Apart from nervous disturbance we are all apt to "see" what we expect to see, and—if our pecuniary interest is involved—perhaps what we unconsciously prefer to see.

One day a young woman, Mrs. Richard Macaulay, came to my office in great distress. Her husband, a cashier in the stock brokerage house of Thompson & Hardwick, at 30 Broad Street, had been arrested charged with the theft of $9,000 U. S. Government 4½ per cent notes belonging to a customer by the name of Cantor. Macaulay had received as he supposed $25,000 in notes from the senior partner, Mr. Thompson, counted them, given Mr. Cantor a receipt for them, pinned them together and taken them to the Nordic Trust Co. across the street to be sold and the proceeds credited to Cantor's account with the firm. When, however, he had pushed the notes with his deposit slip under the wicket of the receiving teller the latter handed them back, pointing out that they only aggregated $16,000. Aghast, Macaulay counted them again and found this to be true—yet five minutes before there had been $25,000! What had happened to the other $9,000? They had been securely fastened together from the moment he had given the receipt to Cantor to that of his arrival at the bank. At first he thought that he might have

---

* In the majority of these cases the accused were poor persons and in many of these cases their defense was, for that reason, inadequate.

dropped them in the cage, but a thorough search disclosed no sign of any note. He was short $9,000! He knew that it would be useless to appeal to his firm. Mr. Cantor was his only hope. Maybe, somehow, the latter had made a mistake.

Macaulay hurried over to Cantor's office and haltingly laid the matter before him.

"Miscounted my notes!" snapped Cantor. "You're short $9,000 in your accounts and you want to make it up out of me. Do I look like that kind of a sucker? I'll give you until three o'clock to make good and, if I don't have the whole $25,000 back by then, I'll have you put in the hoosegow."

The situation was complicated emotionally by the added facts that Mrs. Macaulay was about to become a mother and that she had a sick child at home with a temperature of 106°. No defense seemed possible. Cantor had counted the notes, Thompson had counted them, the defendant had counted them and given Cantor his receipt into the bargain. Yet after talking with Mrs. Macaulay I was convinced that her husband must be the innocent victim of a mistake—just what I couldn't tell.

Next morning at nine o'clock Macaulay was brought before the police magistrate and Cantor appeared as complaining witness. I have never known a man to testify more positively or with greater vindictiveness. This aroused my suspicions, since having their receipt he would have had no difficulty in holding Thompson & Hardwick for the loss. His story was that, a week previous, he had sold certain securities and invested the proceeds in U. S. 4½ notes which were as liquid as currency. Later he had purchased other securities, paid for them out of a portion of the notes, and placed the rest in his safe deposit vault. He had carefully counted them, found that they amounted to exactly $25,000 —two $10,000 notes and a $5,000, folded them and tucked them under the rubber band around a manila envelope. Then, the day before, having bought two hundred shares of Union Pacific, he had gone back to the vault, removed the $25,000 4½s, which he had again counted, and taken them over to Thompson &

Hardwick's. That was all there was to it! He had counted the notes three separate times and each time there had been two $10,000 notes and one $5,000. I could not shake him.

Suspending my cross-examination I called the cashier of the Nordic Trust Co. who identified the notes produced in court as those proffered him by the defendant for the account of Thompson & Hardwick—one $10,000, one $5,000 and one $1,000—still pinned together in their original condition.

Then I called Mr. Thompson and asked him if his firm had had on hand any U. S. 4½ notes other than those received from Cantor. He answered "None." Did he have any knowledge that Mr. Cantor expected to pay for the 200 Union Pacific shares in U. S. 4½s? No.

Upon this testimony I moved that the prisoner be discharged on the ground that it was obvious that all three—Cantor, Thompson and Macaulay—must have miscounted the notes, the only other possible hypothesis being that Macaulay, between the time he had received them and taken them to the bank, had abstracted a $10,000 note and substituted for it a $1,000 note—a manifest impossibility, since no one knew that Cantor was coming in with his 4½s and there were none in the brokerage office.

When the magistrate hesitated, I demanded that Cantor be required to produce his books, upon which it became clear that after consummating his transaction of the previous week, his balance in notes had been only $16,000. Convinced that he had had a net profit of $25,000 he had miscounted the notes three separate times. Mr. Thompson relying on Cantor's statement that the notes totaled $25,000, and the outside note being for $10,000, had misread the second note of $1,000 for another of $10,000. Macaulay, naturally assuming that his employer and his employer's customer knew what they were talking about, had been misled into making the same mistake, even to posting an entry in his books and giving a signed receipt for the wrong amount.

I submit that under most circumstances the evidence of his guilt would have appeared conclusive to any jury. Had Thompson & Hardwick had a $1,000 4½ among their securities poor Macaulay would undoubtedly have gone to prison, the victim of an honest, but almost unbelievable series of mistakes of fact. As it was I had the satisfaction of bringing an action against Cantor in his behalf for malicious prosecution and false imprisonment, and of securing a judgment for $10,000 which in due course was paid.

The method sanctified by the law for testing the accuracy of oral testimony and eliciting the truth is known as cross-examination. Traditionally this consists of sneering and bawling at the witness in an attempt to scare him out of his senses, threatening him and holding him to scorn as an obvious liar, a probable inheritance from the old days of the "hanging judges" in England who regarded themselves as in fact prosecutors for the crown with the duty of sending every prisoner brought before them to gaol. Such was the method employed by my former associate, Mr. Levy of Hotchkiss, Levy & Hogan. I have never thought much of its effectiveness. Brow-beating and vituperation accomplish no more in the courtroom than in ordinary life. It is far better to lull the witness into a sense of security and encourage him to elaborate his evidence, until he involves himself in palpable contradictions or evasions, then turn and rend him.

There is a lot of hokum written about the "art" of cross-examination. For fifty years I have largely earned my living by it and I do not think that much more skill is involved than the exercise of ordinary common sense, careful preparation and knowing when to sit down and let well enough alone. It is precisely the same "art" we employ when we try to demonstrate to any person with whom we are conversing that he is uninformed, inconsistent, illogical, prejudiced, or disingenuous. All that is needed is a moderate amount of intelligence supplemented and reenforced by a knowledge of the facts. The lengthy examples of "masterly" cross-examination to be found in most books on the subject hold the reader's attention, if at all, less as demonstrations of skill than for the sensational or salacious facts that they reveal. The quip, the quick turn, the confrontation of the witness with a damning alternative, the *coup de grace*, so to speak, occupies but a few seconds and can be put in a single paragraph. I do not mean that cross-examination cannot be ingenious, witty, and adroit; but it can be equally dull, protracted and useless.

Great liberties were formerly allowed counsel—particularly if they were leaders of the bar—in exhibiting both their erudition and wit, but the old style verbal interchange, in which legal prima donnas attempted to outsmart one another, would probably not be tolerated in any metropolitan courtroom today, as for example, the famous cross-examination by Joseph Choate of Russell Sage or that of the Rev. Henry Ward Beecher by Judge William Fullerton.

When the late Francis L. Wellman asked for a sample of my own efforts to be included in a new edition of his *Art of Cross Examination* alongside those of Mr. Choate and Sir John Russell —as well as, I might add, several of his own—I could find among the minutes of none of the cases I had tried anything I thought either worthy of perpetuation or of sufficient interest to warrant publication. I think Mr. Wellman was a trifle offended that I did not take his invitation as a command or regard it as enough of a compliment to invoke acceptance, but the page of an old trial record is as dead as a slab of hieroglyphics. Once the moment of tension is over it can never be recaptured. Cross-examination has lost as many cases as it has won, and the jawbone of the legal ass has certainly slain its thousands.

Most cross-examination is what its name implies. As Baron Bramwell said: "The art of cross-examination is not to examine crossly." The extent to which it shall be permitted is a matter of the court's discretion, and one often abused. Any witness who testifies necessarily submits his character to attack, and hence it is proper to ask him whether he has been convicted of felony or been guilty of some act showing moral turpitude. This opens the door to great injustice, for the official standing of the prosecutor is such that his mere interrogation is equivalent to an accusation carrying with it a strong presumption of guilt.

I once had a case which, on second thought, I might have sent to Mr. Wellman for his book, not as any evidence of my ability but of the danger of that sort of cross-examination on the part of an unscrupulous prosecutor.

I had been assigned to the defense of a man named Mooney who had served a short prison term and was now charged with carrying a concealed weapon—a convenient method sometimes availed of by the police to get rid of undesirable citizens. It is enough for present purposes for me to say simply that the case against my client was of the flimsiest character, but Delaney the policeman, who had made the arrest, had urged the prosecutor to convict him if he could. Now while the only testimony against Mooney was that of the officer who claimed that he had taken a loaded pistol from his pocket—which he may well have done after first placing it there—it was legally enough; and unless Mooney took the stand and denied that the weapon was his, the jury would have practically no choice. So I put him on the stand.

The prosecutor was my ancient enemy Francis Patrick O'Brien, and the fact that I was for the defense made him more than ever zealous for a conviction. Having proved that Mooney was an ex-convict, he asked:

"You come from the Gas House district, don't you?"

"No," replied Mooney.

"Ever hear of the Gas House gang?"

"Yes, but I'm not one of them."

"Oh, you're not, eh? I didn't ask you that. Why were you in such a hurry to slip that in?"

"Because," retorted Mooney, "you were trying to make the jury think I was."

"Maybe you're right!" replied O'Brien with a grin. "Now, how many times have you been convicted of crime in other States?"

"Never!" cried Mooney indignantly, "and you can't prove it, either!"

"Well, maybe I can't prove it," admitted O'Brien, "but," he added insinuatingly, "I can inquire how many times you have committed burglaries—say in New Jersey."

Mooney, his face white, turned to the judge.

"Your Honor," he protested, "has this man got the right—"

"Answer the question," admonished Judge Babcock. "This is proper cross-examination."

"Well?" sneered the prosecutor.

"I never committed any burglary."

"No burglaries? What kind of crimes, then, have you committed."

"None!" declared Mooney defiantly.

And then O'Brien pulled the dirtiest trick in court that has ever come to my attention. He took a copy of Inspector Byrnes' *Professional Criminals of America* and, holding it so that the jury could plainly see the title, opened it and ran his finger down a page as if reading what he had found there,

"Did you not, on September 6, 1927," he demanded, "in company with Red Birch, alias the Roach, Toni Sevelli, otherwise known as Toni the Greaser, and Dynamite Tom Meeghan, crack the safe of the American Railway Express at Rahway, New Jersey, and get away with six thousand dollars?"

Mooney leaped to his feet.

"It's a lie!" he shouted. "I never knew any such people. I never was in Rahway in my life!"

"So *you* say!" taunted O'Brien. "But don't you know that both the Roach and the Greaser swore you were there?"

"Hold on, Mr. O'Brien!" admonished Judge Babcock. "If there's an objection I'll exclude that question."

"I don't object," I answered. "Go as far as you like."

"I know nothing about any of it!" protested Mooney. "He's framing me!"

Bang! went Babcock's gavel.

"That's enough!" he remarked. "You will have your chance to explain on your re-direct." But I had already made up my mind what to do and there wasn't going to be any re-direct.

"That's all," said O'Brien ostentatiously tossing *Professional Criminals of America* on the table in front of the jury box.

"If the Court please," I said, "for some reason the district attorney has not seen fit to offer in evidence the loaded pistol which Officer Delaney has produced here and swears he found in the defendant's pocket. Unless this is done I shall move to dismiss."

O'Brien arose languidly.

"The merest oversight, Your Honor! I offer the pistol in evidence."

"I object unless it is made to appear upon the record from whose custody it is produced, how it got here and that it is in the same condition as when received," I said.

"Mr. Tutt is technically correct," ruled Judge Babcock. "If he insists you will have to be sworn."

"I do insist," I said.

So O'Brien with the pistol in his hand ascended the stand, took the oath, and testified that it was in precisely the same condition as when delivered to him a few days before by Delaney.

"Have you any cross-examination?" inquired His Honor.

"I have," I replied. "Are you one of the public prosecutors of this county, Mr. O'Brien?"

"I am," he snapped. "As you very well know."

"And you are sworn to prosecute those of whose guilt you are satisfied, through the introduction of legal evidence in a legal manner?"

"Correct."

"Where were you born?" I asked.

"New York City."

"Do you come from the Gas House section?"

One of the jury sniggered and the judge raised a finger in admonition.

"Your question seems rather unnecessary, Mr. Tutt."

"This is cross-examination," I answered. "But I will withdraw it.—How much did you pay for your appointment as assistant district attorney?"

Judge Babcock brought down his gavel.

"That will do. The jury will disregard the question."

"I have as much right to attack this witness's credibility as he has to attack that of my client," I asserted stoutly. "Did you not pay five thousand dollars to Michael McGurk to be delivered to Joseph Morrison in consideration of your appointment?"

"I did not!" shouted O'Brien. "Is your Honor going to permit me to be insulted in this way?"

But a bewildered look had settled upon the learned justice's countenance. Wasn't what was sauce for the goose sauce for the gander?

"Haven't you regularly contributed ten per cent of your salary each month to the treasury of Tammany Hall?" I persisted.

His Honor flushed. That was getting near home.

"Kindly answer the question," I said.

"I object," roared O'Brien.

"There really must be a limit to this sort of thing!" declared Babcock. "It wouldn't have any bearing on the credibility of the assistant district attorney even if he did."

One of the jurors snorted.

"If you prefer not to answer I won't press it," I remarked. "What is your salary?"

"Seventy-five hundred a year."

"What is ten per cent of that?"

"Come, come, Mr. Tutt. That is a trifling arithmetical problem," commented Babcock.

"If seven hundred and fifty dollars is a trifle," I countered.

The twelve in the box were having a grand time.

"Only a few more trifling questions, Mr. O'Brien," I went on. "Have you ever been convicted of a crime?"

"No!" he replied, but he had turned unexpectedly gray.

"Have you ever committed one?"

O'Brien choked.

"I won't force you to answer that," I continued.

But Babcock thought he saw his chance.

"Have you any basis for that question?" he demanded sharply.

I smiled at the jury and then at the bench.

"Your Honor," I said, "you and I belong to a generation which has old-fashioned ideas of honor. Honor demands that I admit having no basis for most of the questions which I have just asked this witness; yet, in a sense, honor demanded that I should ask them, although I might later have to disown their sincerity. But, sir, I do not abandon my attack upon this witness's credibility. I have but one more question to ask him and upon his answer I stake my client's liberty. Let him answer any way he sees fit—yes, or no, I care not which—let him make any reply at all which may be officially recorded here and not hereafter be disputed or denied by him—and this jury may return a verdict against my client.—It is this; Mr. O'Brien, when you took that book in your hand"—and I lifted Byrne's *Professional Criminals* from where it lay upon the table—"and pretended to read from its pages, were you reading something that was printed there or not? YES—or NO!"

In the silence that followed all those in the courtroom could distinctly hear the ticking of the clock upon the rear wall.

"Tick-tock! Tick-tock! Tick-tock!"—"Yes-no! Yes-no! Yes-no!"

O'Brien squirmed and gazed at the floor.

"Tick-tock! Tick-tock!" went the clock.

"Yes—or no! Yes—or no!" I echoed.

O'Brien hung on dead center. If he answered "Yes"—insisted that he had been reading from the book—I would have put it in evidence and sent him up for perjury. Yet if he answered "No"—admitted that he had made the whole thing up—that there was not a word about Mooney in the book at all—it would be almost as bad. I could see him clutching at the flimsy legal straw of refusing to answer on the ground that his reply might tend to degrade or incriminate him, but that would leave him possibly in a worse position. He'd surely lose his job.

"Tick-tock! Yes-no! Tick-tock! Yes-no! Which—what!"

O'Brien moistened his lips and swallowed twice. He coughed and fumbled for his handkerchief. After all, I could see him thinking, he had done nothing that was not strictly legal. He had not charged that Mooney was a professional crook; he had only asked him the question. You could ask anything you chose so long as you were bound by the witness's answer. Wouldn't that save him? Then that hope faded. While I might be bound by his answer in the case at bar he would be forever bound by the written record. He could never get rid of the millstone his yes or no would hang about his neck. I could have him disbarred.

"No," he muttered in a woolly voice, so low as hardly to be audible. "I—was—not—reading from the book."

"You mean—" began Judge Babcock. "You actually mean that you—" And he turned his back upon O'Brien with a look of disgust.

The Lord had delivered my enemy into my hands. I faced the jury.

"Now, gentlemen," I said, "you may convict my client if you wish. But at least you now know how the administration of justice is sometimes conducted."

Judge Babcock swung around his chair.

"Take your seat, sir!" he said to the unhappy prosecutor. "Gentlemen of the Jury, acting within my judicial discretion I wish to say that in my opinion the proof in this case does not measure up to the standard of quality required for a conviction. I direct an acquittal."

"Hearken unto your verdict as it stands recorded," intoned the clerk. "You say the defendant is not guilty and so say you all."

Most juries—and judges—want "to do justice." Yet it is extremely unlikely that any judge, however able, can in from ten minutes to an hour instruct a jury as to what it has taken him a lifetime to learn himself in such a way that they really understand much of what it is all about. They not only go into the box with preconceived ideas which they are disinclined to surrender, but they are mentally incapable of making the fine distinctions required by the law. Since their verdicts are, save in exceptional cases, general, *i.e.* merely "guilty" or "not guilty," or "for the plaintiff" or "for the defendant," no one has any means of knowing whether they accepted the law as laid down by the judge or what facts they found to be "established." They can disregard the judge's charge with impunity and nothing can be done about it. That they have no moral right to do this makes not the slightest difference to them. Thus, in the jury system, we have to a great extent a government of men and not of laws.

It is frankly alleged by some jurists that this is all to the good, since the jury's ability to defy the law as laid down by the judge enables them to mitigate the injustice of its strict application in harsh cases, while at the same time apparently keeping it intact. That juries could do this in the past is perhaps one reason why death continued to be the penalty for all felonies, not only in England but America, well into the eighteenth century and why over two hundred crimes were still so punishable as late as 1822 in England. If juries had not thus been able to nullify capital punishment, attached by law to the killing of rabbits or the stealing of apples, the situation would have been ameliorated by statute far earlier. Such extreme penalties, if enforced, result either in civil disobedience or revolution.

The same thing is true of a judge sitting without a jury. He can render a general opinion similar to a general jury verdict, or he can hand down an opinion in which he is meticulous in his statement of the law, yet in effect nullify it by finding such facts as perhaps unconsciously appeal to him. In the hands of a dishonest judge this is an invitation to veniality. The first thing he does in writing an insincere opinion is to parade an unassailable regiment of incontestable legal principles—and then accomplish his object by juggling the facts to make them fit the law.

Just as the Constitution is what the Supreme Court says it is, facts are what judges and jurors say they are—and usually refuse to disclose. Steve O'Hare, one of my friends of the criminal bar once told me: "There's no proposition of law too foolish or absurd to advance to a judge in a criminal case and no claim as to fact too foolish for a jury to swallow." Steve had been educated for the Jesuit priesthood but, although he had fallen by the way, he was a kindly man and a sound lawyer. He was astute at taking exceptions on which later to reverse a conviction.

"Young feller," he said to me one day, after a jury had gone out, "there's lots of things in this game you ain't got onto yet. Do you think I care what the jury did? Not a mite! I got a nice little error into this case the very first day, and I've set back ever since. S'pose we *are* convicted? I'll get Jim here out on a certificate of reasonable doubt and it'll be two whole years before the Court of Appeals will get around to the case. Meantime Jim'll be out makin' money to pay me my fee—won't you, Jim? Then your witnesses will all be gone, and nobody'll remember what on earth it was all about. You'll be down in Wall Street practising real law yourself, and the indictment'll kick around the office for a year or so, all covered with dust, and then some day I'll get a friend of mine to come in quietly and move to dismiss. And it'll *be* dismissed! Don't you worry! Why, a thousand other murders will have been committed in this county by the time that happens. Bless your soul! You can't go on tryin' the same man forever. Give the other fellers a chance! You'll see! I've been doin' it for thirty years."

XIX

THE LAW AND LITERATURE

I WAS sitting with Peter Dunne and Arthur Train before the fire in my library after a session of the Bible Class, when the latter said:

"Did it ever occur to you that there's a striking analogy in the difference between law and justice and that between fact and truth?"

"Are you trying to revive the old dispute between the 'realists' and the 'nominalists'?" asked Dunne. "If so, you can refill my glass, Eph—just what you lawyers call a 'refresher'."

"The distinction between fact and truth is old stuff," I commented.

"Perhaps—but not to me!" said Train. "I used to think I was getting at the truth in court, but I see now that the truth is greater than the sum of all the facts. Besides, you can't get the truth from a witness. The rules of evidence don't permit it."

"Mr. Dooley" set down his glass.

"If you'd develop that a bit, maybe I could use it."

"For one thing—" Train lit a fresh cigarette—"the truth, so far as any particular person is concerned, is the result of the impression made upon his brain, and it varies with each one of us. Now his five senses received that impression simultaneously. He didn't hear before he saw, or smell before he felt. Yet when he tells his story on the witness stand he has to arrange his reactions in some wholly arbitrary and artificial order. Second, and far more important, unless the witness is allowed to interpret his sensations and impressions as he experienced them he cannot convey the truth. Yet the law won't let him!"

"How d'you mean won't let him? Doesn't the law compel a man to testify?" asked Dunne.

"Haven't you ever been in court?" I asked.

"Only once—and I pleaded guilty," he said.

Train picked up the thread again.

"The law allows one to testify only to what it calls facts. It won't allow the use of any simile, metaphor or analogy. Homer wouldn't be permitted to talk about a 'wine-dark sea' or Shakespeare about the quality of mercy dropping 'as the gentle rain from heaven.' You can't testify that you were 'sick as a dog,' or your 'feet were like ice,' or that a motor was 'going like Sam Scratch.' "

"I'd be tongue-tied!" muttered Dunne.

"My point is," continued Train, "that one cannot express the truth without every descriptive aid at one's command. Comparison is the writer's necessary and most important technique. Without analogy and metaphor we wouldn't have the delicate imagery of Shelley, the stupendous panorama of Balzac's *Human Comedy,* the pathos and humor of Dickens, the irony of Thackeray, or Keats's immortal 'Ode to the Nightingale'."

"Or the wisdom of 'Mr. Hennessey'!" I added.

"The upshot of which, I take it," said Dunne, "is that as an interpreter of truth literature is superior to what you call evidence?"

"Immeasurably," said Train. "Take for instance that line from Tennyson's 'Ballad of the Revenge': 'And a pinnace like a fluttered bird, came flying from far away.' It is a perfect—and therefore a truthful—description. On the witness stand you would first have to define 'pinnace,' omit all reference to birds, and state that you observed, at a certain distance, a boat or vessel a certain number of feet long, with a specified number of sails, moving on the surface of the water in a specified direction, at such and such a rate of speed."

"I get you," nodded Dunne. "Remember that wonderful verse in the book of Job:

'Hast thou given the horse strength? Hast thou clothed his neck with thunder? Can'st thou make him afraid as a grasshopper? The glory of his nostrils is terrible. He paweth in the valley and rejoiceth in his strength.'

What would a court do to that, I wonder?"

"Play everlasting heck with it!" I said. "The judge would strike out any allusion to grasshoppers as irrelevant, incompetent and immaterial, and as for 'clothing his neck with thunder,' he'd commit old Job either for contempt of court or to Bellevue Hospital for medical observation. How can a horse's neck be 'clothed with thunder'?"

"That's only one side of the picture!" insisted Train. "The law not only excludes what ought to be allowed, but on the theory that fact is too trifling to be omitted since it may somehow turn out to be important, admits much that ought to be kept out. No one can prophesy what is going to attract the idiosyncrasy of an Appellate Court. Hence the law tends to emphasize equally all facts, whether great or small. The result is a loss of proportion and a distorted picture."

I crossed to the bookcase and took down a volume of Judge Cardozo's essays.

"Listen to this," I said, opening to the famous jurist's essay on "Style." " 'There is an accuracy that defeats itself by the over-emphasis of details. I often say that one must permit oneself, and that quite advisedly and deliberately, a certain margin of misstatement. . . . The picture cannot be painted if the significant and insignificant are given equal prominence. One must know how to omit.' "

Dunne laughed.

"I never thought I'd hear a Justice of the Supreme Court of the United States cited as an authority for the proposition that, if one would tell the truth, he must not tell all of it!"

"I go so far," declared Train, "as to assert that the more a statement is couched in legal phraseology, in accordance with the laws of evidence and adapted to legal uses, the less it approaches truth—or perhaps, more accurately, that such a statement never can represent the truth in the usual conception of the term, but only a special kind of truth, which might be called the 'legal truth'."

"Well," said Dunne, "I never could understand what lawyers were talking about anyway."

"That's because they have inherited a jargon of their own," I said. "Old Jeremy Bentham called it 'lawyers cant, which serves them, at every word, to remind them of that common interest by which they are made friends of one another, enemies to the rest of mankind.' "

"Yes," said Dunne, "I've often noticed that a lawyer requires about fifty times as many words to say that a hen crossed the road as it would anyone else. A lawyer is as tautological as a cuckoo-clock!"

"That's in part because originally scriveners were paid by the word," I said. "To use only one, when he could avail himself of three or four, was regarded as treason to his craft."

"No lawyer can spend ten years drawing papers and retain his freedom of expression," declared Train. "It's not only the saids, aforesaids, whereases, hereinafters and befores, it's because the factual attitude becomes part of his make-up. His style ceases to be free. He becomes literal, pedantic, over-precise, unable to see the woods for the trees."

"Not only his style!" I interrupted. "He ceases to be free himself. The legal goblins that hide in his briefs will get him if he doesn't watch out—probably even if he does—and squeeze the juice out of him."

"I seem to have observed," said Dunne, "that—present company excepted of course—lawyers exhibit rather less emotion than most people—even than bankers."

"That's why lawyers can't write," said Train.

"What do you mean they can't write?" demanded Dunne. "You're both a lawyer and a writer. That disproves your own thesis."

"No. I was never in earnest about the law," Train said. "I was always a sort of legal play-boy. Even so, my professional training has decidedly stood in my way."

"On the contrary," I retorted. "I feel sure you owe whatevei success you have had—and you will admit that it is not inconsiderable—to your legal training. The law is pre-eminently a literary profession. Words are the lawyer's media of exchange."

"A debased coinage!"

"Come, come!" I went on. "Some of the greatest essayists, historians and novelists in the English language were lawyers. Look at Justice Holmes. He had one of the most beautiful and limpid styles of our day. Wasn't the Gettysburg address written by a country lawyer?"

"I agree," he answered, "that up to a certain point a legal training has certain literary advantages. I am not speaking of clarity of thought or elegance of expression, and certainly not of the material which a legal career affords. Neither do I take account of those advocates who address juries in rhyme, judges who write humorous opinions on dogs and wines, or the lawyers who occasionally turn out a capable short story. My point is that those who practice law seriously are bound to forfeit freedom of expression and that the longer they stay at it the less they become qualified to give rein to fancy. Lawyers, as a rule, do not become poets, playwrights or novelists—at any rate not of the first rank. They rarely produce great literature."

"You're quite mad!" said Dunne. "How about Scott, Dickens and Thackeray?"

"Dickens was no lawyer," replied Train. "After eating, as he put it, 'a few bad dinners in Gray's Inn' as a solicitor's clerk he became a newspaper man. Thackeray, having frittered away a year in the Middle Temple, inherited £500 and beat it for Paris. Scott, who wrote better and more understandingly of the law than anyone else before or since, although nominally a lawyer and for twenty-five years holding a sinecure as clerk of Sessions, was really a writer and antiquarian—he never practiced. Your best bet would be Samuel Warren with his famous *Ten Thousand a Year*—an infernally bad book by the way!—but Warren studied medicine first and wrote his novel within two years of having been called to the bar."

"Well—Henry Fielding, then? I've got you there!" Dunne pressed him.

"No, you haven't. Fielding was a playwright and producer long before he studied for the bar. After a couple of years on circuit he took a job as police magistrate at £300 a year (he called it 'the dirtiest money on earth') and gave his real energies to writing *Tom Jones* and *Joseph Andrews*."

"You do not convince me," retorted Dunne stubbornly. "I can name dozens of lawyers who were or are successful novelists."

"Not a single one of the first rank!"

"All right," he said. "How about John Galsworthy, Anthony Hope Hawkins, A. P. Herbert, the author of *Water Gypsies*, Owen Wister, and John Buchan—Lord Tweedsmuir?"

Train tossed an ash into the grate.

"It's true that they belonged to the legal profession, but none of them practiced it for more than a year or so. John Buchan came nearer to embarking seriously on law as a career than the rest, but a few months after he was admitted to the bar he went to Africa as secretary to Lord Milner, and later on returning to London soon abandoned law for business. Wister had only two desultory years in an office. The others got out almost immediately."

"You forget Edgar Lee Masters, Robert Grant and F. J. Stimson," insisted Dunne. "And who was the fellow that wrote the librettos for *Trial by Jury* and *Iolanthe*?"

"W. S. Gilbert? His connection with it was brief as well as briefless. He paid £400 in fees and rent in order to become a barrister and quit after four years having earned £75; Grant and Stimson were both literary men of talent, but hardly of the first rank; while Masters began deluging the magazines and newspapers with poetry within a few years of his admission to the bar."

"You seem to have documented yourself pretty thoroughly," I remarked.

"I have," conceded Train. "The subject interested me. I wanted to find out why I didn't write better myself."

"Did you?"

"I think so. Like all men bred to the law I'm too factual, too precise, too obvious, too logical. My dialogue tends to be too complete, to resemble questions to and answers from a witness. I'm too anxious to make clear my point, to prove my case and win the reader's verdict, to write Q.E.D. before I sign off, to dot my i's and cross my t's. Life isn't like that, you know."

"I can see how there might be such a tendency," admitted Dunne.

"I'm sure there is! You don't find it—at least to the same extent—among writers who haven't had a legal training. Kenneth Grahame, who wrote *The Golden Age* and *The Wind in the Willows*, was secretary to the Bank of England; Charles Dodgson —'Lewis Carroll,' who wrote *Alice in Wonderland*—was a mathematician; Somerset Maugham was a surgeon before he became a playwright. Medicine has produced all sorts of imaginative writers, including poets, playwrights and novelists."

"You recall Phyllis McGinley's satiric 'Complaint to the American Medical Association' about doctor-authors in her 'Pocketful of Wry'?

> 'The pen (so springs the constant hope
>   Of all devout physicians)
> Is mightier than the stethoscope
>   And runs to more editions.
> So while he's waged bacillic wars
>   Or sewed a clever suture,
> His mind has hummed with metaphors
>   Laid up against the future.' "

"I dare say there's something in what you say," I agreed. "A surgeon, you see, can take out your appendix without harming his literary style. It's obviously unlikely that young men with marked artistic gifts and a strong urge for creative expression would go to law school, or that older ones engrossed in a profession should turn to another, particularly if they need to make a living."

"It's as true as most generalities," said Train. "Another curious thing is that writers of literature so rarely select the law as their field. It's one thing to attack the law's delays, or the barbarism of imprisonment for debt, through fictional propaganda as did Dickens and Charles Reade, and quite another to write a vital story based on the vast panorama of the law, using the characters to illustrate its development, its relationship to life, its majesty as well as its limitations, and the startling contradiction between law and justice. It would require a maximum of literary skill, combined with profound knowledge not only of jurisprudence but of history. No really great novel, like Tolstoi's *War and Peace* has been written against a legal background—or is ever likely to be."

I went over to the shelf where I had assembled a long row of volumes based to a certain extent on the law—Samuel Warren's *Ten Thousand a Year,* Trollope's *Orley Farm,* Scott's *Guy Mannering,* Dickens' *Bleak House*—half a hundred of them, including Train's own study of criminal justice, *The Blind Goddess.*

"What becomes of my so-called 'legal novels'?" I asked.

"There's no such thing as a 'legal novel'," he replied. "There are only good novels and bad novels."

XX

THE LEGAL CAVALCADE

O CCASIONALLY, as will happen to any lawyer whose name gets into the newspapers, I would be cajoled into giving an after-dinner talk or even into being "the principal speaker" at some banquet of legal brethren. At first I took this to be a tribute to my reputation as an advocate, but an incident which occurred in 1927 disillusioned me and thereafter I avoided all such booby traps for the next ten years.

I had been asked to address a state bar association in a New England city at which all the members of the supreme court were to be present—supposedly a very dignified affair for which I made appropriate preparation. On descending from the train I was welcomed by an expansive person who, introducing himself as The Reception Committee, escorted me to a suite in the nearby hotel at which I was to be lodged and suggested a drink. To this I assented, and in due course we drank. Now I do not say that there was anything actually offensive in this complaisant young man's demeanor, or the odor of bay rum which he exuded, but I could not but suspect that he somehow regarded me in the light of a public entertainer, rather than as his grave and reverend senior at the bar. This suspicion crystallized into conviction when in order to make conversation I remarked :

"I hope what I have to say may prove of interest to your associates."

At this he grinned knowingly.

"Don't worry!" he assured me. "You'll be a knockout all right! You'll fold 'em in their seats. You see, we used to invite some pompous old judge or professor, who put us all to sleep, but we learned our lesson a couple of years ago. We had sent out word that Dean Doolittle of the South-western University Law School would deliver an address on 'Implied Superrogatory Powers' and there had been a good

deal of bellyaching among the members because no one knew
what it meant, and they looked forward to a pretty dreary hour.
Just the same they all came—the dinner is free, you understand.
Well, towards nine o'clock the chairman introduced Dean Doolittle, a young chubby sort of feller in goggles, and he began. He
made a fair start, then tripped over himself, and got all tangled
up so that we wondered if he would ever pull out. He stood there
a few minutes gagging and stammering and then suddenly
shouted 'Oh, to Hell with it!' leaned under the table and pulled
out his accordion. He played on it for forty-five minutes, everything we asked—Sweet Adeline or anything—and we all sang.
Gee, he was a wow! So, as I say, we've learned our lesson and
you can go the limit."

An icy hand clutched my heart.

"Mr. Jones," I said solemnly, "I'm sorry, but I accidentally
left my accordion in New York."

However when in 1937 I was asked by the Interstate Bar
Association to make the address at its annual August convention
at St. Louis, Missouri, I confess to having felt much flattered,
since up to that time in spite of my success at the bar I had
suspected that my brethren in the profession did not take me very
seriously, or at any rate regarded me somewhat in the light of a
legal wanton.

After all I was sixty-eight years old, and had tried cases forty-
five years. If I had learned nothing from my experience and
legal research my professional life had indeed been wasted. But
what could I say to these learned men about the law which
would profit them? Probably nothing; but I could at least tell
them what fun I had got out of it and of my hopes for what it
could accomplish for the good of men.

The law is like a glittering cavalcade woven in parti-colored
thread upon the tapestry of civilization. Its records are full of
humor and tragedy, of ambition, success and failure, of plot and
counter-plot, of romance, chivalry and intrigue. They embody
much of the accumulated wisdom as well as many of the fatuities

of the race. The aftermath of every great adventure appears there in some form or another. The State Trials of England paint a vivid picture in which kings and queens, archbishops and lord chancellors, commoners and felons live, act and speak the language of their time as they never do in the retrospective pages of the historian.

They have plenty of salt in them, too. Take for example the record of the proceedings in 1613 between the Lady Frances Howard, Countess of Essex, and Robert, Earl of Essex, her husband, in the ecclesiastical court before the King's Delegates for a divorce on the alleged ground of his impotency.* The King, according to the custom under such circumstances, appointed as judges six bishops, who in turn empannelled a jury composed of "midwives and matrons" to inquire into the matter, conduct the necessary research and report as to whether the lady had what may be called the *a priori* grounds for her assertion. According to the record, after the countess had veiled herself, these subjected her to the necessary examination and unanimously returned a special verdict to the effect that she was a *"virgo apta"* and, what was more to the point, *"intacta."* The gallant bishops thereupon granted the divorce. Now, *quaere*, did the countess veil her face out of excessive modesty in an age by no means noted for that virtue and sometimes even described as bawdy, or, as is hinted by the reporter in a footnote, was another lady substituted? And who was behind all this parade of bishops and midwives? Did she perhaps have a lover and a noble one? That was what everyone was asking. The to-do was such that the Archbishop of Canterbury wrote a long "memorial" concerning the case, together with a speech which he "intended to make" but which was "printed but not delivered," and King James published a reply to it, concluding "the best thankfulness that you, that are my creature, can use towards me is to reverence and follow my judgment, and not to contradict it" and generally putting that dignitary in his proper place.

* 2 Howell's State Trials, 586–832; 3 Kennet's History of England, 686, 692; 1 Bacon's Works, 78.

Essex *vs.* Essex furnished as much excitement at that time as the Thaw case in ours, which was not lessened by the fact that the Earl immediately married again and had a son by his second wife, thus proving that he was more of a man than the matrons had given him credit for. Anyhow, why read mystery stories when reports of the State Trials can be had for five shillings the copy? It would probably surprise any lady client to find that before shipping her off to Reno for a divorce her lawyer had consulted the decisions of the Consistory Court of England in the 17th Century, although he may well have done so.

The lawyer no more than his client can escape the past. Law has always existed. It started in the Garden of Eden, and while it was God himself who forbad Adam to eat of the fruit of the tree, it is fairly clear that when Cain slew Abel he violated some primitive law against murder. Every civilization has had its code, whether Babylonian, Hebraic, Egyptian, Greek, Roman, Gothic, Norman or English. We have inherited something from all of them. Ecclesiastical or canon law, as it is called, interwoven with Bible tests and excerpts from the epistles of "the Fathers," is solidly imbedded in the English common law and hence is an integral part of American law today. Every time the lawyer reaches for a book upon his shelves the ghost of Charlemagne, of Pope Gregory VII, Thomas Beckett, Cardinal Woolsey, or of Sir Edward Coke stands at his elbow. In those days the church and the state were pretty well jumbled up.

Speaking generally the law is a body of man-made rules designed to enable people to live in harmony with each other and with their rulers. It tends to reduce social disorder and friction, just as surgery and medicine diminish ill-health and suffering. Often both systems have gone hand in hand, and the prophet Moses gave the same attention to the rules of health as of conduct, both being regarded as of equal sanctity by the Hebrews.

All ancient legal systems without exception were supposed to be of divine origin, including that of Hammurabi, King of Babylon, which he claimed to have received directly from Samas, "the judge of heaven and earth," and the mediaeval church did not overlook the practical value of the same suggestion. We have got a long way from that point of view today. We realize that the thesis that human laws are of divine origin is a proposition no sounder than that the Book of Genesis is a more accurate explanation of man's appearance upon earth than the Darwinian theory.

Since law, whatever its origin, was originally based on the necessity for order, only the more egregious forms of misconduct were at first forbidden; while sins, impieties and mere wrongs were left to the individual conscience, to the priest or to paternal discipline. Sin was obviously either a private affair or too vast a field for effective personal control. While God could have his eye in every place, no policeman possibly could do so. Thus the law only incidentally regarded the moral or ethical aspect of an act in determining whether it should be punished. Yet a system which sends a man to jail for walking on the grass or stealing a loaf of bread, while taking no step to castigate him if he allows a child to drown before his eyes, clearly lacks the appeal of justice.

I confess that I have always wanted to see the doctrines of Chistianity translated into public action seven days in the week instead of being reserved for private charity on Sunday. I admit that there is another side to the picture and that "he who is governed least is governed best." I abhor a multiplicity of statutes and governmental interference in one's personal affairs, but there is an irreducible minimum of legislation below which the misfortune of the individual affects the welfare of the state. The old idea was that an individual's business was nobody's business, whereas there is in fact a point at which any man's business becomes everyone's business.

When God created the universe, including the solar system and our own little world, he established certain inviolable physical laws—such as those of chemistry, hydraulics, and thermo-dynamics. Mankind accepted them because it couldn't do anything about them, and various theories grew up as to how human beings were to be compensated for the sufferings which such laws unjustly caused. Buddha, Christ, Mohammed, Tolstoi—all had their explanations. While lawyers use the phrase "Acts of God" and write it into insurance policies, they are referring merely to certain unusual forms of accident, and no judge ever thinks of saying to a jury: "It may be, gentlemen, that in this case a miracle occurred."

It was on the laws of nature that man imposed his own legal structure. But the basis and the building were entirely different in that the latter could be altered. More rooms became necessary and even when this was obvious it required an almost super-human effort to change it. So a substantial proportion of the inhabitants of the earth have always spent their lives out in the rain and cold, often with disastrous consequences not only to themselves but to the people inside as well. Gradually the legal building has been enlarged. From time to time different rulers have had different ideas of architecture and put them into effect, so that strange excrescences have appeared. Some of them were later torn down, but some were left, and parts of the foundations although decayed also remained; while the main purpose of the building—to house people in reasonable comfort—was often over-looked in the effort to patch it up.

The reader will agree that I have already said enough to jus-tify my intial statement in the first chapter of this book that I am a natural rebel. Certainly I have filled plenty of pages with rather acrid criticism of our laws and legal processes. I hope that I have not been unduly captious and that my allegations have been sufficiently documented to convince him of my sincerity.

That law is not justice is of vital significance to everyone. To many of us the idea will not seem new, to others it will come as something of a shock, for the great mass of mankind undoubt-edly invests the law which we have inherited from the past with something of the sanctity which the Israelites accorded to the Ten Commandments which Moses brought down from the mountain.

I discovered this attitude even among my classmates at the Harvard Law School who used to ask me with obvious boredom what I was kicking about. If I tried to tell them they merely shrugged. They had, it seemed, enough trouble with the law as it stood, without looking for more. When I got into active practice I found that most people were either too anxious to maintain the *status quo* or too busy trying to make money to do anything about it. A man who would give a thousand dollars to a charity wouldn't take the time to go to Albany to back a law which might render the charity unnecessary.

Generally speaking I wanted the law to be more efficacious, more speedy and above all more human. So does everyone, you say? Well, perhaps. More efficient and more speedy, yes; but more human? I'm not so sure. This is where self-interest comes in, and in spite of the Beveridge plan and the fact that the so-called common people no longer are prepared to order themselves lowly and reverently before their betters, there are a lot of folks who still believe that *laissez faire* means the privilege of starving to death, or going without a doctor when you are sick, or seeing your children grow up in the ignorance that is alleged to be bliss.

My fervent hope has always been that the law might be directed more and more to the betterment of mankind rather than of its rulers. This has been my hobby and a goodly proportion of the volumes in my library are devoted to it. But it is a very complicated subject, so much so that it would take a lifetime of study to write even an elementary treatise upon it. Yet since this is my autobiography it would be inadequate if I did not put down my ideas.

There have been certain general but definite trends in legal history. During the Dark Ages, when bloodshed and superstition reigned throughout Europe, the Church represented what law there was. Petty counts and barons exercised the right of life and death and the *"jus primae noctis"* over their serfs and spent their time brawling and raping. The only thing they feared was the censure of the bishop or excommunication by the Pope. Things got so bad that in the eleventh century the ecclesiastical authorities decided that something must be done, so they invented what was known as the "Truce of God" forbidding all fighting from Wednesday until Monday, thus insuring, it was hoped, a peaceful and religiously minded week-end.

The lay power of the Church declined as that of the kings increased, and it is interesting that the invention of gunpowder should have contributed so much to the lessening of its material and spiritual influence. Prior to then the heavily armored knight accompanied by his cavalcade could ride around, robbing and cutting throats at his pleasure, but his sword was no match for the highwayman's pistol and soon the outlaws outnumbered the nobles, who had had things entirely their own way. This was one of the reasons why the king, whose title theretofore had carried comparatively little weight, grew steadily in authority until in fact he was the whole works. The "Truce of God" became the "King's Peace," and how the King enforced "his" law and "his" peace on "his" highway was for a long time nobody's business but his own. But throughout this disordered period the Church had been in control of affairs and its statutes and edicts had become part of the law of the land. The priest was a privileged person, "benefit of clergy" prevented his punishment by a civil court, and the struggle between Church and state for temporal authority continued in England for centuries.

Nevertheless the king was the fountain of all law and, since he was king by divine right, compliance with his commands was regarded as a religious duty. As a result he rode rough-shod over what we now regard as natural rights, imprisoning people without trial, seizing their lands and in general doing as he pleased. This could not go on and at length the barons forced King John at Runnymeade to admit in Magna Carta that he was not above the law. It was one of the greatest steps ever made in humanizing the law, but strangely enough, so used were people to the idea of one-man control, that even this did not at first actually safeguard the rights of the individual. A criminal prosecution was still looked upon merely as the means whereby the King enforced his own personal peace. Judges, regarding themselves as agents of the Crown, acted as zealous prosecutors, while juries were punished if they failed to find a verdict of guilty.* Down to the sixteenth century the accused in felony trials was denied the right to counsel and refused even a copy of the indictment, and, although the Crown could call witnesses, the prisoner was allowed neither to do so nor to testify in his own behalf. Not until 1837 was the right of the prisoner to counsel extended to felonies other than treason, although as late as the reign of George III over two hundred offenses were punishable by death. It was difficult for those with humanitarian principles or who believed in the "Sermon on the Mount" to regard the law as divine. As years went on there was, of course, a natural and growing tendency to go easier on the prisoner and to safeguard his rights as guaranteed under Magna Carta. In time he was given the right to testify; he was allowed the protection of the jury, who must be not only unanimous but satisfied beyond any reasonable doubt as to his guilt; the severity of punishment was gradually mitigated and the death penalty practically abolished. Nevertheless a constant struggle continued between the people's representatives and the officers of the Crown.

Then the great Eighteenth Century movement towards freedom and democracy got under way on both sides of the Atlantic. The American Colonies kicked King George in the pants, and in Paris the mob overthrew the Bastille. The people at last were in the saddle. Hereafter there were to be no divine rights except their own. To insure these a Bill of Rights was incorporated in the United States Constitution and because the courts had generally acted either as agents for the king or favored his interests they were largely shorn of their former power. "The Truce of God" which had first turned into "the King's Peace" now became "the Peace of the People"—the concluding phrase in our

* King *vs.* Windham, 2 Kebb 180 (1667).

present criminal indictments which formerly had read "against the Peace of Our Lord the King." The transition had taken nearly a thousand years, but it had occurred—from Church to King, from King to People. Now at last men could breathe the pure air of freedom. There was no longer any tyrant for them to be afraid of. "Liberty, equality and fraternity" were assured forever. The millennium had arrived.

This happy state of affairs lasted nearly a century before a new threat replacing that of the Crown appeared in the form of the legal fiction known as the "corporation." The people still ruled but they did so through elected representatives who, being for the main part small time politicians and exceedingly human, were easily susceptible to appeals to self interest. The corporations who had no souls did have most of the money, and by means of lobbyists and pressure groups, through political influence or downright bribery were able to get what legislation they wanted. They grabbed the natural resources of the country, they secured the passage of laws beneficial only to themselves and they blocked remedial legislation designed to improve the condition of the laboring man.

By the beginning of the twentieth century a new struggle between the "Haves" and the "Have Nots" had replaced the former one between the Crown and the People. Democracy was now accused of being the tool of Plutocracy, and the system as lending itself to the perpetuation of the majority in power and to an increase of special privilege. "The forgotten man," the factory worker, the miner, and the farmer not without justice raised his voice against Wall Street and "the malefactors of great wealth." Living conditions in factory communities were unspeakably bad, yet the financial power of the owners enabled them to avoid the necessity for improvement. I can well recall when any organization of workers was regarded as a criminal conspiracy and could be prosecuted as such; and even when the moral and legal right to organize had become recognized, its value was practically destroyed by the readiness with which the courts issued injunctions against union activities. Similarly actions by employees for personal injuries sustained during their work were nullified by the ancient doctrines of "contributory negligence," "assumption of risk" and the "fellow servant rule." For a workman or machinist to be compensated in the courts for the loss of an eye or an arm was almost unheard of. "Workman's Compensation Acts" passed by State legislatures were invariably voided by the appellate tribunals as unconstitutional, and it was not until 1915 that such a law was sustained by the New York Court of Appeals after a lengthy and bitter fight.

This outcry against the sins of the corporations was also directed against the courts, being encouraged by the technicality and complication of legal procedure and of the laws themselves, which in many cases admittedly could not accomplish justice when applying archaic precedents to new economic situations unless juries and judges more or less "took the law into their own hands," deciding first what ought to be done and then trying to find some legal excuse for doing so. Even the Constitution was "interpreted" to cover modern conditions.

The danger of this judicial disingenuousness was apparent: A court's jurisdiction could become as personal as that of a sovereign. Judges did not in terms repudiate the law, but they differentiated it to such an extent that the effect in fact was the same. Their motives were honorable, they tended to follow the equities, yet "hard cases make bad law," and many jurists thought that it would have been better frankly to overrule previous decisions if they would have resulted in present injustice, than to make untenable decisions. Hence the practical appeal of so-called "administrative tribunals." The former decentralization of legal authority—such as distributing that of the judge among a fact-finding jury of twelve non-experts—gave way, except in criminal cases, in favor of speed, certainty and actual justice, to that of greater power in a single judge, commission or other governmental agent. "The factual approach," where each case was decided on its own bottom, gained in favor. Red tape was cut, new rules of procedure formulated, a system of "administrative law" by commission came into increasingly wide use; since the mass of business was so great that, unless decisions could be made promptly and with finality, the government could not properly function. But only by a stretch of the imagination could this be regarded as a development along democratic lines. It was in fact a retrogression towards the strengthening of central government.

When it comes to the adequacy of the substantive law, and its established procedure, to achieve justice under the complex developments of modern civilization, even conservative lawyers and judges cannot forbear a shrug—at least in the privacy of their homes. Life implies growth and hence change and this is as true of law as of anything else. No sooner is a law made than *rigor mortis* sets in, and new and unforeseen conditions arise that often render an originally just law unjust. A highly intelligent and entirely unselfish legislature attempting to keep statutory pace with concurrent social and economic developments would be like a dog chasing its tail. Civilization spins ever faster and faster, and even if we do not follow Henry Adams in his prophecy of its resulting doom, one must frankly confess that the law often acts less as a lubricant than as a clog. Our traditional legal system actually tends to gum the whole works.

Jerome used to say, when commenting upon the idiosyncracies of juries, the delay and uncertainty and hence the ineffectiveness of criminal law, that an excellent substitute for it would be some wise old guy in a turban (he usually nominated the late Jacob H. Schiff for the job) who should sit on a platform in City Hall Park with a scimitar across his knees, hear such accusations as were brought before him and lop off such heads as he thought deserved it.* He declared that in that event crime would undoubtedly decrease.

* The fact that the courts are careful not to define "fraud" seems to indicate a recognition of the desirability of allowing some individual latitude of interpretation. Lord Hardwick said: "The Court very wisely hath never laid down any general rule beyond which it will not go, lest other means of evading the equity of the Court should be found out." Lawley *vs.* Hooper, 3 ATR, 278 (1745). See Stonemets *vs.* Head, 248 Mo. 243 (1913).

There is a great deal of truth in this jest. It might be carried further. Instead of the present spectacle of judges wriggling to distinguish their cases from former precedents in order that something approaching justice may be accomplished, why not do away with all forms of law and empower every judge, without regard to "principles" originating in decisions made perhaps long ago under utterly different conditions, to decide each case that comes before him in accordance with his own idea of justice? Their ideas would doubtless differ somewhat, but probably not more than do the present decisions. Some people think that this is in fact what they do now.

Popular dissatisfaction with the law also arises from the inordinate delay involved in invoking its provisions. There are numerous instances where a preliminary hospital delay involved in locating the interne, whose conventional duty it was to hand the operating surgeon the proper instrument, has resulted in the death of the patient; there are vastly more where the law's delay has resulted in the death of legal rights. Even where a legislature has enacted an ameliorative statute, there is a sort of No Man's Land between the passage of the act and its final interpretation. It is necessary to wait until the courts have construed it to know what its legal meaning is, and for this a test case has to be brought. Prior to that time its interpretation is open to anyone—plaintiff, defendant, criminal or judge—any one of whom is likely to disagree with the ultimate conclusion of the court of last resort. Thus there may well be a period of five to ten years, or longer, when no one can say positively what the law is, what sort of act is penalized by a fine and what by a jail sentence, and by the time this is done the statute may well be obsolete. There is also the technicality and frequent absurdity of the laws of evidence.

While I am unwilling to go so far as to say that "the rules of evidence are all nonsense," I do not see why, in the interest of expedition and lucidity, a witness should not be allowed to "tell his story in his own way" as is the procedure in continental countries. The rules enforced in our courts are quite at variance with those invoked by witnesses and jurymen in getting at the facts in their own daily experience. It would be far simpler and more expeditious to "let it all in," subjecting the testimony to the ordinary tests of probability than, as is now the case, to exclude so much that has probative value.

But the chief difficulty with the law viewed from the progress of society is due to its lack of humanity. This is what I have been leading up to in the foregoing pages and what has haunted me for fifty years. The law in spite of its supposedly divine derivation has inevitably been used for the benefit and aggrandizement of those in power—the Church, the King, the Majority—rather than for the best interests of all the people. Moreover, from the days of Moses it has always told us what we must *not* do instead of what we *must* do. It has been preponderantly "thou shalt not," although it might just as well have been "thou shalt." As Roscoe Pound points out, "there is nothing to prevent legal recognition of the moral principle of obligation and the working out of legal rules to give it effect." Today you can let a man be killed before your eyes when you might have saved him without danger to yourself and avoid any civil or criminal liability.

Yet in spite of everything the law gradually and in time, adapts itself to scientific discovery, and economic and social development. "The life of the law has not been logic: it has been experience," says Mr. Justice Holmes in the introductory chapter to his great work on "The Common Law." * "The felt necessities of the time, the prevalent moral and political theories, institutions of public policy, avowed or unconscious, even the prejudices which judges share with their fellow-men, have had a good deal more to do than the syllogism in determining the rules by which men should be governed. The law embodies the story of a nation's development through many centuries, and it cannot be dealt with as if it contained only the axioms and corollaries of a book of mathematics. In order to know what it is, we must know what it has been, and what it tends to become.

* Boston: Little, Brown & Co., 1881.

. . . The substance of the law at any given time pretty nearly corresponds, so far as it goes, with what is then considered to be convenient; but its form and machinery, and the degree to which it is able to work out desired results, depend very much upon the past. . . . The truth is that the law is always approaching, and never reaching, consistency. It is forever adopting new principles from life at one end, and it always retains old ones from history at the other, which have not yet been absorbed or sloughed off. It will become entirely consistent only when it ceases to grow."

The law has made a good deal of progress during the last twenty-five years towards recognizing a heretofore unacknowledged moral responsibility on the part of each individual citizen towards his fellows and of all collectively towards each. We have learned that we all have a "social interest in the general security, which is best maintained by holding those who conduct enterprises in which others are employed to an absolute liability" for the acts of their servants. No one today is startled by the prevalence of Workmen's Compensation Acts or even at the suggestion that insurance against accident, whether the assured is or is not an employee, is something that could well be passed along to the community.

We know that certain acts must be punished as contrary to the public welfare, even where a person is without conscious fault, as in the selling of drugs contrary to the Anti-Narcotic Act. The thing has simply got to be stamped out!

We are alert to the enormous value of having the state take an active interest in the family, through the establishment of juvenile courts and a jealous watchfulness over the control of children and the dependent members of a household.

There has, of course, been a revolution in the status of married women and the establishment of their separate rights. Small claims courts have been instituted to facilitate the settlement of debts and disputes among the poor. We have seen the benefit to the community of zoning laws even if they do put a limitation upon the use of private property;* we place bounds upon the right of a creditor or injured party to exact satisfaction by throwing his opponent into jail or penalizing him unduly; we have laws in the public interest relating to irrigation, and the protection of wild life including migratory birds;† there is a tendency to hold that where an individual has suffered an injury through a public agency he should be compensated out of the public funds; and socialization is especially noticeable in the limitation of the right to contract in labor relations, in insurance, and in fact in almost every branch of contract law. These instances may not strike the lay reader as significant, but they are progressive steps towards an attitude which regards the general welfare as more important than minor individual rights, and as such they are important.

The pace is slow but the legal cavalcade moves on and in the right direction. Most of the kings and emperors have lost their crowns and plod along on foot, while their former serfs, no longer in rags, ride the chargers they bestrode. But the pennants still fly gallantly and the trumpets echo to the challenge of "Liberty and Equality" and of "Justice for the Common Man."

* See Village of Euclid, Ohio et al. *vs.* Ambler Realty Co. (1926), 272 U. S. 365, upholding the validity of zoning ordinances.
† State of Missouri *vs.* Holland (1919), 252 U. S. 416.

XXI

"TUTT AND MR. TUTT"

THIS autobiography, as the introduction indicates, was undertaken purely in self defense. I can see now that it was a mistake in the first place to have allowed the use of my actual name for that of a fictional character; but it arose out of spontaneous good-nature and no one concerned, least of all myself, had the faintest suspicion of what the result would be. Now the harm is done and unfortunately it is not a case of "least said soonest mended." The "Ephraim Tutt" of popular literature is not myself save in outward form and appearance, and yet there is just enough of me embodied in him to create the illusion of identity.

This book is an attempt to set myself right, my plea of "confession and avoidance" as we say in the law. Arthur Train's Ephraim Tutt is not the real Ephraim Tutt, an obvious fact which, if you have read thus far, you will have already perceived for yourself. His Tutt is not even consistent. The character changes from story to story—from that of mountebank to philosopher, from shyster to philanthropist, from law-breaker to upholder of the Constitution. I cannot afford to have such a distorted image of myself go down into history, since, if it did, whatever I have written or said throughout my life would be suspect. I intended to surrender only my privacy, not my reputation.

It came about in March 1919 when I had just succeeded in securing the acquittal of an Italian charged with murder. Angelo Serafino was a simple-minded Italian, a native of Palermo, who earned his living by blacking boots at the Manhattan terminal of the Brooklyn Bridge. He was desperately in love with a really beautiful girl by the name of Rosalina Cellini. Prior to this Rosalina had had an unfortunate love affair with one Tomasso Crocedero who had jilted her and, in consequence, her reputation had suffered. This did not bother Angelo and in due course he and Rosalina were married. But Crocedero, although unwilling to marry the girl himself, resented the idea that anyone else should have her and seized every opportunity to twit Angelo about her past. He hung about his discarded mistress, publicly scoffing at her husband, making horns with his fingers, and seeking to give the impression that he still enjoyed her favors. Angelo stood it as long as he could, then sought out Crocedero in his barber shop and put a bullet through his head.

He had been promptly arrested, indicted and, since he had no money to employ counsel, Tutt and I had been assigned by the court to defend him. Rosalina, his wife, came to my office to give me their side of the case. Her hands and finger nails were far from clean, but her neck rose from the folds of her shawl like a column of slightly discolored Carrara marble, upon which her head with its coils of heavy hair was poised with the grace of a Roman empress. She was utterly dejected, since it appeared that Angelo refused to make any defense but openly gloried in his deed. "I killa him—I killa him again," he had reiterated.

"Will they be able to prove where he bought the pistol?" I asked.

"He didn't buy it," she said, a glint in her black eyes. "I bought it. I'd ha' shot Crocedero myself if Angelo hadn't."

If ever there was a case of wilful, deliberate murder this was it: but if there ever was a case where the deceased had invited his fate, perhaps deserved it, and in which the defendant enlisted all my sympathies this was it also. Angelo came from a country where killing in hot blood was regarded as no great matter and he had, in a sense, acted in self-defense in slaying the would-be murderer of his wife's reputation. But I knew that cat could hardly be made to fight before a "blue ribbon" New York County jury whose specialty was that of regularly convicting every defendant brought before them. I had no defense, and no hope, and in addition I momentarily expected Angelo to spring to his feet and shout as he had in the Tombs: "I killa him! You killa me if you want!"

My only chance lay in being able to capture the sympathies of some single juryman who might bring about a disagreement. No tough old bachelors, no Irish need apply! I wanted twelve, weak-headed, soft-hearted, spineless Casper Milquetoasts who had, if possible, daughters of approximately Rosalina's age. By noontime at the trial I had exhausted all my peremptory challenges and not even a foreman had been selected. Then the clerk drew another slip from the box and to my horror called the name of "Patrick Henry Walsh"! He was square-jawed and ruddy, with a long relentless upper lip and a brogue that would have charmed a Mavis off a tree. He looked like a professional executioner and he acted like one, but he denied any prejudice against Italians and I could not disqualify him.

"Oi'll give him the benefit of the doubt," he said dryly taking his seat in the box, "but if Oi think he's guilty Oi'll convict him."

My heart sank. As the case proceeded it sank lower and lower, particularly as at sporadic intervals I could hear Angelo's suppressed "I killa him! I killa him again!" When the evidence was closed I hadn't a leg to stand on—not a shred of evidence in Angelo's behalf. By three o'clock everyone in the courtroom knew that he was already half way to the electric chair. I did the best I could in my speech to the jury. I discanted on the law of homicide, on the constitutional rights of American citizens, and the sanctity of marriage, I waxed eloquent over Italy and the Italian character, lauded Cavour, Garibaldi and Mazzini, implying that Angelo was their lineal descendant, and I was just making the world safe for democracy at Caporetto when the judge adjourned court and told me I could conclude in the morning.

I had made a good enough speech, but I hadn't said a thing and the jury knew it. I was licked; Angelo would be electrocuted. I could not face the tragedy of the morrow; neither could I sleep. All night, as in a coma, I wandered the deserted streets of the city until towards sunrise I found myself utterly exhausted in front of the twin spires of St. Patrick's. Remembering that a cathedral is never closed I went in and sank down on one of the rear seats, where, resting my head on my arms on the back of the bench in front, I fell fast asleep. I awoke to broad daylight with hardly time enough to reach the courthouse before the case was called. The jury were in their seats and I could think of nothing to say to them except:

"Do not forget your awful responsibility, gentlemen. If you entertain a reasonable doubt upon the evidence you have sworn upon your oaths to give it to the defendant."

The prosecutor made an eloquent address conclusive as to my client's guilt. The judge charged in a way to show the jury that they had no alternative but to convict. They picked up their hats and coats and retired. The funeral rites were all concluded except for the final commitment of the corpse to Mother Earth. We waited in silence.

Suddenly without warning Angelo's voice arose in a defiant shriek:

"I killa that man! He maka small of my wife. He no good— bad egg! I killa him once—I killa him again!"

Horrified, I offered to reopen the case and enter a plea to murder in the second degree. The judge refused. Hours passed. At length the twelve hangmen announced that they had agreed and filed in.

"How say you? Do you find the defendant guilty or not guilty?" asked the clerk.

I gripped the rail with one hand and, closing my eyes, supported Angelo with my other arm. It was all over.

"We foind the defendant *not* guilty," announced the foreman.

"What!" cried the judge and prosecution incredulously.

"I said we foind the defendant not guilty!" stubbornly replied Patrick Henry Walsh.

The judge turned on me furiously.

"This acquittal is a blot upon the administration of criminal justice," he shouted. "It's a disgrace to the city, an unconscionable verdict, a reflection upon the intelligence of the jury!—Defendant discharged."

He hurried from the room: So did the prosecutor. I stood alone with Angelo, endeavoring to grasp what had occurred. What miracle had intervened to save my client from electrocution? Then I felt a rough, warm hand clasped over mine upon the rail and heard Mr. Walsh say in his rich Irish brogue:

"At first we couldn't see that there was much to be said for your side of the case, Counsellor; but whin Oi sthepped into St. Patrick's on me way down to court this mornin' and spied ye prayin' there fer guidance, I knew ye wouldn't be defendin' a guilty man, and so we decided to give him the benefit of the doubt."

I was so exhausted by the trial that, in spite of its exhilarating result, I felt the need of a few days' rest. So taking Train with me I went to Atlantic City where we ran into George Horace Lorimer, then editor of *The Saturday Evening Post*. One evening after dinner, as an illustration of the unpredictability of the action of a jury, I told them how Angelo Serafino had come to be acquitted of a murder which he undoubtedly had committed.

"Do you object to my using that as the basis for a story?" asked Train.

"It's yours," I replied. "It's in the public domain anyway."

"Potash & Perlmutter" was playing down on the pier and we strolled over for the last act. As we walked back to the hotel Lorimer said: "Why couldn't a story about two lawyers be made as amusing as one about two garment makers?" He stopped and looked at me. " 'Tutt!' " he exclaimed. "What a name for a central character! Would you mind our using it?"

Feeling rather jovial and hardly thinking I retorted:

"Go ahead! Put in the whole damn firm if you like."

Lorimer turned to Train.

"All right!" he remarked with his usual abruptness. "You can go ahead and write a series about a law firm called 'Tutt & Tutt' and use that Crocedero murder as the introductory story."

That is all there was to it, and I did not think of the matter again until one of my friends called my attention to a story entitled "The Human Element" in the issue for June 7, 1919, in which I figured. It was *fait accompli*; the crime had been committed; the horse was out of the stable door; and there was no use crying over spilt milk.

Twenty-three years have passed since then and to date there have been nearly a hundred "Tutt Stories," collected in some eleven volumes, all illustrated by Arthur William Brown. His drawings of myself are said to be excellent and I can personally vouch for the accuracy of those of my office force. The first model to pose for the character was Frank Wilson, a retired actor. Since then he has been succeeded in turn by three others, Reginald Carrington, John Whiffin, and William Balfour. Brown's pictures are an important factor in the popularity of the stories, and I have heard Train say that if he is my literary father, Brown is my pictorial mother. At first it was rather startling to see my own lineaments staring me in the face and to find attributed to me sentiments and actions of which I had no previous knowledge. I have had to stand a good deal of good-natured kidding, but I am quite willing to play Charlie McCarthy to his Edgar Bergen, and to allow myself to be thus sacrificed—if it be a sacrifice—on the altar of justice.

Because the law they set forth is sound, these books—particularly "Mr. Tutt's Case Book" *—are frequently used in law schools to illustrate legal principles. Train tells me that he has received letters from numerous candidates for the bar, in widely separated places, who despairing of success and abandoning the idea of going on with their examinations, happened to pick up a copy of one of the Tutt books and acquired sufficient information overnight to pass triumphantly next day.

The following from Edward S. Miller, of Millville, New Jersey, is an illustration:

Dear Sir:
   My father, an attorney for thirty-five years, got me to read some of Mr. Tutt when I was all of twelve. My father has been gone

* Charles Scribner's Sons, New York, $4.00.

these ten years and I am now in my last year of law school, but I still follow Mr. Tutt avidly. The fact is, now I have something more than a casual reader interest in Mr. Tutt.

Last June, the night before taking an examination in Evidence, instead of studying I read a volume of Mr. Tutt. The next day, out of eight questions in the examination, there were three in which I swear I was hopelessly ignorant of the answers in my own right. But in each case the point of the question had been covered by Mr. Tutt in the stories I had read the night before. Since I got an eighty-four in the exam, you may readily understand why you and Mr. Tutt will take the bar exams with me next year.

The stories, some of them by this time as familiar to lawyers as folk tales, are not infrequently cited from the bench in both trial and appellate courts as quasi-legal authorities. I have in fact had the somewhat upsetting experience of having my own statement of the law—as expounded by Train—hurled in my teeth by a presiding judge.

A curious coincidence occurred towards the end of the year 1933 in the State of Pennsylvania, where two litigations happened to be going on in the probate courts of two different counties, but involving precisely the same questions of law and procedure. Each action was an attempt to set aside a will on the ground of fraud and undue influence, and in each court the lawyers for the contestants had been prevented from introducing the diaries of the testatrix to prove that fraudulent statements had in fact been made to her by a third party which had influenced her testamentary intentions—the ground being that such were hearsay.

Both courts adjourned from Christmas to January 2nd. On December 30, 1933 the New Year edition of the *Saturday Evening Post* appeared containing a story by Train entitled "Mr. Tutt Takes A Chance" in which a similar problem was presented. I am supposed to have overcome the difficulty by entering an alternate plea to the effect that the testatrix was mentally incompetent to make a will and by offering the entries in the diaries, not as proof of the facts contained therein, but as bearing upon her condition of mind.* If the statements in the diary were false she was obviously unbalanced; if they were true it was equally clear that a fraud had been perpetrated upon her.

The trial counsel for the contestants in each action read the story, reversed his tactics on the strength of it, and won his case.

That the stories have had repercussions even among lawmakers is demonstrated by what happened as a result of the publication of "Mr. Tutt Stages a Rodeo" in the *Saturday Evening Post* for February 15, 1935, based on Section 7, Chapter 140 of the Revised Statutes of the State of Maine, at that time reading:

Sec. 7: An innholder who, upon request, refuses to receive and make suitable provision for a stranger or traveller, and also for his horses and cattle, when he may under the provisions of this Chapter be required to do so, shall be punished by a fine of not more than fifty dollars.

Sec. 8: An innholder who violates Section 7 shall forfeit his license.

The story recounts how, returning from a fishing trip in Canada with Bonnie Doon, I was obliged to stop over in a Maine city—presumably Bangor or Portland—and on account of my disreputable appearance was refused admittance to a newly erected modern hotel. My protests proving of no avail I indignantly sought accommodations elsewhere from whence, having remedied my sartorial deficiencies and availed myself of the services of a barber, I returned outwardly disguised as a gentleman, and was duly received by the landlord and assigned a room. I thereupon promptly demanded that he provide stabling, hay and provender for my cattle—a herd of steers which at that moment appeared outside, running hither and thither and bellowing loudly.

At first the proprietor did not take the situation seriously, but after his hotel flower-beds had been partially ruined and one of the steers had climbed up the front steps, stampeding the guests,

* See Marx. *vs.* McGlynn, 88 N. Y. 370.

he admitted his error, I forgave him, and the cattle which Bonnie
had hired for the occasion continued on their way to the slaughter-
house. The tale seems to have sent a shiver down the spines of
all the innkeepers in Maine, who raised such a chorus of protest
against the danger of the existing statute to their business interests that it was immediately repealed by the State Legislature.
This seems to substantiate Theodore Roosevelt's theory that the
best way to get rid of an archaic or otherwise undesirable law is
to enforce it.

The Premier of New Brunswick assures me that my friend's
fishing stories have brought millions of dollars into the Province,
and I was once invited to a banquet tendered by its officials in
recognition of the favorable publicity it had thus received. I
regret that in these yarns Train invariably describes me as killing
enormous salmon in the most unlikely places. Unfortunately it is
not true that one has but to cast a fly on the most innocuous
New Brunswick stream to make fast to a mighty fish. Forty pound
Atlantic salmon are, to say the least, extremely rare and a forty-
five pound fish is a trophy. On certain rivers, owing to the amount
of netting at the mouths, one might as well try to get a rise in the
Central Park Reservoir in New York City. Yet occasionally on
almost any river, one can take a single salmon which has dodged
the nets below and managed to make its way upstream.

I once killed, at first cast in late August, a thirty pound fish
on a pool beside a railroad siding where there had been no
salmon seen that season. The news of my fluke brought hundreds
of anglers to the scene, for several weeks the small hotel was
crowded, and the river was jammed with canoes. No other
salmon, however, rose to the fly. Next year on my way to northern Canada I stopped over night at this same hotel and was
eating my supper in the dining room when two fishermen came
in. Each had on a suit of brand new khaki, patched with every
conceivable kind of pocket and receptacle. They were armed
cap-à-pie, belted, buckled, and booted like lancers at a mediaeval
joust. They ate in gloomy silence.

"I thought it might help our case if I dressed up like Mr. Tutt."

My somewhat old fashioned clothes, which Arthur Train has shamelessly exploited for his literary purposes, have been made the basis for many a cartoon.

Courtesy of the *Saturday Evening Post*.

"Well, gentlemen," I said finally, "I hope you are enjoying yourselves. How many fish have you killed today?"

"Didn't catch any," answered the larger of the two, a bespectacled man of considerable girth. "Didn't have a rise. In fact we've been here a week and haven't seen a fish."

"We're having a swell time, though!" put in his companion more cheerfully. "You see, we come from New Jersey, and neither of us have ever been fishing before. But last winter we read a story about a man named Tutt, who seemed to have wonderful luck everywhere he went, and we made up our minds that, before we died, we'd each of us catch an Atlantic salmon."

I concluded my meal as speedily as I could, sneaked out to the office and forbade my friend, the proprietor, to disclose my identity on pain of death.

But after all, what difference did it make? Those two old boys were started in the right direction, and I am convinced that the following year saw them casting their flies, perhaps not there, but certainly somewhere else, and really "having a swell time."

Arthur Train's salmon stories have made me friends all over the United States and Canada, and I am the recipient of countless gifts in the shape of hand-made flies and even of rods, as well as of invitations to fish at various camps and on private water from persons whom I have never seen. Some of these letters are touching in their love of nature, and most of the writers seem to live during eleven months in the year only for the sake of their annual vacation in the woods. Truly we belong to the brotherhood of the blessed, even if our feet are no longer young!

XXII

POOLS AND RIPPLES

FISHING was the one sport which had my father's approval. While, like all Puritans, he believed that whatever made for enjoyment must be wrong, he was prepared to overlook the fun I got out of it since it contributed towards the family larder. As a boy when I went fishing with Cal Coolidge I always loved the pungent smell of dank earth, of rotten logs and leaf mould, of Indian grass and balsam fir, the flecked sunlight on the rocks and eddies, the bright green moss, the golden-brown cascades. I still love them, and I still love to fish; but I realize now that catching the fish is but a small fraction of the enjoyment derived from the feeling that one is a part of nature.

Often, when on a too-sunny day the fish would not bite, I have lain flat on an overhanging bank and watched what Oliver St. John Gogarty calls "the balanced trout" hanging in the current beneath. Stealthily I would lower my arm into the icy water behind one of them, moving my hand imperceptibly forward until I could stroke it with utmost delicacy beneath the gills and belly. Gradualy my numbed fingers would circle the trout's body until with a sudden clutch I would yank it out of the water. We used to call this "tickling trout." Some say that it cannot be done, but I have caught hundreds in that way.*

Having learned to tickle a trout into docility, I have since then frequently done the same thing with a judge upon the bench. The manoeuvre must be carried out imperceptibly to him;—the first stroke, a merely deferential bow perhaps; the next, a smile of appreciation at a ruling; another, a subtle tribute to his learning or to his wisdom in some past case; and still another, a not too obvious appeal to his greatness of heart. Soon he will unconsciously have come over to your side. It is foolish ever to antago-

* "Here comes the trout that must be caught with tickling." *Twelfth Night:* Act ii, sc. 5, l. 24.

nize a judge. Poor devil! He has to sit mum most of the time listening to the wrangles of counsel and the windy speeches of legal spell-binders. For Heaven's sake, give him a break. Let him do a little talking himself. Allow him the satisfaction of proving you to be wrong. Of course you will put up a vigorous argument, but you should never act as if His Honor was a nincompoop if he takes the other side. Save the vials of your wrath for the opposing attorney and his witnesses—and let it know no bounds. The old bozo up on the bench enjoys it. And, when you except to his ruling, by all means do so deprecatingly and as if you fully realized that he was probably right.

In the woods things fall into their own perspective. Artificial values exist no longer. Half my pleasure in fishing comes from contact with my guides. Some of the most picturesque characters I have ever met were among the river men of New Brunswick. There was Donald McKay of Boisetown, for instance, nearly eighty years old, with an eye like a hawk, who could still shoot a raft of logs unerringly through the narrow stone piles guarding a bridge. When I first knew him he was seventy-three, had had nine children by previous alliances, and had just married a girl of eighteen. Donald was tall and erect with gaunt regular features and long white hair. He looked almost as saintlike as Recorder Goff and it took time to adjust oneself to his profanity, which produced the effect of a major, but highly obscene, prophet descending out of a cloud and exploding into invective. He had spent all his life on the river, working in lumber camps in winter and guiding in summer. Normally silent, the offer of a cigar or a drink of whiskey would inevitably open him up. Then he would point out the places along the river where he had camped in former days with Grover Cleveland and Joe Jefferson. "Jesus!" he'd remark, "Those fellers was great story tellers! The boys are tellin' them same yarns up here in the woods yit—good ones, too!"

My chief interest in Donald lay in his matter-of-course acceptance of the supernatural. His conversation turned largely on "warnings" and "forerunners." There were, he said, men and women known as "blood stoppers" who, by their mere proximity and unless running water intervened, could stop the flow of blood from a wound. He'd seen it done hundreds of times, as had everyone around there. There were lots of "blood stoppers" all over New Brunswick and the Gaspé. In some of his anecdotes instances of clairvoyance played an equal part with "blood stopping." A lumberman deep in the woods would sever a vein and instantly his brother, several miles away, would know what had happened and start with the nearest "blood stopper" towards the place where the accident had occurred. The injured man might be lying unconscious, the vital fluid pouring from the vein, but it would cease as soon as the "blood stopper" crossed the last stream between them.

There was, beyond any doubt to my mind, some supernormal means of communication, or psychic grapevine, between these woodsmen. Donald and I might be coming down the Miramichi from a point sixty or more miles away, where there was no railroad, no telephone, no telegraph, and where there had been no visitors, yet as we passed some lonely voyageur laboriously poling his canoe upstream he would know everything we had been doing, including how many fish we had killed. If I asked Donald about it he would merely nod his white mane sagely and remark: "We got our way o' knowin'."

Even in the woods I could not entirely escape the responsibilities of my profession and fortunately on at least two occasions was able to assist justice in triumphing over the technicalities of law. I was once, for example, coming down the Nipsicodiac River which flows into the Bay of Chaleau at Ste. Marie des Isles where one takes the train. It is a long day's run at best and the trip usually ends after dark. Just as we pushed off that morning the warden remarked that the president of the Canadian Southern, Mr. F. W. Micklejohn, had a camp at Stillwater where the track crosses the river on a long narrow bridge about twenty miles above Ste. Marie. He offered to telephone Micklejohn, whom he knew slightly, and ask him to put me up for the night and to flag the west-bound train next morning. Since this would save me a twenty-mile paddle I welcomed the suggestion.

So Donald and I started down stream all set for an easy day. I was feeling rested and happy; the ripples sparkled in the sunlight; the air was soft and laden with the scent of balsam—God was in His Heaven, everything was all right! We had a grand day on the river and at about seven o'clock that evening, at the top of the Stillwater pool, Donald suggested that I make a few casts on the way. As we rounded a point concealing a bungalow, an incoherent bellow came from a canoe anchored fifty yards away. It was Mr. Micklejohn, very angry and very drunk. He was obviously too boiled to care who I was, and I would not have accepted his hospitality even had he extended it. But, unfortunately, we still had twenty-odd miles to go and already the stars were coming out. Ahead loomed the long single-tracked bridge.

"The bastard only owns one side of the river," said Donald. "Some folks named Ferguson live on the other. They got burnt out and had to live in tents all last winter, but they're good people and I'm sure they'll put us up."

Jim Ferguson and his French Canadian wife gave us a hearty welcome. The spot where his tents were now pitched had once been the site of the thriving town of Stillwater composed of lumbermen and farmers, whose cleared fields extended a quarter mile back from the river. A small steamer had plied between it and Ste. Marie bringing the mail, passengers, and supplies. Five generations of Fergusons had lived and died there, then smallpox had ravaged the little community, the logging industry had declined, the young folks had moved away, until at last only Jim, his wife and their two children were left. The steamer had been discontinued. But Jim had stuck it out and in the end had prospered. Then Micklejohn had come along and had tried to buy his fishing rights, and, when he had refused to sell them, had done all he could to make his life burdensome. One night a fire had started somewhere near the railroad track and, gathering headway, had swept across the fields, destroying his home, his barn and everything he had. Now he was back where he had started. He had brought suit against the railroad for $25,000, but his lawyers advised him that, although it was morally certain that the fire had resulted from a spark from an engine—even if Micklejohn hadn't set it himself—the evidence was probably insufficient to sustain a judgment.

I took a flashlight and went down to the bridge and examined the draw, which I found consisted merely of a twenty-foot section of track with a trunion at one end. The buttresses were hopelessly out of plumb, the joints of the machinery rusted and eaten away, the bolts in the counterweights gone, the lever frozen from disuse. It would have cost at least $30,000 to put that draw into commission.

Next day, taking Jim Ferguson with me, I paddled down to Ste. Marie, where I poked about a bit, made friends with a local K.C. and looked up the law covering navigable waters. I found that the Canadian Southern had built the drawbridge over the Nipsicodiac by authority of the Ministry of Public Works "on condition that it be operated as such." Accordingly, I made an informal application in chambers to Sir Douglas Hartley, Judge in Admiralty of the Exchequer Court for that district, to compel the Canadian Southern to maintain its draw or have the bridge removed as a public nuisance. They are friendly people down there in New Brunswick and, since Sir Douglas didn't want to take brother Micklejohn too much by surprise and also, I fancy, because he didn't object to a pleasant sail upriver, he got in touch with Mr. Cameron Hall, the attorney for the railroad, the provincial bridge engineer and the sheriff, and we all piled onto a tug and steamed up to the Stillwater Bridge. While Sir Douglas talked with Micklejohn, Cameron Hall, the engineer and I examined the draw.

"You're jolly well right about our not being able to operate that draw," said Hall, accepting one of my stogies, "but of course you know equally well that you have no case, because the town for the convenience of which the draw was required has ceased to exist."

"It's still on the map," I said, "and I know at least four people who live there—five, if you count Micklejohn."

"I don't count him!" replied Hall. "But you'll admit that the conditions under which the authority to build the bridge was issued have radically changed. To compel the railroad under present circumstances to operate a draw would be ridiculous."

"That very point was decided against you by Cox, J. in Dumfries *vs.* Quebec Central," I countered. "He held that it was not the use to which a stream was actually put, but the use to which it might be put, without a change of conditions, that determined its navigability. If you opened the draw this tug could go right up the river to Stillwater, and that's where I insist on going."

He laughed good-naturedly, and beckoned me to a spot on the bridge, out of hearing of the others.

"As one fisherman to another, how much do you want?" he asked.

"Twenty-five thousand dollars," I said. "Twenty-four thousand to settle Ferguson's damage suit, and an extra thousand for waiving the maintenance of this draw."

"It's a deal," he said.

The most objectionable fisherman I ever encountered was Judge Philo Quelch who belonged to a small club of which I was a member on the Tobique. He was a cadaverous person with a coffin-shaped face, a querulous, rasping voice, and a legal manner which, perhaps, was but natural considering his profession. Yet a legal manner is a poor manner among sportsmen; as is too great a regard for the technical niceties of one's rights. Quelch was learned in piscatorial as in other branches of the law, and when he chose to be so could be fairly agreeable, but there was something about him which made others dislike him more when he was trying to be pleasant than when he was being frankly nasty, which was most of the time.

One night he expounded at great length the doctrines regarding property rights in animals. He even went so far as to declare that, if one man hooked a fish another had the legal right to gaff and keep it, on the ground that he and not the first man had actually reduced it to possession.* Regarding our custom to draw lots daily to determine who should fish any particular pool, Quelch claimed that this right was exclusive and that under no circumstances could one member take a fish from another's allotted pool even if it had carried him there against his will.

"Suppose," I asked him, "I hooked a fish in the Upper Pool and it carried me down into the Home Pool where you were fishing, what would you do?"

"Whoever draws the Home Pool has a right to the undisturbed possession of it. Under the circumstances you describe I could legally hook, gaff, net or otherwise take the fish as being in my water," ruled Quelch.

Next morning the judge drew the Home Pool. He fished there all day. Just at dusk—that indeterminate, translucent veil which, like a mist, screens and magnifies, transforming the commonest objects—he heard a great hullabaloo upstream. First Donald McKay appeared, gaff in hand, leaping from rock to rock, closely followed by Angus Ogilvy and myself, my rod bent, my line taut. A minute more and we were just above the falls below which Quelch was fishing. Etiquette and good fellowship under such circumstances demand that every member shall leave what he is doing and watch the kill. But Quelch did not budge. Stolidly he went on with his casting, with hardly a look upstream.

"Thar he goes!" shouted Angus as a black streak slithered over the falls into the foam-flecked whirling current of the Home Pool.

I scrambled down over the rocks and ran along the shore

* Pierson vs. Post, 3 Caines Cas. 175 (N. Y. 1808); Liesner vs. Wanie, 156 Wis. 16; Young vs. Hitchens, 62 B. 606 (1844 Eng.).

opposite the sand bar from which Quelch was casting. Looking across at me he called harshly:

"Get off my water!"

"I can't!" I answered. "I'm fast to a salmon."

"Makes no difference! You're a trespasser!"

Just then my line slackened for a moment and a black back rose to sight, only instantly to disappear again. I reeled frantically.

"I tell you to get off my water!" shouted Quelch. "If you kill a salmon here, I shall claim him as mine!"

"Nonsense!" I retorted. "You can't prevent another member from following a fish into your water."

"The courts will decide that!" he countered.

The black object rose once more to the surface some twenty-odd feet lower down the pool. At the same time Quelch raised his rod. Ping! His line became taut, his rod whipped into a half circle, and with a leer of elation he began to reel in. Incredible as it seemed, he had succeeded in hooking my fish foul at the first cast.

"I hooked that fish!" I panted.

"That gives you no legal claim. You haven't reduced him to possession! A salmon is *ferae naturae*—"

"*Ferae naturae* be damned!" I bawled, as, at that precise instant, my line parted and my rod straightened so that I nearly fell over backward.

A grin of triumph gathered upon the face of the Honorable Quelch at the realization that the gods had thus unexpectedly intervened in his behalf. All he had to do now was to land the fish. He was a good fisherman and knew that, even if he could not hold it in the swift water, he might be able to steer it into the back eddy; so he let it run the length of the pool and then swung it across the current. It was a daring and clever manoeuvre —and it succeeded. Back came the salmon upstream into the dead water on the other side of the bar and, with the strain on the line thus relieved, Quelch reeled in until he had shortened his line by fifty or more feet. Making a complete circle around the sand spit, the fish re-entered the Home Pool, and taking advantage of the rapids below the falls and the powerful current in front of the clubhouse again made for the lower river.

This time it became obvious that the judge meant to bring the struggle to an end, for he began to reel in with all his strength. Slowly the line shortened. One of his guides climbed into his canoe and swung it across the end of the spit in order to intercept the salmon should it make a final rush; while the other waded into the water with his gaff held in readiness to strike.

Inch by inch, the salmon came in, not, as usual, turning over so as to exhibit its belly, but with its back flush with the surface. Quelch walked to the river's edge.

"Now!" he yelled dramatically. "Let him have it!"

Amid a silence like the vacuum between two worlds, the guide reached forward with his gaff and struck. Generally, under such circumstances, the salmon puts up a frantic battle for life, floundering about and scattering the water in every direction. But in this instance nothing of the sort occurred. The gaff encountered no resistance and, with but slight effort, Quelch's guide lifted his quarry from the water. Quickly he dropped it—but not before a chorus of jeers and catcalls had arisen from the opposite bank. Shamefacedly he waded backward toward the spit, dragging behind him—a waterlogged pair of blue overalls! Quelch stared at them stupidly. Gingerly he picked them up by one leg. They were his own which he had left hanging from a peg upon the veranda.

"You're quite sure those pants are *ferae naturae?*" I inquired.

Next day the judge packed up his dunnage and moved further on.

It was not until 1933 that I joined the piscatorial elite. I was on my way down river to Cadogan, the capitol of St. Lawrence Province, with Angus Ogilvie, Donald's nephew, and had stopped at noon to "bile." While he made the coffee I put on a Silver Doctor, dropped it above an eddy and next instant was fast to a fish. That salmon towed us three miles down stream before, after a final leap, he turned upon his side and I steered him into shallow water. Just as Angus was about to gaff him there was a crunching of sand behind us and someone shouted: "You're poaching! This is private property!"

"Hello, Crockett!" answered Angus. "We aren't poaching. This fish was hooked three miles above here on the Tilford water."

"I found you here on our property killing a fish in front of the Wanic clubhouse," retorted the guardian curtly. "I ought to run you in, but I'll be reasonable. Free the fish, get into your canoe and paddle off as fast as you can."

He was a stern, bearded man, he had a shotgun in the hollow of his arm, and he looked full of hatred, malice and all uncharitableness.

At that instant, and apparently in acceptance of Crockett's invitation to depart, the salmon came to life. What he did will always remain a mystery to me, but to all intents and purposes, he stood up out of the water and walked away on his tail across the pool, shaking his head vigorously from side to side. Nearing the opposite bank he gave a particularly violent jerk, the leader parted and I found myself holding a rod to which was attached merely a line.

"I trust, sir, that you are now satisfied!" I remarked icily.

"I won't be satisfied until I see you off our property," retorted Crockett. "Start along and keep right on going. Don't let me find you camping around the bend when I come along. If I do, there'll be trouble."

Angus as a farewell gesture ejected a thin brown stream of tobacco juice in Mr. Crockett's direction, and with a few quick strokes drove the canoe to within a few feet of the opposite bank and began looking carefully into the shallow water.

It was nearly dark. The golden javelins that had bathed the forest had slipped up and up until, resting for a second or two upon the tips of the pines, they had leaped into space. The pool itself was a black glitter reflecting the blue patches overhead.

"There they are!" he exclaimed, leaning over and lifting a dripping key-ring from the water. "This isn't the first time that fish has broke loose. Some time or other, when he'd been hooked before, he struck his head agin' a rock and sulked and they slid a bunch of keys down the line to stir him up. I saw 'em when he jigged. But say! Weren't you using a Silver Doctor?"

Tangled among the keys was a six-foot mist-colored double-leader to which was attached a brilliant scarlet-and-white Parmacheene Belle.

We beached our canoe ten miles below the clubhouse, safe from the interference of Mr. Crockett; the moon had come up and was peering through the trees; the air was perfumed with wood smoke and tobacco.

"I bet that fish would ha' weighed fifty pound in midsummer," quoth Angus as he squatted in front of the cooking fire. "You don't often find a salmon carrying another fellow's tackle along with him. They usually manage to rub it off somehow. I figure this one was hooked beside the gills at the very end of last season and broke away. That's how he happened to be wearing that Parmacheene Belle. . . . Eggs is ready!"

"Who are the men that own the Wanic lease?" I asked.

"I dunno exactly. But they're all millionaires—some of the biggest men in Canada. They've got a railroad president and a couple of bankers and a regular Church of England bishop. They don't kill themselves fishing. They're old fellers and they like to be comfortable. They set around and play cards and tell stories and, when they feel in the mood for it, they go out and kill a salmon or two."

"How long did you say they'd been coming here?"

"Twenty years to my knowledge. They went to college together, or something."

"Lucky dogs! I should call a vacation like that pretty near to heaven, even without a bishop."

That night, on my bed of balsam tips, I dreamed that an

enormous salmon, dressed in the white-and-scarlet robes of a bishop and weighing at least five hundred pounds, came walking upon his tail across a pool of black glass and, offering me a gigantic bunch of keys, said:

"I will give you the keys of heaven! I will give you the keys of heaven!—Get out of here and keep going!"

We reached Cadogan the next afternoon. The train did not leave until eight the following morning, and, after a wash-up and shave, I bought a copy of the Cadogan Gazette, lit a stogy and sat down on the verandah of the hotel. Reduced to reading the advertisements, my eye caught the following:

SALE OF SALMON ANGLING LEASES
CADOGAN, ST. LAWRENCE, CANADA

The Exclusive right of Fishing—with rod only—in front of ungranted Crown Lands on the Musquash, Crooked and Santapedia Rivers in St. Lawrence will be offered for sale at Public Auction, at this Office, at eleven o'clock to-morrow morning.

SANTAPEDIA RIVER (IN ST. LAWRENCE)

No.		Upset price per annum
1—From Tom's Brook to Red Bank Fork	. . .	$1,000
2—From Red Bank Fork to Stillwater Pool	. . .	1,500
3—From Stillwater Pool to Portage Brook	. . . .	1,000
4—From Portage Brook to the Ox Bow	. . . .	3,500
5—From the Ox Bow to Victoria County Line	. .	1,000

That was just where I had been fishing—the Tilford water—the Wanic Club water! Surely there must be some mistake! I hurried out into the street.

"Angus!" I said, showing him the paper. "What do you think of that?"

"It's nothing. The leases have run out and the government has got to put 'em up at auction according to law. But the same parties always bid 'em in. The Wanic crowd will have a representative there. They'll go as high as they have to—naturally."

I folded the paper and placed it in my breast pocket.

"They always bid 'em in, do they? Believe me, Angus, this time they'll have to do some bidding!"

Cadogan is a fine old English town, conservative, orderly, comfortable and slow-going. There is an excellent hotel, the King Edward, which in June and July is crowded with fishermen on their way to and from the woods. A lieutenant-governor is in residence.

When shortly before eleven o'clock next morning I attended at the office of the Deputy Minister of Lands and Mines, such a gathering had assembled that he adjourned the meeting to the hall of the provincial legislature. Most of those present were attorneys or guardians acting for absent principals, with a few bargain hunters; but, in spite of the large attendance, competition on individual leases did not run high and in the case of the first two the previous holder was able to renew it at the former price.

"And now," said the deputy minister, a sandy, genial-looking man with a cheerio manner, looking around the chamber, "we come to Number Three. The three miles from Stillwater Pool to Portage Brook. What is your pleasure?"

"One thousand dollars," came in a high squeak from a rusty little man in spectacles on the center aisle.

"Thank you," nodded Mr. Cheerio. "One thousand dollars. Do I hear any other bids?" This was the stretch where I had hooked Leviathan.

"Fifteen hundred," I said quietly. The rusty little man turned and squinted through his goggles at this unexpected intervention. A five-hundred-dollar jump had been unheard of up to that time in the proceedings.

"Er—sixteen hundred!" he countered.

"Two thousand!" I retorted.

"This is some of the best fishing in Canada," interposed Mr. Cheerio. The rusty one looked anxiously about the room without finding any apparent relief. Then he stood up. His face was flushed.

"Might I have an opportunity to call up Mr. Tilford on the telephone?" he inquired. "My authority is limited—"

"I protest!" I objected. "One can't conduct auctions by telephone. Where is this gentleman?"

"In Montreal."

There was a burst of laughter from the spectators. Mr. Cheerio smiled.

"Mr. Tilford ought to be here," I said. "I press my objection."

"I'm afraid we can't interrupt the proceedings," agreed Mr. Cheerio. "Do I hear any more bids?"

"Well, I don't know what to do!" declared the rusty one, mopping his forehead. "I'll take a chance, though! Twenty-one hundred!"

"Twenty-five!" I shot back.

"Any more bids?"

Mr. Cheerio looked inquiringly at the little man.

"Sold! Number Three sold for twenty-five hundred dollars to —what is the name?"

"Tutt," I said. —"Ephraim Tutt of New York."

The rusty man took off his goggles helplessly, arose and walked slowly out.

"Mr. Tilford will be very much disappointed," I heard him say.

Mr. Cheerio banged with his gavel.

"Number Four—from Portage Brook to the Ox Bow—the best lease on the river," said he brightly. "Upset price thirty-five hundred dollars. What am I offered?"

There was no response. The audience stirred. My heart thumped as it had never done save once when I had hooked Leviathan. I waited, hardly breathing.

"Anybody here from the Wanic Club? Anybody here representing Bishop Charteris?" continued Mr. Cheerio.

Silence. Two men—one in high boots—got up suddenly and went out. Mr. Cheerio waited a moment or two. It was obvious that something most unexpected had occurred.

"Well," he remarked, "if there are no bids—"

"Thirty-five hundred dollars," said I.

The two men who had gone to the door returned.

"Thirty-six!" shouted one of them.

"Thirty-seven!"

"Thirty-eight!" came from the door.

"Thirty-nine!" I responded blithely.

Two others now joined the original couple, whispering excitedly.

"Any more bids?" inquired Mr. Cheerio.

"Four thousand!" continued one of the quartet defiantly.

"Forty-five hundred!" I rejoined.

"Forty-six hundred!" called out the last consultant.

"Five thousand!" I volleyed.

A murmur ran around the chamber. What was the use? The speculative spirit evaporated.

"Any more bids?" The deputy minister held his gavel in air for a short *locus penitentiae*. Then he banged it down. "Sold for five thousand dollars to Mr. Ephraim Tutt! I feel pretty sure that there has been some mistake," he added. "Bishop Charteris and his friends have had that lease for heaven knows how long! —However—the next item is Number Five, from the Ox Bow to the Victoria County Line. What am I offered?"

"Twenty-five hundred dollars," I answered, and got it.

In the dining room of the King Edward, an hour later, I encountered the Deputy Minister of Lands and Mines. His manner was no longer cheerio.

"I can hardly believe that Bishop Charteris intended to let his lease go when his friends enjoy it so," he remarked stiffly. "I think myself that he must have overlooked the fact that the lease had run out. I remember now he told me the last time he was here that he expected to spend the winter in Egypt. They all will be terribly upset. I know how they look forward to coming here together every year."

I had begun to feel rather sorry for the members of the Wanic

Club. I had been righteously angry at my treatment by the guardian, and had I gone to the auction and bid the lease away from them in fair fight, no matter at what cost, I would have felt fully justified. But to get it by default robbed the victory of all zest. That evening I sat down and wrote a letter on the King Edward stationery to Sewell T. Warburton, the president of the Utopia Trust in New York, offering to assign my lease to the Wanic Club at cost. As a fisherman I could picture Mr. Warburton's astonishment and gratitude. They might even offer to make me a member of the Wanic Club. Anyhow they'd be sure to offer me the hospitality of the river.

Three days later, at Quebec, I received Mr. Warburton's typewritten reply:

E. Tutt, Esq.,
Hotel Frontenac,
Quebec, Canada,

Dear Sir: Your communication regarding lease of fishing rights on the Santapedia River, together with suggestion that I send you five thousand dollars in return for an assignment of same, is at hand. I beg to say that your offer does not interest me. I might add that we are quite capable of handling our own affairs without interference from strangers.

Truly yours,

S. T. WARBURTON.

So that was the way he treated my generosity! This snob Warburton was worse than that hound of a Crockett. "Like master, like man!" This would end their fishing on the Santapedia forever!

Stepping across to the telegraph office, I sent a wire to Angus Ogilvy, authorizing him to take possession of the Wanic property and to notify Crockett that he was fired. The last lines of the telegram read:

TELL HIM TO START ALONG AND KEEP RIGHT ON GOING STOP TELL HIM NOT TO LET ME FIND HIM CAMPING AROUND THE BEND WHEN I COME ALONG FOR IF I DO THERE'LL BE TROUBLE

I had no sooner got back to New York than I received a second letter from Mr. Warburton in which he stated, with an effort at jocularity, that his original reply had been sent under an entire misapprehension of the facts, which I, as a broad-minded man of the world, would no doubt understand and overlook, and that the Wanic Club would be most grateful to accept my offer to turn over to them the Santapedia lease at the price I had paid for it, and that with sincere regards and much appreciation, he begged to remain, "cordially yours, Sewell T. Warburton." I threw it in the scrap-basket.

Five days elapsed. Followed a third communication, upon the paper of the Union Club, from Mr. Warburton, in which he abandoned all attempts to treat the affair jocosely, apologizing for the boorishness of his first letter and owning himself entirely and inexcusably in the wrong. No one could have eaten more humble pie. I let him wait for a week and then succinctly informed Mr. Warburton that the lease was not for sale. For two whole days he tried to get me on the phone and couldn't! Then one morning Willie Toothaker brought in a card on which was inscribed the name SEWELL T. WARBURTON.

"I have come to make a personal apology for my first letter to you," said the banker. "There was no excuse for it. Of course at the time I didn't know who you were. Also, I'd had an annoying day. I am sorry. I regret my letter." He looked at me as if to say: "I can't do more than that, can I?"

I bowed in return.

"I understand the situation perfectly," I said. "I accept your apology."

"May I hope then that you'll reconsider your refusal to assign us your lease? Five of us have fished the six miles of river you now control, for twenty years. We go there every spring on the fifteenth of June and stay three weeks. It is the only real vacation any of us have. We look forward to it as the bright spot of the year. We're all of us getting on. I'm the youngest, and I'm sixty-five. We could get another river, but we love the Santapedia. It's good fishing. But it's not the fishing and it isn't the money! It's a matter of sentiment. I hope you won't make my friends suffer for my mistake!"

"I am sorry," I replied. "I cannot renew my offer."

"In that case," remarked Mr. Warburton, "I will make it a business matter. It is entirely my fault and I am willing to pay for it. I will give you ten thousand dollars for the lease."

"I am sorry," I repeated. "It is not for sale."

Mr. Warburton got up. "Then there is nothing more to be said. You are quite within your rights. May I ask when you expect to go up there?"

"On the fifteenth of June, for about three weeks."

"Alone?"

"Alone."

"Would you be willing to lease the fishing before or after the period you are there?"

"No," I said. "I prefer to reserve the use of the property to myself—and friends."

Mr. Warburton bowed. "In any case you have my apology," he said. "Good morning!"

The Intercolonial Express arrives at the provincial capital in the late afternoon. I had looked forward to a rather dull afternoon and evening, but as I stepped from the Pullman upon the station platform, I was surprised to find myself greeted by a military-looking young man who, with a half-salute, inquired pleasantly.

"Have I the honor of addressing Mr. Ephraim Tutt of New York?"

"Guilty!" I answered, struggling with my rod case.

The youth offered his hand. "My name is Smith. I'm the lieutenant-governor's secretary. He wished me to deliver this letter."

It was an invitation to dine with the lieutenant-governor that evening at the latter's mansion at eight o'clock.

"The governor asked me to say, Mr. Tutt, that the affair would be most informal and that he very much hoped you would give him the pleasure of your company."

It was still broad daylight when I drove up to the big Colonial mansion which in more ceremonious localities of the British Empire would have been termed "Government House." Mr. Smith was in waiting and immediately escorted me to the high-ceilinged, old-fashioned drawing room. A group of gentlemen were standing before the fireplace, and at my advent one of them —a big, bronzed man with kindly gray eyes—disengaged himself from the others and came forward to greet me.

"I am delighted to see you, Mr. Tutt," said he. "We are a small party, but what we lack in quantity I hope will be compensated for by quality. Mr. Tutt, permit me to introduce my friends the Right Reverend, the Bishop of St. Albans; Mr. Arbuthnot, president of the British Columbia Railways; President Norton of the British Colonial Trust Company; President Ives of the Royal British Bank of Canada; and Mr. Warburton of New York. I believe you know one another?"

"It is a pleasure to meet you, gentlemen," I said.

So this was the Wanic Club! I could not but admit that even if they were bankers and railroad men they were a fine, genial-looking lot of old boys. So they were going to try to make up to me, were they? A lot of good it would do them. But meanwhile a drink was a drink!

The lieutenant-governor poured the cocktails himself out of a huge frosted shaker.

"Gentlemen! The King!" he said, raising his glass.

Everybody hastily muttered "King!" and drank.

"King!" said I with the rest. Having swallowed the cocktail, I said it again.

"King!" I repeated very distinctly, looking at the lieutenant-governor.

"May I give you another?" inquired His Excellency.

"I really feel that I should drink His Majesty's health at least twice," I replied.

The Bishop of St. Albans smiled at him. "I'll give you a toast!" he volunteered. "To the king—of game fish! *Salmo salar!*"

At the dinner table I found myself upon His Excellency's right, opposite the bishop, and next to the president of the British Columbia Railways. I had never tasted more delectable food or better wines, and the Cordon Rouge, 1918, began with the fish and did not apparently finish at all. An easy air of good-fellowship prevailed. These men had been everywhere, knew everybody worth knowing and were themselves engaged in enterprises of world importance. The talk was excellent, the stories amusing, and although I sniffed a rodent—I recalled having seen a private car on the end of my train—I thoroughly enjoyed myself. All that I had to do was to nod benignly every now and then, and say "King!" It was only when the coffee and cigars had been passed that I noticed a certain air of expectancy on the part of the assembled guests. Then and not until then did His Excellency, lifting his glass of port, allow the concealed feline to thrust her nose out of the opening of the bag in which up to that time he had kept her carefully concealed.

"And now, Mr. Tutt—a glass of wine with you, sir!—I hope that you will not be averse to discussing a little matter with my friends—my very old friends—who have come here at my suggestion to meet you."

"I am sorry, but I never mix business and society," I answered.

"What we wish to discuss is not exactly business," interposed Bishop Charteris hastily. "It is rather in the nature of pleasure. And what more appropriate time than after a good dinner over a glass of port and our cigars?"

"Hear! Hear!" murmured the president of the British Columbian Railways.

So they were trying the old game of giving me a dinner and then trying to sell me a bill of goods? To hell with them!

"I'm sorry," I replied firmly. "I cannot break my rule. I have had a most agreeable evening. If you gentlemen have anything you wish to talk over with me—and I tell you quite frankly I have no intention of changing my fishing expedition to Canada into a business trip—I am willing to meet you tomorrow morning at the office of your lawyers."

"Mr. Tutt is right," interjected Mr. Warburton nervously. "This isn't the time for business. Let's forget it until tomorrow morning. Suppose we ask Mr. Tutt to meet us at Selborne's office at ten o'clock?"

As if to compensate for their *faux pas*, the members of the Wanic Club made themselves doubly agreeable for the rest of the evening. These hard-boiled business men and bankers argued about the relative merits of the Jock Scot and the Durham Ranger, and fought their salmon over again, until the years fell from them and they became again the boys they still were at heart.

"Charteris," suggested His Excellency at length, "tell Mr. Tutt about your struggle with Leviathan."

I pricked up my ears. "Leviathan!"

"There was nothing very remarkable about Leviathan," smiled the Bishop of St. Albans, "except his size and his peculiar method of escape. I stayed upriver a day or two after the others had gone last year and was just putting my gunny sack into the canoe to go downstream when I saw a heavy swirl in the middle of the pool right in front of the clubhouse. Well, I couldn't resist the temptation. 'I'll try just one cast,' I said, and in two minutes I had a fly drifting over the spot where I had seen the rise. Next instant I was fast to the biggest salmon I'd ever had on my line. To make a long story short, I played him for two hours and he took me eleven miles on my way to Cadogan. My guide was just going to gaff him when he unexpectedly came to life and—believe me or not!—that fish stood right up out of the water on its tail, walked across the pool jigging from side to side, broke my leader and went off with my fly and two yards of leader in his mouth. And that's the solemn truth!"

"I believe you," I replied. "And what's more I think I can tell you the fly you were using, a most unusual fly for a salmon, although excellent for trout. Wasn't it a Parmacheene Belle?"

"Bless my soul!" exclaimed the bishop. "How did you guess it."

I couldn't help having a fraternal feeling for the silver-haired old ecclesiastic.

"It wasn't a guess," I chuckled. "If you hooked Leviathan again, you'd probably find a Silver Doctor in its place." And I told them of my fight with *salmo salar* three weeks before, not omitting the episode with Guardian Crockett.

"I never did like that fellow," declared President Norton at the end of the story. "Fancy his treating a stranger that way! He ought to be discharged."

"He is!" said I. "Well, gentlemen—the King!"

As I drove back under a frosty crescent moon to the King Edward I found it difficult to analyze my state of mind. I had been twice insulted by representatives of the Wanic Club—outrageously insulted—and now by a quaint turn of Fortune's wheel my enemies had been delivered into my hands. Did they imagine that they could bribe me with a dinner at the lieutenant-governor's and a bottle of champagne? I'd show these rich men that money was no excuse for arrogance.

At ten o'clock next morning I repaired to the office of Lawyer Selborne. My six companions of the evening before, including the lieutenant-governor, were already assembled.

"Gentlemen," I said, "my train leaves in an hour. Let us dispose of whatever you wish to discuss as quickly as possible."

"Mr. Tutt," replied His Excellency, "these gentlemen are my very good friends. We were classmates at college, forty-seven years ago—nearly half a century," he sighed. "For twenty years they have met here for three weeks each summer and renewed their youth. Frequently I have been one of the party. They are all elderly men. They love the Santapedia and they love their little clubhouse. They could rent other fishing, but it wouldn't be the same thing. They realize that you have been cavalierly treated. On the other hand, it seems hard that all should suffer for the mistake of one. They are not here to do the cry-baby act. Money means very little to them. They are willing to pay not only what the fishing is worth but enough to net you a handsome profit. You already control six miles of water without the Wanic. They are willing to pay you fifteen thousand dollars for what cost you but five. How about it?"

"I have no desire to sell," I replied. "I did not take the lease to make money out of it. I want the fishing. If that is what you wished to see me about—" I got up.

"We will give you twenty thousand," said President Ives of the Royal British Bank of Canada.

"The lease is not for sale," I said, picking up my hat.

"It is all my fault," broke in Mr. Warburton. "I will personally offer Mr. Tutt twenty-five thousand dollars for his lease, out of my own pocket. You certainly cannot refuse such a sum as that!"

"Can't I?" I countered. "I do!"

"Then you absolutely refuse to have any mercy on these gentlemen?" asked the lieutenant-governor.

"It is not a question of mercy," I said. "They wish to buy something I don't want to sell, that is all! They can fish a thousand other places. But one thing is certain: I am going to fish the Santapedia from Portage Brook to the Ox Bow and nothing shall stop me!"

My eyes swept the circle of crestfallen faces—then I bowed and walked out into the corridor, loitering within earshot. The five members of the Wanic Club stared after me with expressions ranging from incredulity to rage.

"The old bird must be cuckoo!" I heard President Arbuthnot exclaim.

"Either cuckoo or smart as hell," grunted President Ives.

"It's a dirty trick," commented President Norton. "He's taking a malicious revenge. Think of his not being satisfied to sting us for four thousand apiece. What sort of an old he-devil is he?"

The bishop smiled. "If he wants to fish for salmon as much as all that, maybe he's a sportsman," he pondered.

"Well, gentlemen," said His Excellency, "it looks as if you'd have to find somewhere else to fish. I've done all I can. After all, he had pretty rough treatment and if he's not willing to accept damages I swear I can't blame him much."

"I'm seventy-one years old," quoth President Ives. "I can't live forever. I can't go chasing all over Canada for salmon. I'm here with my rod in my hand and I'm willing to stand the gaff and pay him whatever he wants."

"So am I," agreed President Arbuthnot. "No matter what it costs us, I'm for raising the ante."

"We've still got three-quarters of an hour before the train leaves for St. Croix," mused President Norton. "How about one last effort? He's got us. The only thing is to decide how high we are willing to go."

Ten minutes later the five elderly gentlemen composing the membership of the Wanic Club, headed by the Bishop of St. Albans, ascended the steps of the King Edward and inquired for Mr. Ephraim Tutt. I sent word that since I was engaged in changing my clothes, I could not at the same moment go downstairs to receive my visitors. Should they, however, care to come up to my room, I would be delighted to see them.

In single file the Right Reverend, the Bishop of St. Albans; the president of the Royal British Bank of Canada; the president of the British Columbian Railways; the president of the British Colonial Trust Company; and the president of the Utopia Trust Company of New York—collectively representing a substantial fraction of the moral influence, as well as several hundred millions of the financial resources of the Dominion—climbed up the two flights of stairs. There was a knock. I opened the door. The floor, bed and chairs were strewn with fishing paraphernalia; there was no place to sit down without incurring danger of being impaled upon a hook.

"Well, gentlemen," said I, "is there anything further I can do for you?"

"May we come in?" asked the Bishop.

"Certainly, if you don't mind standing up," I replied, thrusting various objects from the bed into the gunny sack. "There's only a few minutes before train time. But come in!"

Grimly they entered and disposed themselves along the wall like a row of disgraced school boys.

"Mr. Tutt," said the Bishop of St. Albans, "we have come to make a final appeal to your kindness of heart. We know that your sense of justice would not lead you to refuse our request merely because your pride had been wounded. We have made all the amends we can for the offense offered you. I am sure that you are too high-minded to exact revenge. We realize that you have conceived as great a liking for the Santapedia as ourselves and that, if you surrender it to us, we must compensate you for it. We are very fond of the place and of our clubhouse. You can hardly appreciate what the loss would mean to a handful of lonely old fellows like ourselves. We are prepared to pay you what to the outside public would seem a fantastic sum. We have talked the matter over carefully. If you will assign us your lease I am authorized to offer you the courtesy of our club at all times and the sum of fifty thousand dollars."

I was sitting on the edge of the bed like a criminal judge facing five culprits in the dock.

"Bishop Charteris, you cannot tell me anything I do not already know about your interest in the Santapedia River. I shall not discuss my own motives in the matter. I have decided upon my course and shall adhere to it. I do not seek to make a profit out of my sport. I refuse your offer."

The Lord Bishop of St. Albans looked as if he were going to cry. He made a deprecatory gesture and fell back.

"Will you take sixty thousand?" asked President Ives.

I looked him straight in the eyes. "My lease is not for sale."

"How about seventy-five thousand?" inquired President Norton.

"I will not sell for seventy-five thousand," I returned inexorably.

Bishop Charteris wrung his hands. "What manner of man is this?" he seemed to say.

Mr. Warburton stepped forward.

"I am probably a fool! But this situation is due to my stupidity. If you will relinquish the lease I will make you a personal offer of one hundred thousand dollars," he said. "If you refuse it I must conclude that you are either quite mad or—"

I held up my hand.

"Your offer is refused. I regret, gentlemen, that I must finish my packing." I bowed and moved toward the door.

"Well, what will you take?" asked President Arbuthnot defiantly. "Name your own price."

I eyed the disconsolate faces before me.

"I will put a price on my lease on one condition," I said slowly —"which is that you agree to take it or leave it without further discussion. Is that clearly understood?"

Bishop Charteris nodded. "We have no choice," he said.

"Very well then," I said. "Provided we can all fish the stream together in harmony—you making use of my water and I of yours—I will lease you the six miles from Portage Brook to the Ox Bow for—"

No one so much as drew a breath. Not even a boot creaked.

"—one cent per annum for five years."

For several seconds there was a graveyard silence. Then Bishop Charteris took my hand in a hard grip. His eyes were moist.

"I said you were a sportsman," he whispered.

It was as if he were giving me his episcopal blessing—and I had rather have had it than the *croix de guerre* with palms. We shook hands all round.

"What shall we be?" asked Warburton. "Your tenants-at-sufferance?"

"No," I smiled back at him. "Tenants-at-good-will."

XXIII

MY INDIAN SUMMER

I HAD been twenty-eight when I last saw Esther Farr, and although the features in her photograph above my desk were so dim as to be hardly discernible, her image was as vivid in my recollection as if I had seen her yesterday. Her husband, it seemed, had completely recovered his health and now in his late seventies, garrulous and something of a busy-body, was always in evidence on formal occasions at Ramona College as the presidential consort.

"He really ought to be the president," she wrote. "He would enjoy it so much."

Being a prominent figure in the educational world, Esther frequently came East to attend conventions or meetings, many of them in New York. Sometimes he accompanied her, sometimes not. But we had long ago concluded that it would be better for us not to meet.

We had written each other almost every month during that entire period, opening our hearts, as perhaps we might not have done had we been actually together. I described my cases, my philanthropic work, my reading, my social life such as it was, and my adventures in the woods; she in turn told me of her administrative duties and problems, the books and articles she was writing and some of the campus gossip. It was a strange, although not unheard of, relationship. I had adored her for forty years and for me our romance was as fragrant as the first night I had taken her home under the harvest moon. As long as she was alive, no matter where, it would have been impossible for me to think of another woman. Although she was three thousand miles away, her influence was omnipresent. I unconsciously tested every proposed act by whether she would approve or not. I am not religious in the ordinary sense, but, if I were, no creed could have held me to a standard of conduct as steadfastly as my love for Esther.

433

I don't suppose either of us ever thought what the other looked like, whether we were getting gray, careworn or wrinkled. It wouldn't have mattered. The years were past—Alas, how many! —when I had quoted to her Alice Meynell's beautiful lines:

> "I must not think of thee . . .
> I must stop short of thee the whole day long.
>
> .   .   .   .
>
> But when sleep comes to close each difficult day . . .
> With the first dream that comes with the first sleep
> I run, I run, I am gathered to thy heart."

We had become resigned to our lot, yet often late in the evening as I smoked my stogy before the fire in my library in London Terrace I yearned for her bodily presence. What bliss it would have been to have her sitting there opposite me. To pour out all the words unspoken through the years! To look into her soft brown eyes! If longing could have conjured up her presence she would have come. Indeed, more than once, as I drowsed there thinking of her, I had seemed to see her smiling at me and afterwards, when the sweet vision had dissolved, to smell the faint odor of the perfume she had always used.

My address before the Interstate Bar Association had been favorably received and later printed in the *Columbia Law Review* where, while its general humanitarian spirit was editorially commended, its historico-legal errors were no less carefully pointed out. It was even indicated that reading between the lines I might be suspected of being a bit of a fascist. This was a little too much! I, Eph Tutt, a Fascist? At once I wrote a rejoinder in which I suggested that people who lived in glass houses had better refrain from throwing stones and that, if one wanted to find a good collegiate example of a benevolent despotism, a spy-glass would not be needed to locate one in upper Manhattan. This raised quite a rumpus, involving various aspects of the life of the university including the method of award of the Pulitzer Prizes, while the *New Yorker* seized the opportunity to print a "profile" of President Nicholas Murray Butler, in which it disclosed the generally unknown, and certainly surprising, fact that in the dim mists of long ago he had once been indicted on a charge of criminal libel for calling the President of the New York Board of Education "an intellectual mastodon." In the ensuing hilarity, to my great relief, I found myself forgotten—or at least so I thought.

Then an odd thing happened. A couple of months afterwards I received word that Columbia University would be pleased to bestow upon me an honorary degree of doctor of laws. Now I am no multimillionaire to take honorary degrees in my stride and thrust them in the bottom drawer of my desk. I had nothing to give Columbia in return and I accepted the gesture at its face value.

That Commencement was the high spot in my life. Somewhat before the appointed hour I took my place among the trustees and other notables on the platform at the top of the steps leading to the Low Memorial Library, marvelling that an old lawyer like myself, who had been so often caricatured and lampooned, should be esteemed worthy of distinction. It was a warm spring day with white clouds making a slowly moving backdrop for the magnificent building that housed the learning of the ages, while at the foot of the stairs sat the banked rows of undergraduates and the impressive looking scholars in their robes. At the conclusion of the ceremonies President Butler, in his doctor's gown, began awarding the honorary degrees with an appropriate eulogy for each recipient. I caught my own name and with blurred vision stepped forward.

"Ephraim Tutt, lawyer and advocate—" I did not hear the rest of it. The academic hood was placed on my shoulders and Dr. Butler handed me a roll of parchment. There was a mild outburst of hand-clapping. I returned to my seat and sat down— "Doctor Ephraim Tutt." The faces beside me nodded, my composure returned, now I could enjoy myself. Name after name was called and I chuckled at the realization of the momentary discomfort of their owners.

Suddenly—I could hardly believe my ears—I heard the name

Esther Farr. For a moment I felt faint, and my throat contracted. Esther! Would I see her at last! People were looking towards the row behind me, but I did not turn around. I could not. The moment of recognition between us must not be strained. There was a slight rustle, a chair creaked, and a charge of electricity leapt from me as Esther's gown brushed my shoulder—or did her finger tips touch it lightly? Then she was standing beside Dr. Butler. As from a great distance came the words:

"President of Ramona College, historian, scholar, outstanding educator, wise counsellor of youth, sympathetic interpreter of the intellectual aspirations of women."

She looked towards me with the same lovely smile I knew so well. If her hair had become slightly gray I did not notice it. All I knew was that this was still the Esther of my youth and of my dreams, with the same sweetly sensitive mouth, proud courageous chin and veiled brown eyes. Straight and almost as slender as I remembered her, there was a new nobility in her carriage. She had not grown old, she had merely matured.

I don't recall what happened after that, or how we got up to Fort Tryon where we sat on the grass in the shade talking most of the afternoon. I remember bringing her a sandwich and a cup of coffee from a nearby cafeteria, later wandering through the rhododendron-bordered paths of the rock gardens to the Cloisters, and then sitting together on a bench from which we could look far up the Hudson to the pale blue outlines of the hills above Haverstraw. We had forty years to cover, yet now they dissolved to nothing. Once again we were in my little Grecian temple of a law office at Pottsville reading and dreaming of the future. Once again we walked by moonlight under the falling leaves on Main Street. We were not a day older. At least I didn't feel so and I don't think Esther did. The sun sank over the Palisades and the purple shadows crept across the water.

I had telephoned Mandy that I was bringing a guest to dinner and now I said: "I want you to see my house. You're going to dine with me there tonight, you know!" She did not dissent and we lingered there until the afterglow had faded and lights began to twinkle along the Jersey shore, then walked to the subway and, getting out at Twenty-third Street, took a taxi to London Terrace. The windows were all alight and in the powdery dusk the trees and bushes, now in full leaf, had the purple bloom of grapes. I opened the iron gate and Esther—my Esther!—entered and walked up the brick path towards the door.

I had expected that she would burst into rapture at the sight of my house with its vine-clad balconies and blossoming shrubbery but she only said "How really lovely!" "She's tired, poor dear!" I thought. "I ought to have taken better care of her and not kept her out all day." Then the door opened and the C.J. rushed out followed by a widely grinning Mandy.

Now the C.J. has a well-defined technique. In welcoming me he gives two short appreciative barks, then races in circles for a minute or two, pays his respects to the plane tree and then leads the way to the front steps. If a stranger makes his appearance alone the C.J. subjects him to a fictitiously savage onslaught in order to test his good faith. If I am accompanied by a friend the C.J., after a few hostile barks, declares a temporary armistice and, growling, conducts a preliminary investigation, which, if satisfactory, results in the newcomer being given the freedom of the domain. In this instance, however, the C.J. was evidently so captivated by Esther's appearance that he merely gave her a passing whiff and at once indulged in his customary scurry. Mandy was waiting.

"Ah's sho' glad to see you, Miss Farr!" she exclaimed delightedly. "You can wash yo' hands and rest yo' hat on de secon' flo' rear."

Five minutes later we were sitting together at my dining room table eating the most savory meal that Mandy had ever cooked. Any restraint that had existed between us during the afternoon had vanished. It seemed in no way strange that Esther should be presiding at my table, but on the contrary just as it should be. We were gayer than we had ever been together. I told her about

Priscilla's belated attempt to entangle me and become the *chatelaine* of London Terrace, about Rosa Lewis and my adventures in London at the Cavendish. For a college president Esther showed an extraordinary curiosity in all the details. In fact she didn't seem like a college president at all, rather like a girl of twenty. After the *Crêpes Suzette* we had coffee in the dining room and then went upstairs to the library.

I got out a bottle of Burgundy and Esther seated herself in the low swaybacked rocker before the fireplace where I had so often imagined her, with her feet crossed, her delicate hands resting on the arms of the chair, her head thrown back, looking at me with those half-veiled eyes. There was even the same subtle fragrance I seemed to have remembered. I was a hard-boiled Yankee lawyer. Yet what were time and space? Could her astral body have visited me from time to time during the years?

"Why are you staring at me so, Ephraim?" she asked.

"I was thinking how natural it seems to have you here. I've dreamed that you were sitting there just like that more than once."

" 'The Brushwood Boy'?"

"That takes two, you know!"

She did not pursue the subject further. Instead, she lit a cigarette: "What's in that bottle, Ephraim?"

"Burgundy," I said. "Bottled sunlight from the *Côte d'Or.*"

"I think I'd like a little bottled sunlight."

I poured her a glass and she raised it to me. Then her eyes wandered across the room to the bookcase.

"What's happened to Daniel Webster?" she remarked casually.

"Being mended," I answered. "I knocked his ear off. Hold on! What's this! If you've never been here before how did you know his bust used to be there?"

She looked embarrassed.

"Why, you've just said I'd been here!" she parried.

Then all at once it came to me how the C.J. had paid no

attention to her, how Mandy had called her "Miss Farr" and how Esther herself had expressed so little appreciation regarding the appearance of the house.

"Esther!" I said sternly, "that 'Brushwood Boy' stuff is all right in its place, but don't try to deceive me. This isn't your first visit to London Terrace. You've been here before."

"Well, what if I have!" she challenged me.

"But our bond—our agreement not to see each other!"

"I didn't see you—only your house. Well, if you must know, twice before this when I've been in New York I've called up Mandy and found when you were going to be out and come here and sat in the library just like this."

So the perfume had been real. Esther looked at me whimsically.

"Don't you think we're old enough now to see each other occasionally—after forty years, Ephraim?"

They say that towards the end of a man's life the years whip by like telegraph poles past a train. That has not been my experience. Since I reached the age of sixty I have not been conscious of the flight of time at all. I no longer think of something as happening in any particular year—except possibly the Panic of 1929 and the outbreak of the World War ten years later. I have no children so I cannot, as I am told most mothers do, correlate events to the year Jessie had the measles or Sonny broke his leg. Now that I have found Esther again, although I see her by no means as often as I could wish, I realize that my life has held more of romance than falls to the lot of most men. Nothing has marred it and nothing can. Whatever I am my ideal of her has made me, and time is no longer of the essence.

I know of course that I haven't made the most of my abilities—every honest man must feel the same way about himself; but I have always thrown my weight on the side of such causes as I believed to be just. In the first days of the feminist movement I was one of the comparatively few men who marched amid the jeers of the bystanders in the Woman's Suffrage Parade up Fifth Avenue; although a Democrat I followed Theodore Roosevelt in 1912 into the Progressive Party; while four years later I voted for Woodrow Wilson, and for Cox in 1920, because I believed that the United States should assume its responsibilities in world affairs by cooperating with the League of Nations. Since then I have been a somewhat qualified New Dealer. But the insincerities, equivocations and compromises incident to success in party politics revolt me. I can have no lasting loyalty to any political organization the basic motive of which is self-interest, or the mere perpetuation of majority control. I like to watch the game, but I prefer to be free to stand on the side lines and criticize the play. I know that this may itself be but a form of selfishness on my part, yet I cannot help it. I am made that way.

The truth probably is that I am a superficial person and easily bewildered; I have little interest in theories, for I have so often seen the accepted truths of today become the falsehoods of tomorrow. I equally dislike the smooth young intellectuals who prove what is wrong with society and what to do about it in 350 pages, and the glib orators who know that if they shout loud enough and long enough they will convince even themselves of what they say. I believe the curse of the world to be that it is governed by talkers, whose influence has been multiplied a million fold by the radio. The really great man is usually modest and too often shy. He may have ability, experience and wisdom but unless he is articulate he becomes a push-over for the first roughneck who has the gift of gab and can talk on his feet. The Hitlers, Mussolinis, and the Huey Longs—not the John Deweys—are the ones whom the voters listen to. I do not care for government of, for or by the larynx.

I am an opportunist. I distrust too long views. Let the morrow "take thought for the things of itself; sufficient unto the day is the evil thereof." I want an immediate return for my money. I believe in acting when the need is instant even if mistakes are made, rather than in the scientific delay which may accomplish more good in a hypothetical future. No doubt it is unsound charity to give a bleary-eyed old souse a dime for a cup of coffee, but when I look at his blistered feet bursting through the soles of his ragged shoes I haven't the heart to tell him to walk two miles to a wood yard. It is bad philanthropy but it is good for the arteries. What difference does it make whether he is helped by me individually or by a scientifically run agency, so long as he get his belly filled? Let John Rockefeller deal in wholesale charity—I'm a retailer. That is why I treat the funds left me by Miss Pidgeon as a trust for emergency relief. Neither do I much care whether the applicant for aid is morally deserving or not. The Good Samaritan didn't investigate the unfortunate victim of the thieves before binding up his wounds and guaranteeing his board for an indefinite period at the inn. Nor did the father who killed the fatted calf for his prodigal son concern· himself as to the latter's previous riotous living. I would far rather be swindled a few times than grow callous to suffering. Too much repression may cause one's human sympathy to wither and eventually to die for lack of nourishment.

London Terrace has been torn down to be replaced by a gigantic apartment-hotel and I have moved uptown into a small brownstone house in the East Sixties. There is a "C.J. IV," but no front grass plot or plane tree for his delectation, yet the back yard is large and sunny—long enough to practice casting in—and a clever young landscape gardener has planted out with cedars the surrounding laundry poles and fire escapes so that I can sit and smoke there of a summer evening in comparative privacy. I have transferred my library bodily to my new establishment—fireplace, carpet, hangings, books and furniture—and when lounging before my sea-coal fire it is hard for me to realize that I am not on Twenty-third Street. Mandy, the priceless Mandy, is still with me, and she has lost none of her skill, as my friends can testify. The faded photographs of my mother and Esther Farr hang, as before, above my desk.

Now that these reminiscences are nearing an end I ask myself whether they have any significance. Certainly more important than any other lesson to be drawn from my professional experiences is the distinction between law and justice. Over the portals of the new United States Supreme Court Building in Washington are inscribed the words: "Justice through Law." This does not mean that Law and Justice are one, but only that it is the ideal of a democratic form of government.

Once, after arguing a case in the Supreme Court, I overtook Justice Oliver Wendell Holmes walking on Pennsylvania Avenue with my friend Learned Hand, now a judge of the New York Circuit Court of Appeals. We chatted for a block or so together and, as Holmes turned to leave us, Hand congratulated him on the "justice" of a decision he had just handed down.

Holmes turned and shaking his forefinger at him said almost sharply:

"Listen, young feller! I'm not on the bench to do justice, but to play the game according to the rules. It's not my business to decide whether a particular law is a wise or rational provision, or whether a particular decision will, or will not, result in individual injustice. The law is one thing: justice, as you use the word, is another."

As the present Chief Justice of the United States told someone with regard to a certain piece of New Deal legislation the constitutionality of which had been questioned: "It's perfectly constitutional, and—it's perfectly foolish."

Only in the theoretical sense that, despite its deficiencies, our legal system treats all men as equals, rich and powerful or poor and humble, and that it has behind it the genuine desire of all the people that the laws should, so far as possible, be right and fair, can the Law be said to be just.

Society cannot exist without laws. Without regularity and order, life, to say nothing of progress, would be impossible. Unless the sun had its orbit, the stars their courses, and the seasons duly succeeded one another there would be only chaos. We must know that summer will follow spring or we cannot sow our crops, and unless we are assured of their use after harvest we will not sow them at all. We must know what to expect both from nature and from our fellows. This order we call law,—on the one hand, the law of the universe or of nature, and, on the other, the law of man.

The law's historical development has been—in spite of many setbacks—towards equality and hence towards justice; but not until very recently was the doctrine promulgated that all classes of men, and not merely the men in each class, were "created equal,"—not in our own country, for example, until the Civil War resulted in the abolition of slavery.

From this necessity for equality arose the so-called "Lex Talionis." If one knocked another man's eye or tooth out, he had his own eye or tooth knocked out. "Tit for tat!" But this doctrine of retaliation made so much trouble that eventually compensation in money was substituted. Thus originated our common law theory of damages and of fines, paid by individuals, communities and, later on, by nations. Yet, on the face of it, justice can be attained neither by retaliation, the assessment of damages, nor by fine or imprisonment. At best they are only a very imperfect substitute.

The defect in all early Continental legal systems was the idea that the King was the source of law and was not bound by it. The greatest contribution which the Anglo-Saxon race has made to social philosophy is the thesis that the only safe way to secure a maximum of justice for the individual is not through the arbitrary dictates of kings or emperors or dictators, however wise, but through the blundering processes by which the people make and enforce their own rules and thus work out their own justice, however defective it may be. This principle is the foundation of our own theory of constitutional government. But even if we are theoretically secure against kings and dictators, and even where the attempt is made to administer the law impartially, it is far from being justice.

The law has been called the perfection of reason, but there

are many ways of reasoning about the same thing and what seems reasonable to one judge will not seem so to another. His decision may well depend on the state of his digestion—just as equity, according to Sir John Selden, depended on "the length of the Lord Chancellor's foot." It is impossible in many instances for any one to know what the law is. It changes from one day to the next. The "nine old men" of the United States Supreme Court are not so infirm that they cannot perform the most surprising handsprings.

There are so many laws and ordinances—town, city, state, and federal—that one cannot help violating some of them much of the time. Every man, woman, child and dog in the country is enmeshed in statutes of which he is totally unconscious until some hostile official or personal enemy decides to put him on the spot. Government departments, commissions and "administrative tribunals" issue in microscopic print, and in language unintelligible to the layman, regulations having the force of acts of Congress and involving criminal penalties. One has first to purchase a magnifying glass and then hire a lawyer to find out what one may or may not do. Usually the lawyer does not know either; which may also even be true of the authors of the regulations.

Law is not justice because, while available to the rich, it is often beyond the means of the poor. The "little bug" is caught in the web of laws which the "big bug" buys or forces his way out of. It takes no account of a man's moral responsibility and classifies all offenders in definite categories irrespective of their moral guilt. It does not consider the physical or mental weakness of the accused, his environment, his heredity or the nature of the temptation to which he was exposed. There is no equality in punishment. One judge sentences a prisoner to ten years at hard labor, while another judge gives a defendant equally guilty six months for the same offense. Justice is what a man deserves and that is known only to his Maker.

The law is a brush-pile of ancient technicalities and outworn fictions. Even if the rules of evidence were not arbitrary, often absurd and, as has been said, "admirably adapted to the exclusion of truth," juries consistently ignore the law as laid down by the judge, disregard such facts as they have been permitted to learn, and base their verdicts upon bias or prejudice.

There are good laws and bad laws, but whether good or bad they can be used for corrupt purposes, to further the ambitions of prosecutors, or to protect political crooks. Democracy cannot abolish despotism. While we have "a government of laws and not of men," the unfortunate fact remains that all laws must be administered by imperfect men. Sooner or later you come to a man—in a blue coat with brass buttons, or at a desk in an office, or on a woolsack, or in the White House—and then the question of how far ours is to be a government of laws or of men depends upon him.

There is lynch law in every State of the Union. There are many lawyers, including myself, who believe that the legal current which electrocuted Hauptmann for the alleged murder of Charles Lindbergh, Jr. had to leap a surprisingly long way.

I had been struck by all this when I was serving as an assistant to the Tammany district attorney of New York County. No man of any sensibilities whatever—to say nothing of a young one with many—could fail, while watching the daily procession of unfortunate prisoners haled to the bar to be struck with what Professor Wigmore calls "the contrast that has so long been the theme of philosophers and jurists, namely the relation of law to justice—in particular, the contrast between the rule of law that forms the ostensible issue in the litigation and the merits of the parties when all the circumstances are considered—in short, the justice of the case."

It came upon me as a momentous discovery. I don't suppose that I had ever had a philosophy, although I had studied the subject under Professors James, Royce, Santayana, Palmer and Münsterberg at Harvard, who had merely reduced me to a sort of amiable acquiescence in a game which was far too abstruse for my limited understanding. But now I had achieved one, not from books but from experience, for there dawned upon me the striking analogy between law and justice—and life itself and justice. There was in fact no justice in either worthy of the name. Just as the laws of nature were harsh and implacable, whose results must needs be set aright, if at all, in an hypothetical Hereafter, so the laws of man rarely, or never, accomplished justice in any individual case. We merely did the best we could by applying legal rules-of-thumb based on the doctrine of averages, which we hoped in the long run—a very long run indeed—did make for justice.

And what was the practical answer? That jurors, within the technical limits set by the statutes, and sometimes aided by prosecutors on the one hand and attorneys on the other, did the best they could to even things up. That was the saving grace of an otherwise intolerable situation. It was up to the jury, just as it was up to individuals in their daily lives outside the courtroom, to ameliorate the unfortunate fate of their fellows who otherwise would be required to pay too great a penalty for their misdeeds— to apply in fact wherever possible the rules of ethics rather than of strict law or at least to allow considerable play to ethical considerations.

Thus such pleas as "This poor fellow didn't know any better," or "He didn't realize what he was doing" or "If you jail this man you punish his innocent wife and children more than you do him," etc., had a certain moral validity, even if technically of no avail under the strict rule that motive and intent were two distinct things, that a man was held to intend the natural and reasonable consequences of his acts even if his intelligence was too limited to foresee them, that drunkenness was no excuse for crime, and that an insane man was responsible for what he did, so long as he could distinguish right from wrong.

In a word I learned that juries, so far from doing what they were supposed to do, really treated crimes as sins, and temporarily acted as vicarious representatives of the Almighty in deciding what ought to be done about the transgressors; that on the whole, although it wasn't the law, this, considering the way the law was administered, was sometimes not such a bad thing; that, by and large, the Good Samaritan was better than the Man-who-passed-by-on-the-other-side, even if the chap in the gutter had got only what he legally deserved; that even the worst had something admirable about them and should be judged, not according to legislative standards, but by their own, for which usually they were not responsible—held good or bad "according to their lights"; that the really important thing was, not what their standards were, but that they should have standards at all; in fine that only sympathy and understanding could make life or law bearable; and that kindness, loyalty and courage were better tests of a man's virtue than his respect for the letter of the statutes.

How are we to attain the individual justice which can never be secured through the courts for the reasons that the law punishes the criminals but lets the sinners go, and that its penalties are as inflexible and relentless as those of physics? When a man accidentally touches a live wire and is instantly killed, perhaps leaving a destitute wife and children, we don't merely say "Tough luck." We get busy and do something about it ourselves, since the mere fact that he violated a law of nature is no reason for abandoning his family to their fate. We recognize that helping the poor and unfortunate is part of our job as good citizens; and we try to improve the conditions under which the accident occurred so that it may not happen again.

In the same way a man may cross a technical legal line, be sent to prison, and be stamped as an ex-convict for the rest of his life. His family are disgraced. Yet perhaps the law he violated was a bad law, or he didn't get a fair trial, or there were extenuating circumstances which the court could not legally recognize. He and his family deserve our sympathy and our help just as much as in the case of the man killed by the live wire. It is not enough to say "Let the law take its course" for we know how crude and unjust the law can be. Neither is it enough to say, "Oh, he got what he deserved." How do you know that he did?

There was in my childhood, and probably still is, a place on the Green Mountain watershed where a brook flows down the mountainside until it meets a rock lying in mid-stream. At this point it bifurcates, one rivulet running northwest down Cold River into Lake Champlain, emptying at last into the St. Lawrence—the other southeast to the Black River, thence to the Connecticut, and so to the Atlantic Ocean. It is an even bet which course a chip tossed into the rill above that rock will take. Just how it bumps against the rock alters its ultimate destination. A slight breath of wind will deflect it either way.

It seems to me that a man's life is like such a chip tossed into such a stream. Sooner or later—probably sooner—his course is going to be deflected, through what may be no fault of his, to what is known as crime or virtue, wealth or poverty, success or failure. I confess I have no patience with those who coldly say that he "has made his bed and can lie in it" or that he "had his choice." Maybe he did and maybe he didn't, and what influenced that choice, if in fact he made it, may in turn have been due to some trifling cause for which he deserves no moral blame. You cannot say "Well, that's how things are," and let it go at that. If we're content to abandon humanity either to the laws of nature or to the laws of man the world would be a miserable place to live in. We must have faith in our fellows just as we must have faith in God. Without it civilization will return to the wilderness and we shall become mere packs of wolves—each ready to tear his neighbor in pieces. Those who do not possess that faith—who refuse to believe in the innate goodness of human nature, who look for evil in every man and deny him the benefit of any doubt—are the mean people who see only the reflection of their own mean natures in the acts of others.

The truest democracy is that society in which the individual is allowed to exercise the utmost freedom of thought and action consistent with order. The totalitarian theory—the theory of government in the dark ages—attempts to fetter the minds and souls of men with rigid laws enforced through terror; but it failed and always will fail since it only serves to breed revolution. Order and civilization go hand in hand, their progress always being marked by the gradual substitution of moral, religious, and humanitarian sanctions for those of fear. The higher the civilization the fewer laws it needs; the more it will rely upon sympathy, kindness, and loyalty.

As Lord Moulton has said: "Mere obedience to Law does not measure the greatness of a nation. It can easily be obtained by a strong executive, and most easily of all from a timorous people. Nor is the license of behavior which so often accompanies the absence of Law, and which is miscalled Liberty, a proof of greatness. The true test is the extent to which the individuals composing the Nation can be trusted to obey self-imposed law. . . . Between 'can do' and 'may do' ought to exist the whole realm which recognizes the sway of duty, fairness, sympathy, taste, and all the other things that make life beautiful and society possible." *

So far as we have any real justice in this world we get it less through the courts than by virtue of the inherent decency of our fellowmen. The law is only a means to an end and often a very inadequate means at that. It is so overgrown and tangled up that no one really knows what it is today or what it will be tomorrow. It's like a bird on a bough that is as likely to hop one way as another. So don't take it as a guide but trust rather to your conscience, for no law can relieve you from the duty of being a gentleman and a sportsman. The only way to attain justice is by doing it ourselves every day—with our own hands—to each other —at home—and in the world outside. If each of us tried to right the wrongs that occur before his eyes, to relieve the distress of those with whom he comes into direct contact, we could do away with organized charity and there would be little need for law.

Looking back over nearly three quarters of a century I agree with my old friend Judge Tompkins that, had I my life to live over again, I would spend twice as much of it in fishing. Certainly

* "Law and Manners," an address by the Rt. Hon. Lord Moulton, Nov. 4, 1912.

my thoughts when idle turn instinctively to the woods rather than to the courts. Nature is the Great Mother of us all, always ready, if we seek her aid, to calm our throbbing nerves and stroke our fevered brows. We run to her like the sick and troubled children that we are and she never fails to nurse us back to health. She is always calling to her tired and nerve-wracked sons, ready to smooth out the confusion of their minds, heal their bodily ills and bring peace to their embarrassed souls. From her womb we came; it is to her arms that we return at the end to sleep. From her bosom we draw our sustenance and our vitality. Whether we lie upon balsam beds under the starry canopy of night, or throw ourselves face down at noon to rest upon some patch of reindeer moss, her breath pungent with the odor of leaf mould and rotting bark, of juniper, checkerberry and Indian grass, is a mysterious elixir more potent than all the alchemies to give us strength. Did not the giant Antaeus, in his struggle with Hercules, redouble his vigor whenever his foot touched earth?

Mother Nature is a wise old woman, nine-tenths of whose secrets are as yet unknown to us. How she must smile at our chatter about atoms and electrons, at our meaningless measurements of so-called time, our contradictory ethics, our vaporings about metaphysics, at our political theorizing, our fascism, our communism, our democracy. She rules us all no matter what we call ourselves. Our most learned scientists cannot solve her simplest secrets. We do not know what calls back the carrier pigeon to his loft or why the salmon returns to the exact river of his nativity.

I do not inquire into the whys and wherefores of things; it is enough for me that they are so; the game of metaphysics interests me but mildly, and I begrudge to it the time that otherwise might be spent in living; it makes no difference to me whether the food I eat or the brick that falls on my head are what they seem or not, they are quite enough so for my purposes. I am not greatly concerned over ultimates, and I feel quite confident that, as Holmes used to express it, I am in the belly of the Cosmos and not it in mine.

I suppose I am what is called a hedonist. I love the hot sun, the wind, and the rain—to be around with the common crowd, to share their rough jests, their problems and their troubles, to smell the sweat of their bodies, to feel that I am part of all and of them. I like the fun of catching trout, the taste of good food and wine, the affection of my fellows, the excitement of a good fight, the satisfaction of throwing all I have into an effort irrespective of achievement, in "the joy of life become an end in itself."

And after it is over?

Well, most of mankind has always believed in a future life and what the human race has accepted as true since the dawn of time is as likely to be so as the theories of modern science which, after all, proceeds by trial and error and is constantly finding unsuspected truth in old wives' tales and sailors' proverbs. It is, of course, no stranger that we should live forever than that we should live at all. Anyhow we all act as if we believed in a future life, and if we are wrong "at least we have made a pleasurable mistake." In any event I know that "the time to be happy is now, the place to be happy is here," and that the best happiness is that reflected from the hearts of others.

Would it be so bad if a tired old fellow like myself should find, after his human life has ended, that he has become a boulder lapped by dancing ripples or the swaying branch of a tall pine whispering in the wind? I should be content.

INDEX

A

"Act of God," 36, 37, 50, 385
Adams, Henry, 391; quoted, 13
Adams, Franklin P., 254, 255
Adams, Maude, 211
Addams, Jane, 254
"Administrative law," system of, 391
Agassiz, Alexander, quoted, 213
Age, full, 334
Alciatore, Antoine, 197
Alciatore, Roy, 197
Alice In Wonderland, by Lewis Carroll, 378
Allen, Frederick Lewis, 257
America, revolt against convention, in, 321 ff
American legal procedure compared with English, 293, 294; business fascism, 241 ff
American Metal Company, 259
Ames, James Barr, 37, 38
Anderson, Mary, 287
Animals, trial of, for crimes, 200, 201; *sine animo revertendi,* 200; early laws regarding, 200; law today, 200; in Middle Ages, 201; property *rights* in, 413
Anstruther, Dame Eva, 280, 282 ff
argumentum ad hominem, 191
Aristotle quoted, 339
Armstrong Insurance Committee of Investigation, 214
"Arrest, false," 60
Art of Cross Examination, by Francis L. Wellman, 363
"Assize." *See* Jury
Attachment, writ of, 300
Atwood, Sally Wilson, case of, 191 ff
Auerback, Joseph S., 357
Autobiography of Lincoln Steffens, 217 n.
Aymar, Lucy, 353 ff

B

Babson, William ("Wild Bill"), 149 ff
Babu, Sadi, case of, 117 ff
Babu, Mahommed Ali, 340, 344, 345
Baker, Ray Stannard, 214

Balfour, William, 401
"Ballad of the Revenge," by Alfred Tennyson, 373
Bannard, Otto, 135
Bar of Other Days, The, by Joseph S. Auerback, 357
Barker, Granville, 280
Barrie, Sir James, 280
Barrister's Hall, 28
Barrows, Cap, case of, 60, 61, 187, 243 ff
Barrymore, Ethel, 161, 210, 212
Bartlett, Rose, 6
Barton, William Kissam, case of, 335 ff
Baxter, Caleb, 339
Beale, Joseph Henry, 37
Beard, Charles A., quoted, 205
Beards, 26, 27
Beaulieu, Abbey, 280 ff
Beckett, Otis, 121, 122
Beecher, The Rev. Henry Ward, 363
Beekman, Althea, 231 ff
Beerbohm, Max, 280
Beeston *vs.* Stoops, citing Havens *vs.* Sackett, 66 n.
Belasco, David, 326, 327
"Bell in Hand," the, 28, 39
Belloc, Hilaire, 280
"Benefit of Clergy," 387
Bennett, Arnold, 280
Bentley, Major, 70
Berkeley Hotel, 263
Best, Betty, 46, 64, 67 ff, 81
Best, Ma, 45 ff, 59 ff, 82, 187
"Bible Class, The," 202, 203, 261
Bicycle riding, 26
Bill of Rights, 224, 225, 388
"Billionaire era," 260
Black River Academy, 12 ff
Blake & Co., E. J., 247
Blake, Rufus M., 239 ff
Blackstone's *Commentaries,* 334
Blind Goddess, The, by Arthur Train, 379
Boardman, Eliot, 22
Boardman, Eliot, Jr., 23, 35, 320
Boardman, Priscilla, 23, 38, 80; Tutt proposes to, 35, 36; again meets Tutt, 318 ff, 438
Bonico, Tony, case of, 106, 107

453